Willard Gibbs

WILLARD GIBBS
Portrait in middle life.

Willard Gibbs

BY MURIEL RUKEYSER

Doubleday, Doran & Company, Inc.

GARDEN CITY   1942   NEW YORK

PRINTED AT THE *Country Life Press,* GARDEN CITY, N. Y., U. S. A.

Author's Note

THIS IS NOT an authorized biography.

Naturally, while relatives of a distinguished person are still living, an authorized account is, properly speaking, out of the question.

There are many ways to approach the story of an imagination which has had a powerful effect on our lives, and which at the same time is an emblem of pure imagination, particularly in this country, particularly against a background of war. I offer this simply as one approach; it is the first full-length treatment of Gibbs, and if it breaks the way for many others to follow, it will have done well.

The war has made it impossible to obtain certain material which may still exist in Germany.

There is reason to believe that there is further evidence in the United States, as well. Several eminent admirers of Willard Gibbs, it is to be hoped, will produce further contributions to his story; and it is likely that there is undiscovered evidence. The author welcomes any addition to the significant life and impact of Willard Gibbs—from Ralph Van Name, E. B. Wilson, and John Johnston, and from anyone who can add further truth to his image as it enlarges on our scene.

M. R.

[v]

To physical chemistry he gave form and content for a hundred years.

WILHELM OSTWALD

"They laugh best who laugh last." Wait till we're dead twenty years. Look at the way they're now treating poor Willard Gibbs, who during his lifetime can hardly have been considered any great shakes at New Haven.

WILLIAM JAMES

Contents

Contents

Illustrations

Willard Gibbs

CHAPTER ONE

Introduction : On Presumption

WHATEVER HAS HAPPENED, whatever is going to happen in the world, it is the living moment that contains the sum of the excitement, this moment in which we touch life and all the energy of the past and future. Here is all the developing greatness of the dream of the world, the pure flash of momentary imagination, the vision of life lived outside of triumph or defeat, in continual triumph and defeat, in the present, alive. All the crafts of subtlety, all the effort, all the loneliness and death, the thin and blazing threads of reason, the spill of blessing, the passion behind these silences—all the invention turns to one end : the fertilizing of the moment, so that there may be more life. Spring, and the years, and the wars, and the ideas rejected, the swarming and anonymous people rejected, and the slow climb of thought to be more whole, the few accepted flames of truth in a darkness of battle and further rejection and further battle. We know the darkness of the past, we have a conscious body of knowledge—and under it, the black country of a lost and wasted and anonymous world, an early America of knowledge; jungle-land, wasteful as nature, prodigal.

Our living moment rides this confusion; is torn by the dead wars; seizes the old knowledge; speeds on the imagination of the living and the dead, and passes, fertilized. But the hidden life today continues among all the silence, and in the midst of war. The hidden life of the senses, the vivid, speculative life of the mind. The man over his table, glass shine of the test-tubes reflected in the eyes; the woman staring into her thought of the when one encyclopaedic scholar could list all human knowledge, or one science could account for method. The combining sciences, with all their pitfalls, are our threshold.

The gifts of Willard Gibbs to the world have barely been opened. He made no experiments. He pursued law; he said, "I wish to know systems"; and his systems hold. The experiments based on his principles are going on now; the course of wars, as well as of sciences, has already been changed by them.

Many biographies end with the death of their subject. The life of Willard Gibbs must be continued to the latest date. In the history of science, his life offers a bridge between classical mechanics and contemporary quantum mechanics; his work on equilibrium, vector analysis, and statistical mechanics has set in momentum a vast body of research and experiment. His direct value has been tremendous.

But it is his indirect value, the secondary influence that he has had, that gives him a unique place in the history of the imagination and, particularly, in the history of American culture.

This was a man whose acceptance of his culture seemed to stop short only at the borders of his scientific labor. Silent, inhibited, remote, he was able to separate the elements of his own life as the town he lived in was able to separate the parts of its community—a separation which in his work he recognized as an impossibility. His gift was in the combining forms, and the language for them, which he set forth—and which were to find their reflections in the discoveries of writers, sociologists, as well as those whose fields lay as far apart as life insurance and high explosives. Many of his formulas were re-discovered. It has been said that it is easier to re-discover Gibbs than to read him. He wrote for physicists and chemists in mathematical terms, and they were not willing to read that language. He was in the position of a great poet whose idiom must reach its audience through dilution after dilution, in the work of prose writers and lesser poets, imitators and contemporaries who in their detailed flashes indicate his wider constellations.

He was in the position of the worker in pure imagination : scientist, poet, abstract artist, pioneer of system—those few working closest to the spirit in any field. They are few indeed in any knowledge, in any country. It is of the greatness of such men : their long days, their quiet hours blasted by the approach of a

Introduction : On Presumption

Whatever has happened, whatever is going to happen in the world, it is the living moment that contains the sum of the excitement, this moment in which we touch life and all the energy of the past and future. Here is all the developing greatness of the dream of the world, the pure flash of momentary imagination, the vision of life lived outside of triumph or defeat, in continual triumph and defeat, in the present, alive. All the crafts of subtlety, all the effort, all the loneliness and death, the thin and blazing threads of reason, the spill of blessing, the passion behind these silences—all the invention turns to one end : the fertilizing of the moment, so that there may be more life. Spring, and the years, and the wars, and the ideas rejected, the swarming and anonymous people rejected, and the slow climb of thought to be more whole, the few accepted flames of truth in a darkness of battle and further rejection and further battle. We know the darkness of the past, we have a conscious body of knowledge—and under it, the black country of a lost and wasted and anonymous world, an early America of knowledge; jungle-land, wasteful as nature, prodigal.

Our living moment rides this confusion; is torn by the dead wars; seizes the old knowledge; speeds on the imagination of the living and the dead, and passes, fertilized. But the hidden life today continues among all the silence, and in the midst of war. The hidden life of the senses, the vivid, speculative life of the mind. The man over his table, glass shine of the test-tubes reflected in the eyes; the woman staring into her thought of the child not yet born; the boy at his gun, his face vulnerable and delicate under the iron cup of a helmet; the broad, many-ridged back over a lathe—the hidden lives of those we see. Or, springing up over the country, the night-time width of America. We see, in this moment of the world, the lives of many people brought to a time of stress. The streams are challenged, all the meanings are again in question.

It is at this moment that we turn.

It is quite clear that we will live and die fighting for our beliefs. In that life we see our only safety. It is for us the life of the spirit as well as daily life, the life of the flesh.

In the imaginations which tapped that energy, in the energy itself and its release, we see our power. Man, the mystery; man, the pure force; man, the taproot of naked vision, the source himself, will look in such a moment for deeper sources, for the sources of power that can bring a fuller life to a desperate time. We cut away the old life, cutting down to the root. And the root of such power, of such invention, is in the imaginative lives of certain men and women, responding in their way and with their proper kinds of love to the wishes of history—that is, to the wishes of the people at that moment, however disguised, however premature and dark.

We look for these sources of power.

Willard Gibbs is such a source of power. Living in the Middle Period of the American people—from the point at which we stand—doing his work in silence, in isolation, in the years of rejection directly after the Civil War, when abstract work was wanted least of all, when the cry was for application and invention and the tools that would expand the growing fortunes of the diamond boys, his wish was for systems. He lived closer than any inventor, any poet, any scientific worker in pure imagination to the life of the inventive and organizing spirit in America. It was a life which accomplished the setting up of a system. Of the four great men of his time in this country—Lincoln, Melville, Whitman, Gibbs—he was one of the two who were occupied in the actual *setting up* of a system that was indicated in the main stream of their tradition; a system that would find it necessary to kill the axioms of their thought in order to find life. Whitman, in all his work, expressed face after face of a loose belief in order to set down the contemporary scene, stroke by stroke and look for look as he knew it; and Melville in the greatest of his books set afloat a cosmos, without land and without women, but with the burning qualities of the real world. Lincoln was the tragic shadow of a conflict inherent in the wishes of this country; he acted out a duel of principles that had been started years before his time; and by his life and death hastened our own duel. He opened the country to another expansion, an expansion of contradictions in which freedom and the wish to subordinate ran wild over the West, and filled back into the East and the wounded South. The age he closed was a war of principles, and the age he introduced was that of Morgan, Gould, Vanderbilt —the age of Edison and not the age of Gibbs.

Among the four, Gibbs is the unknown one. This man, the father of physical chemistry, that science which above all others will shape the course of the war we now are in and the course of our lives after this war—the man who has been called the greatest mind of the nineteenth century—of whom it is said that his name will live after all others, except possibly Lincoln's—is an unknown man to us. In his own field, he has full recognition. When people are used to talking in terms of "best," "first," "greatest," they call Gibbs the "greatest American scientist." When such groups vote, they have voted Gibbs and Benjamin Franklin to be our greatest scientific geniuses. But Franklin was a citizen of the world; he lived in courts and drawing-rooms and the halls of ambassadors at last; his work and its importance was known in his own time to the public of three countries.

Even Gibbs's name is not known to the general public.

But, in such a list of the great, we see time catching up with them. We see their lives filtering down through their influences; their books are read, their battles buried, and all their inventions superseded. We know them well; or we begin to know them, and then see their images corrupted by half-knowledge and misinterpretation and misuse of their gifts. We feel them in their impact on other minds. And here we see Gibbs's ramifying thought, which struck deep to the other sciences, until biologists knew that their future was Gibbsian, until metallurgists saw that he had the key, until it was clear that the combining science with which he worked was to be the clue to many contemporary mysteries. For our time depends, not on single points of knowledge, but on clusters and combinations. The time is long past when one encyclopaedic scholar could list all human knowledge, or one science could account for method. The combining sciences, with all their pitfalls, are our threshold.

The gifts of Willard Gibbs to the world have barely been opened. He made no experiments. He pursued law; he said, "I wish to know systems"; and his systems hold. The experiments based on his principles are going on now; the course of wars, as well as of sciences, has already been changed by them.

Many biographies end with the death of their subject. The life of Willard Gibbs must be continued to the latest date. In the history of science, his life offers a bridge between classical mechanics and contemporary quantum mechanics; his work on equilibrium, vector analysis, and statistical mechanics has set in momentum a vast body of research and experiment. His direct value has been tremendous.

But it is his indirect value, the secondary influence that he has had, that gives him a unique place in the history of the imagination and, particularly, in the history of American culture.

This was a man whose acceptance of his culture seemed to stop short only at the borders of his scientific labor. Silent, inhibited, remote, he was able to separate the elements of his own life as the town he lived in was able to separate the parts of its community—a separation which in his work he recognized as an impossibility. His gift was in the combining forms, and the language for them, which he set forth—and which were to find their reflections in the discoveries of writers, sociologists, as well as those whose fields lay as far apart as life insurance and high explosives. Many of his formulas were re-discovered. It has been said that it is easier to re-discover Gibbs than to read him. He wrote for physicists and chemists in mathematical terms, and they were not willing to read that language. He was in the position of a great poet whose idiom must reach its audience through dilution after dilution, in the work of prose writers and lesser poets, imitators and contemporaries who in their detailed flashes indicate his wider constellations.

He was in the position of the worker in pure imagination: scientist, poet, abstract artist, pioneer of system—those few working closest to the spirit in any field. They are few indeed in any knowledge, in any country. It is of the greatness of such men: their long days, their quiet hours blasted by the approach of a

Introduction: On Presumption

lightning entrance to discovery, their tortures before human insufficiency, and their self-contained pride, that can never be threatened, and that has made their imaginations heroes. That greatness, obscured, attacked by time, covered by friends, covered by those who loved them clumsily, covered by the life that surrounded them. This is of them, and their great wish : to discover, to make known, to find a language for discovery.

America is full of the anonymity of such greatness. Hackles and teeth of mountains, the cities a fume of light, the tremendous and half-wasted plains, the immense secrets of the half-wasted past, and behind them, the unknown faces of thousands of men and women whose real pride was unknown even to themselves, the pride of breaking and creation, of throwing away one's years in a human depth of invention and pioneering.

But there are those whose names we know, those who held the greatness of the times, and of coming times, and added to that greatness before they died. We know their names, we know their silent faces, the features of our explorers, our ancestors. We visit their graves, for their graves are our recollection. We ask our questions about them, and find or are denied the answers. Wars overtake the cities, but these names they do not overtake. They enter our lives. And no matter what isolation they have suffered, no matter what obscurity was their shelter, or how they have hidden themselves, they are involved in the world.

The past of democracy has been a double stream, furiously twining in marriage and war and exchange. The split and the prophecy of conflict came very early : John Quincy Adams saw it plain. As far back as 1820 he knew the tragic outcome, and he dreaded it, for it threatened his two prime beliefs : in God and in the American people. Gibbs was a product of this double and breaking tradition, and he was isolated by his partial existence. New Haven, and Yale; with these he was identified, and although he broke traditions in his work, these two traditions went completely unquestioned.

He was born in 1839 in New Haven, went to school there, went to Yale and graduated and taught there, studied abroad for three years intercalated with illness before he returned to work and teach at Yale until his death in 1903. He never married, nor moved from his family's house. He seemed to be at peace with himself. He had his classes and his work-table; his walks and conversations. And always Time the enemy, and the fury Tradition. Gibbs tore himself down until his life was nothing but self and science, and then he tore the self away. Or let it wither away, until it became vestigial, something he could take along daily, that made no demands, that interfered with nothing.

That was how he was : tall enough and thin, frail but not sickly, the climax of a long line of Harvard and Princeton and Yale men. Scholars, theologians, librarians; remote, guarded, isolated men, and extraordinary and intellectual women. And at the end, this father and this son of the same name, Josiah Willard Gibbs, walking along the silent New Haven streets, their heads averted, the pale far sea-look of the New Englander in their eyes. And behind them, their gifts, predicted in the father (who made the relations of language his chief study) and echoed in a marvellous and architectural science in the son.

What was it in those years, in New England, that made them bury their greatness? It was not true in Massachusetts; the Concord group, the only true "group" this country has ever produced, were full in their sky early in that time; the Adams family were looking for every scrap of reinforcement for their own ideas about the American genius; the Peirces were teaching at Harvard, Agassiz was there, and Pumpelly, and Clarence King. But this was not Cambridge, this was New Haven, a town that had never been on any frontier; this was not Harvard, but Yale.

What obscured his name?

He worked alone; there was no spectacle involved, neither the fireworks of experiment and a visible proof, nor the novelty of a principle that seems to stem from nowhere, because the links are so intricately joined, and the gaps in reasoning so unexpected. No; he built up a structure of thought, and followed his reasons as far as he wished. It was at that point that they demanded discovery.

It was at that point that they were not discovered. Continual re-discovery of his work has confirmed him again and again. The process has done more; it has given him a further life. No one work has had the significance and the burial that Gibbs's work has undergone. No great man whose work has already reached an age—for first in Germany and England and Holland,

and finally in the United States, his work began to reach its own existence—has met with such ambivalence. Gibbs has now received the highest recognition by his successors; his work has been taken up and advanced. But there is no public notice. There is only a blank, and a confusion of names. His Works have been collected, and his true biography, as that of any producing person is bound to be, is in his Works; and a full scientific commentary has been published as companion volumes. But what of the life of this man? What was the nature of his mind? And the greatness? What was that? What places Gibbs with Newton and Einstein?

The story of Gibbs is that of the pure imagination in a wartime period. This is the adventure of the system-building spirit in a time of the breaking of systems, the daring "I Give You" to a future that must rise out of wounds. War and after-war are filled with hatred, and this hatred turns against the imagination, against poetry, against structure of any kind. It wants detail, it wants the practical and concrete. The detail of invention can be understood. It is clear to an age that is occupied with material tearing-down and building. The Middle Period of the United States, the period surrounding the Civil War, included the years of Willard Gibbs. It was a time of battering expansion, land grants, the railroads ramming through the West, watered stock and cheap labor, the new-found cheap energy of steam, the loose translations of democracy into any kind of can-do brutality. Its spokesmen were for it; its greatest spokesman, Whitman, grew old and acquiescent. He had despaired of himself, but not of his age. He had to speak for the system he knew, for he had no other system to offer. This was in a world of war and suffering. This was the world of understanding.

Gibbs lived in the other world. His mixtures, his dynamics, his treatment of chemical potential, his ensembles, belong to the un-understanding world of matter, whose orbits cross our human lives at every step, whose commands we obey, and by the knowledge of whose ways we learn ourselves. Without a biography, he has died; his friends are dead; and those who are old now knew him as their teacher, or as a family friend, or at dead, half-forgotten faculty meetings. His work, which spread over the

world, offers to each specialist whatever he wishes to find in it
—alloys, explosives, a theory of history, medicine, fuel changes,
the design of engines for aircraft and automobiles, social equilibrium, information on vital statistics, cement structure, the behavior of alloys and crystal habit, much of the vast chemical industry
that is now a quarter of American industry—and countless biological advances in cell equilibrium, in work involving permeable
membranes and colloids. This was the synthetic scientist, the
man who did not experiment, the man who never made a mistake.

He cut through a forest of axioms. He worked only with
essentials, and built up a language to make his work more pure.

He was, in this, working in the deepest of American traditions.
From the beginnings, from the European discovery of this continent, we have broken the fastest bonds. We have been heretics
and axiom-breakers, wilful outcasts, exiles. We are a nation of
eager refugees; we were planted as that. When the seaboard was
settled, and a second generation learned a sense of place, and the
new desires arrived, sweeping westward, the desire for unity
came, too. Unity, at any cost. Integration was the word of the
Puritans. To integrate themselves they were willing to amputate
emotions, the complexity in which the mortal mixes himself and
mires himself and grows; they were willing to amputate, or they
would never have sailed, and broken with the mother world.

Blockhouse and stockade have given way to the brick-and-
white, compact New England towns. Early Revolution had settled into a pattern of individualism that sprang with a jungle
flourish into the burst of competition which followed. Planta-
tions, farmsteads, county seats; and a few giant towns, muddy,
uneven, and still charming. The white steeples of the Protestant
churches; the long, desolate highways, general store, and black-
smith's shop. The chain of seaboard cities, along a route which
was to grow into the first road of the country—Portland, Portsmouth, Boston, Providence, New Haven, New York forming
its northern nodes.

Even as the country began to settle—and the symptoms of its
settling were symptoms of power and waste, the slums of Boston, the Panic of 1837—interest in "the law" was beginning to
grow, the feeling of safety that leads a people to litigiousness was
falling over the country. The brilliance of new concepts was

Introduction: On Presumption

shining strangely from under that cloud of safety, an appearance lit, even then, by the storm-light of approaching war. It was clear to the citizens who rode the top of the nineteenth century that we were freemen set on a crusade, members of the largest tribe ever banded together by purpose, and growing with a velocity never before known, according to the rules of a violent and lonesome status quo.

But the status quo itself is almost an outlaw term, if you consider the meanings of the country. Tabu-breakers who fought together for protections, who settled together and bred another generation of tabu-breakers to streak through a green wilderness, and other generations to break their tabus. Even New Haven, which never had to fight its Indians, as most of the other settlements had—even New Haven, whose college, founded in 1701 by the Congregationalist Church, was always half and more than half of the town—was built on a rock. This town can never betray its American tradition of axiom-breaking.

In the center of New Haven is its Green, forum and park to any New England town, that tree about which the house is built. The hub of this Green is Center Church, a beautiful traditional building modeled after St. Martin's-in-the-Fields, in London. With one difference. The two cornerstones of Center Church are two monuments set up to Goffe and Whalley, the Regicides —two of those judges who condemned Charles I to death, and fled England at the Restoration. King-killers! Breakers of the deepest tabu of any ruled people. Three of these men had been concealed and protected in New Haven, and took their lives up again. Their graves are in the church's cornerstones. But it is high explosive that is buried in that gesture : violence, and daring, and the promise of new freedoms. And that, in a quiet town, accepting gracefully the limits of its high red palisades of rock and its curve of Sound—accepting its church, its college, its law.

But buried in its center, the hub of an American city, are those cornerstones.

If Gibbs's life refuses to end with his death, it seeks its own beginnings, too. He goes back, in time, to the beginnings of that search for unity of method which he made his own search. If

he is generally unknown, he is known, too—his single-minded-
ness, his keenness, and the hunt for unity drives into this moment,
to the youngest boy and girl walking along the walls at night,
working over the bright table, finding a way, a formula, a balance—and back to the early phrases, to Epicurus and Lucretius,
the poets of the sum of things; Lucretius, who wrote :

> Nor was the mass of matter more compact
> nor ever set at wider intervals,
> for nothing increases and nothing perishes.
> Therefore the motion of the atoms themselves
> is the same now as it has ever been,
> and so hereafter will their motion be;
> and what has been born will evermore be born
> in the same way; will be, and will grow strong
> with strength as it is given by natural law.
> For nothing can ever change the sum of things;
> there is no hiding-place, nothing *outside*,
> no source-place where another power might rise
> bursting, to change the nature and course of things.

> There is nothing to marvel at in this point :
> that although all things are in constant motion,
> the sum seems steadily to be at rest,
> unless something disclose its proper movement.
> For the nature of origins lies far from the senses;
> far under and hidden—you cannot see so far,
> they hide all movement from you—even in scenes
> which we perceive, motion is often lost.
> As on a distant hill, cropping rich grass,
> go grazing woolly sheep, roaming the pasture
> gemmy with dew inviting them, and they play,
> and the full-fed lambs butt each other and run.
> All this is blurred to us by distance, seen
> as a whiteness at rest on a green hill.
> Too, when great armies cover the wide plains
> in their manoeuvres, fighting a mock-war,
> the glow rises to the sky and all the hills
> flash back splendor of bronze and the deep ground
> shakes at the weight of heavy marching feet,
> and the mountains echo to the stars of heaven
> while circling horsemen gallop through the plains,

Introduction: On Presumption

course suddenly around and the ground is rung.
Even then there is a place on the high hills
where they stand still, a brightness on a field.

In the poems of balance and unity, the science found its word.
Willard Gibbs, of all Americans, was to be the greatest to set
up a system based on the unity and the inquiry into unity which
has concerned this country since it claimed independence through
union. His work was done at a time when it was more clear than
it had ever been before that complexity must be reckoned with
at every step, that unity might be a dream that was lost forever,
and that no one system would do for the times.

The poets and scientists, those who have given themselves
most closely to the creation and description of systems, speak
to the ripeness of their age; live conscious that their own nature
is to be translated into the terms of the systems of which they
speak. To the poet, his own nature is his chief instrument, his
device in terms of which all other unities are mensurable; cadence
and meaning and loneliness are measured by himself. To the
physical scientist, his own nature is apart, he deals with a world
of law in which there is no understanding. And, to a specialist
in scientific knowledge, the poet is likely to seem far off and
irresponsible, beyond the labyrinth of his aims and the intricate
specific habit of his method. The world of the poet, however,
is the scientist's world. Their claim on systems is the same claim.
Their writings anticipate each other; welcome each other; indeed
embrace. As Lucretius answered Epicurus, Gibbs answers Whitman, however unconsciously and from a distant effort. And it is
the poet's claim to ask these questions about a great scientist :
What was his work and life? What kind of love produced them?
What was his impact on the world?

This is presumption. According to the specialists, these questions may be *asked* by anyone, yes; but they are to be answered
by the specialists alone. Who can solve the personality of a dead
physical chemist? Some old mathematician, who has spent his
years preparing for such an end, to whom most other questions
have begun to lose reality—he, perhaps, is fit to answer. Or someone whose contact with the scene has been deep from the beginning—someone whose study has served to illuminate the phase
rule, that formulation of Gibbs which cuts so simply through a

[*11*]

scientific knot and is so formidable to define in lay terms—someone who has worked in vector analysis at Sheff, who remembers
seeing Professor Gibbs edging down Chapel Street against a
football crowd—someone who was brought up in his tradition,
his religion, his town, his science.

It is by a long road of presumption that I come to Willard
Gibbs. When one is a woman, when one is writing poems, when
one is drawn through a passion to know people today and the
web in which they, suffering, find themselves, to learn the people,
to dissect the web, one deals with the processes themselves. To
know the processes and the machines of process : plane and
dynamo, gun and dam. To see and declare the full disaster that
the people have brought on themselves by letting these processes
slip out of the control of the people. To look for the sources of
energy, sources that will enable us to find the strength for the
leaps that must be made. To find sources, in our own people, in
the living people. And to be able to trace the gifts made to us
to two roots : the infinite anonymous bodies of the dead, and
the unique few who, out of great wealth of spirit, were able to
make their own gifts. Of these few, some have been lost through
waste and its carelessness. This carelessness is complicated and
specialized. It is a main symptom of the disease of our schools,
which let the *kinds* of knowledge fall away from each other, and
waste knowledge, and time, and people. All our training plays
into this; our arts do; and our government. It is a disease of organization, it makes more waste and war.

Presumption it is to call it a disease, to say that it is one of the
reasons Gibbs was lost, and the main reason he has not yet been
found.

Lost, I say, and *found;* but he was never lost. It was that he
has not reached far enough, and that we have not reached far
enough to meet him. And this is what it means to reach him.

To journey through his work, the first paper on models, the
great second and third papers, the climactic formulas, and the
flashes of description; the letters, so rigid, so kind, enlightening
point after point; the generous biographies, the sparseness and
lack of personal material. To see a careful withdrawal from personal life, a careful destruction of any personal tokens.

To journey through his streets, the quiet, the brick, the sidewalks and walls built after his time, and try to see again those

Introduction: On Presumption

vanished seasons of elms and gardens, silent thoroughfares, sounds less shrill than any of the bells and wheels we hear. There are the destroyed houses, the destroyed and superannuated laboratories, the libraries destroyed and set up again behind façades he would not recognize. There are the swift advances made over his own work, the great discoveries published a moment after he died; enormous motion in the outside world, and in New Haven, three blocks he made his own, being seen in them, walking in them a route of habit's small circle, thrown like Kant's track in Koenigsberg against the immense arc of his interior life.

To journey through the questions of his life : What was this man? What impact? What restrictions? What gift?

To find his life vanishing as if he had been a snow man living in snow, to find partial answers, silences, refusal. For much of it perseveres, the covering and the burial.

His work endures.

The questions endure.

And if presumption is the only way to cut through and bind these meanings together, then More Audacity must be the word again.

For there are meanings here that blaze up for our moment, meanings of struggle and wish and loneliness, meanings of war and structure and democracy that tie in with what we shall be doing tomorrow; meanings that must be reached.

It was going to be an age of experiment.

The world was extending itself. Europe was full, as it had always been, of self-destruction; America was gathering itself together for leap after leap to the west; Asia was vast and unsuspected to the rest, Africa open only at the edges, and there being bled for everybody's profit. We have to stand far off and see the world turning, its sands, its green, its mountains, its little colored towns, farther and farther off until the thoughts of people are a blur, the world is a blur of a hundred years ago. The round blurred earth, a hundred years ago to our presumption, and there are two ships visible on the curve of its blue oceans. Two ships unconscious of each other, sailing different seas, and carrying vastly different cargoes. But closely interlocked for us now, rocking on their oceans a hundred years ago.

One of these ships was the *Java*, a three-master, sailing from Rotterdam to Surabaya, carrying 100,000 bricks and Robert Mayer. Young Dr. Mayer was twenty-seven; he was serving as ship's doctor, he had lived in the romantic and political Germany of the '30s, studying and wandering, getting himself thrown in jail for belonging to a forbidden secret society in Tübingen, going on hunger strike there, out and visiting the cities of Austria and France, and at last making his preparations to sail to Batavia before he took up his practice at home. On the long voyage out, he broke his hundred days of monotony by reading through Lavoisier. In this chemistry, the images of Mayer's discovery were made clear to him, and their colors burned into his brain : the colors of burning, the bright blood of the arteries, the dark blood of the veins. Burning, burning, he thought; Lavoisier says that animal heat is the result of burning. Bright blood burns. It sheds its oxygen, it burns, and adds carbonic acid. Bright blood burns dark.

It was in the roadstead off Surabaya that it happened, and it came to him flash after flash : it was here that he first discovered the law of the conservation of energy. Twenty-eight sailors had come down with fever when they finally got to Surabaya, and Robert Mayer, while he was bleeding one of them, marked how red the blood was, how red; as red as the arterial spurt, and not like blood from a vein at all. Red blood, full of oxygen. It contained much more oxygen here in the tropics than northern blood would hold. Less heat was given off from the body, then, less oxygen shed. That raises all the questions about work and heat. The work of the body, and the heat of the body. He remembers sailors' oracles, the proverbs about the hot stormy sea that can never be as cold as calm water. He remembers the proofs in Lavoisier of conservation in the relations between work and heat. There are the old lines :

> For nothing can ever change the sum of things;
> there is no hiding-place, nothing *outside* . . .

Robert Mayer stays aboard when the others go off into the seductive heat and noises of the Indies. He wants to make law out of this. Nothing is lost, there are correspondences, he writes. The nature of these energies is the same; they have equivalents;

they change, they are reciprocal, they dance and seem to disappear, but they are not lost. The connections are there. "The day will come, it is certain," he writes, "when these truths will become the common property of science."

The other ship was the *Amistad*.

CHAPTER TWO
The "Amistad" Mutiny

IN THE SPRING OF 1839 a long, low, black schooner set sail from Havana with a cargo of assorted merchandise and fifty-three kidnapped Africans, its crew, and the two Spanish owners who had bought the slaves, against all the treaties then in existence.

The slave trade on the west coast of Africa was a thriving and universal business in February 1839, the most profitable business of the country. Everybody who could be was engaged in it. Extensive wars were being fought, and the captives taken in these tribal wars could be shipped down the streams and river to the slave-ports, or herded from the slopes through the low-lying rice fields. They would find their way to the slave factories on the Atlantic coast at last, whose depots were on islands in the rivers and lagoons. Towns made war for no other reason than to obtain slaves; in the peaceable villages, many Africans were sold for their crimes, and many for their debts. Black men captured other black men from these villages, and brought them to the coast; no white man had yet been into the interior, and none dared be the first. But the slave-traders on this coast were the educated men of Sierra Leone; they were trained at the slave-depots, made their periodic trips inland, and became the principal dealers.

There was an island in the Gallinas River, the place called by the Spaniards Lomboko. A hundred years ago, a large number of these natives were brought here, and put on a boat sailing for Havana under the Portuguese flag.

They were confined on board the slaver according to the customs. Seated in a space three feet three inches high, they had scarcely room to sit or to lie down. There were a good many men in this chamber, but far more women and children. All the slaves were fastened in couples, chained tightly by the wrists and ankles with irons that left deep scars of laceration. They were kept like this day and night, sleeping twisted on the floor, and crouching by day between those decks, crowded to overflowing. They suffered every hour. They were given rice to eat, more than they could swallow, plenty of rice, but hardly anything to drink. They were ill; they wanted water; many men, women, and children died on that passage.

They were spared the last sudden horror of many of these slave-ships, running the long journey from Africa to the New World—the horror of being dragged above decks and flung all in irons overboard, at the sight of another ship, the dark chained bodies twirling down through the middle ocean. They were not hidden as many had been behind the coils of rope and under piles of cargo, as on one boat 240 people had been hidden, so that only the sight of a black leg gave away the presence of a village-ful of Africans to the boarding party, come to search the ship.

For all of this suffering was illegal; it all ran counter to the laws and decrees and treaties among the countries of Europe and America. The robber-chiefs of Africa, the Atlantic pirates, and the representatives of three continents were going against the de-cree of Spain of 1817. All slaves imported from Africa after 1820, according to that decree, were automatically declared free. In May 1818 the minister in Washington of the Spanish govern-ment, Don Onis, communicated to the government of the United States the treaty between Great Britain and Spain to that effect, and the agreement between Spain and the United States was revised in February 1819, after long negotiations between Don Onis and John Quincy Adams, then Secretary of State.

But the slave-markets of Havana did a tremendous business. That pale extensive city waited at the end of the long crossing for more slaves, its width sectioned off like a slaughterhouse into the teeming barracoons, fitted up exclusively for the housing and sale of lately landed Africans. And this new shipload, after their kidnapping and waiting in Sierra Leone, and the two-month crossing of the Middle Passage, landed by night at a small village near Havana. Their wounds were deep, they had been beaten and flogged, and some of them had had vinegar and gunpowder rubbed into their open flesh.

Cuba was beautiful. The aromatic island, with its rush of green, its rapid plants, the stone-works of the harbor, after the long sea. But its coveted harbors were crowded with this traffic, and the masonry of the Morro Castle hid behind them, according to a letter written to Adams in 1836, advocating Atlantic and Caribbean naval bases, "a mean and degraded people." But the brooks and the fields and the fortifications! "They were the most numerous fortifications in the Caribbean, and their people had the least energy for defending them." It was easy to see what value this "American Britain" had, this chain of islands : Summer Island, or Bermuda, was another, and naval officers were talking also to General Jackson about the misunderstood bars and shoals and islands of the sea, all the way from here to Charleston.

Africans did not see this land. It was like what they had left : the slave-cages in the marshy, vivid-green fields. Their village was like what they had left : huts like their huts in the glare of day, and the strong angular shadows of sub-tropical night. They stayed here for about ten days, until several white men arrived. Among these men was Ruiz, whom they learned to call by his Spanish nickname, Pipi. He looked them over, selected the ones he liked, and lined them up in the fierce sun. And then he went down the line making the traditional tests, feeling of them in every part, opening their mouths to see if their teeth were sound; the examination was carried to a degree of minuteness.

It was time to separate these terrible companions. Forty-nine of them had been bought by Señor Don José Ruiz, and four by Señor Don Pedro Montez, and these were taken from the others. When it was time to part at Havana, there was weeping among the women and children, and some of the men wept. Cinquez, a powerful young rice planter, a natural leader even on that journey, wept. He had been kidnapped from his home, where he left a wife and three children, and now this remnant, all taken from his country, were to be parted again. Another young planter, a short active man named Grabeau, did not weep—he felt it was not manly—but sat aside from the others, with Kimbo, older than most of the others, who had been a king's slave. They talked to each other for the last time of their friends and their country. At night, the fifty-three were led through the narrow streets of

Havana. The white walls stood out plain, slashed and sectioned by the deep black shadows : a thick crowded city, bigger than anything they had ever seen, far and lost from the thatch and fields of their country, where they had worshipped the spirits living in the cotton tree, the stream, and on the mountain.

They were put on board a long, low, black schooner when they reached Havana Harbor—a schooner already loaded and ready, swinging at anchor there, with the letters AMISTAD painted large on her. During that night, they were kept in irons again—heavier irons than before, locked on their hands and feet and necks. During the day they were more mildly treated : some of them were freed of their chains, although the Spaniards took care never to free them all at once. They communicated with their new owner by signs, or through Antonio, the cabin-boy, who was the only one on the ship who spoke both Spanish and the dialect they all had in common.

The *Amistad* was bound for Guanaja, the intermediate port for Principe, and the Spaniards held papers certifying that these were their slaves. But, down in the hold, the Africans did not understand why they should be on this new boat, nor where they were being taken. When the mulatto cook, Selestino Ferrer, who was the slave of Captain Ramón Ferrer, came down with the cabin-boy to feed them, they asked him their questions, through Antonio; they knew they were completely lost, they were very hungry, and the hot nights and days were made longer by thirst. There was much whipping, and their questions were not answered. On the fourth day out, the cook and the cabin-boy looked at each other when the questions were again repeated; then the cabin-boy, Antonio, laughed and said that they were just sailing at the pleasure of the Spaniards, and, as for the Africans, *they* were to be cooked and eaten whenever the Spaniards got ready for them.

During the three days out from Havana, the wind had been ahead. On this fourth day and night, it rained; a storm came up, and all hands were on deck, hard at work. Late in the evening, mattresses were thrown down for them. Clouds covered the sky; the moon had not yet risen; it was very dark. All of the crew but the man at the helm were asleep by eleven o'clock. But the Africans, below deck, were not asleep; they were up and working at their chains and whispering in short tense phrases, passing on the information about the knives they had seen, the long knives used to cut sugar cane.

At three in the morning, there was a noise in the forecastle.

None of the Spaniards ever knew how the thing began; but the freed Africans were among them, swinging their machetes. Ruiz picked up an oar and clubbed at the four men who had seized him, and then, up the deck, he heard his yell of "No! No!" followed by a boy's cry of murder. He heard the captain scream to Antonio to go below and get some bread. In the black and cloudy night, it was very late to think of pacifying these men by throwing them scraps. Antonio rushed up, in time to see the captain struck across the face two or three times; the cook was struck oftener. Neither of them groaned before he died.

By now the rest of the Africans were unchained and pouring onto the deck, armed with machetes; and when the man at the wheel and the other hand saw this, they ran for the small canoe, lowered it, and escaped into the clouded sea. Montez ran up on deck, and they met him with knives; he defended himself with his own knife and a stick until he was slashed twice, on the head and on the arm. Then he ran for it, scurrying below and wrapping himself in a sail in his panic, trying to hide between two barrels. They came after him, as he burrowed farther in, trying frantically to work himself into a crevice of safety. They would have killed him, but another black man followed and ordered the first not to kill Montez, but to bring him back on deck.

The decks were covered with blood. Ruiz was begging as he stood there, yelling not to be killed, calling that they spare the life of the old man, Montez. The Africans tied the two Spaniards together by the hands until they had had time to go down to the passengers' cabin and go through the trunks. Then they set to work. They had accomplished their purpose; they had their freedom, and they had killed the two great threats to their lives, the captain and the cook. They threw the bodies overboard and washed down the slippery deck. There were some who wanted the cabin-boy killed. He was African by birth, but he had lived a long time in Cuba as the slave of the captain, whose name he used. The fact of his years in Cuba saved his life, for he was the only link of communication between the Africans and the Spaniards. Cinquez assumed responsibility here; he stopped in his inventory of the cargo, and gave order that Antonio Ferrer was not to be killed, as he was needed for the rest of the voyage.

All night long the Africans washed the decks and went through the schooner they had captured. She was a fairly new ship, clipper-built in Baltimore only six years before, of 120 tons burden. The vessel and cargo were worth $40,000 when they left Havana. The Africans had been bought at a price between twenty and thirty thousand dollars; and vessel and cargo had been insured in Havana, as under the captaincy of Ramón Ferrer.

With favorable winds, the *Amistad* should have made Principe in two days. The distance was only about one hundred leagues. But, when the winds are adverse, the short voyage sometimes takes as much as fifteen days.

The *Amistad* was not going on to Principe. All that the Africans knew was that they lived two moons due east. They gave the Spaniards their orders accordingly. Through Antonio, they ordered Ruiz and Montez to hold the course due east by the sun. Montez had been a sea captain before he went into business for himself at Principe. He was now about fifty years old, and although he had been given wounds in the night whose scars he would always carry, from this time on the Africans were friendly to him, and promised that once they had reached the coast of Africa, he would be permitted to find his way home.

After the floggings and starvation, the vinegar, chains, and terribly cramped quarters, it was sweet to have the freedom of the ship, the clothing that was among the cargo in place of the slave rags, and to know that the sea stretching so far and blue before them led home, to the African village with its palm trees, its round huts and cone-shaped thatch, the beads and blankets, pointed teeth and peace. But the Spaniards were trying to work out a very different plan.

Ruiz, who had been unconscious for most of the day after the uprising, began to recover from his head-wound, and he and Montez plotted together at the wheel. A heavy gale was coming on, and in the clouds over the high seas, the sun was covered. The Africans relied completely on the Spaniards for their knowledge of navigation; they were inland people, all of them, knowing the mountains of the interior, the fenced towns and rice fields, and now they faced an unknown sea; they steered by the sun, and the sun was hidden. The Spaniards had an idea.

They had started out six or seven leagues from land. Now they headed for open sea. During the next four days, they boxed about in the Bahama Channel, and then the *Amistad* was steered for the island of St. Andrew, near New Providence. From here she went on to the Green Key, where they cast anchor. And again she headed out. During the day the Africans sailed eastward, eastward, toward home and full freedom, and threatened the lives of the Spaniards when the wind changed, they were so suspicious and dreaded so to be captured a second time. But at night, steering by the stars, Pedro Montez and José Ruiz headed north and west. And so the fabulous voyage continued, until ominous stories began to appear in Eastern newspapers, advising of the "long, low, black schooner," seen first at one point, and then at another on an altogether different course, following no possible route that any observer could discover. By day east, by night northwest, the *Amistad* zigzagged up the Atlantic, within hail of other ships from time to time, casting anchor when water and supplies were needed, losing their anchor at New Providence. For sixty-three days they sailed, while ten of their number died, while the Spaniards hoped continually that they would fall in with some warship, or be able to run into some port, and while the Africans looked continually for the coasts of home. Several times vessels drew up alongside, and they were boarded; once even an American schooner sent a party on board. That was on the 18th of August, 1839, and the stories of this phantom ship were already in the papers; but the American boat was friendly; it sold the *Amistad* a demijohn of water for a doubloon, and the Spaniards, locked up below, could not even shout until the American boat was out of sight. Two days later, they were twenty-five miles from New York, and Pilot Boat No. 3 came alongside and gave them some apples. Now it was clear what the Spaniards' trick had done. It had taken them almost due north, to a strange country and a strange civilization, from Africa and the Spanish depots and the Spanish bright town of Havana up the Atlantic to Long Island.

The Africans knew they were not anywhere near home. When Pilot Boat No. 4 came up, it found them armed, refusing to allow anyone on board. The *Amistad* headed along the coast, and on the 24th it was off Montauk Point, the tip of Long Island, with its wiry sharp grasses, its sand dunes—the end of America.

Here Cinquez ordered the ship steered for Montauk Light, whose tall freestone tower stood 250 feet above the beach, flashing its two lights—one blinking white, one shining steady and red over Shagwong Reef. Cinquez hoped he could go ashore here, but the tide drifted the boat up the bay, and it finally was anchored just off Culloden Point.

On the morning of the 26th, Cinquez and ten other men went ashore for water. The little houses on the Point looked strange to them, thick and thick-colored after the thatch and stucco. They were the little trim places of the lighthouse-keeper and a few fishermen. The white dunes were brilliant in the late summer sunlight, and out on the bright water, their ship was very black. The still beach was hot, but windy—and quite still until a dog barked, and then, from a second house, another dog barked. From around the cove a straggling line of white men came to meet the Africans. The black men plowed through the soft sand. They were spots of brilliant and impressive color. The first man, Cinquez, the leader, was naked to the waist. He was about twenty-six years old, dark and powerful, erect and handsome, the symmetrical lines of his fine face curving in toward the eyes and mouth. He stood five feet eight, and that was tall for his race; he had already proved himself a match for any two men on the schooner; he had kept order during the long voyage; and now, as he stood on the beach in his white trousers, his white planter's hat, and with a brilliant and many-colored necklace against his naked chest, he commanded the respect of any man. Behind him were the wild colors of Spanish shawls, used as trousers; gauze and Canton crepe wound around the dark throats. One man had an ornate and beautiful bridle in his hand; one wore a linen cambric shirt with complicated embroidery worked across the bosom. They jingled doubloons in their hands. They were the strangest boatload that had ever landed at Montauk Point.

Cinquez pointed toward the dogs that ran beside the white men, held out some money, and the first sale was made : a couple of dogs bought at the rate of three doubloons each. But what they had come for was water. Cinquez sent three men up to one of the houses with the white patrol.

News travelled rapidly from house to house on the Point. Captain Green, who lived near the tip of the island, had read

about the "long, low, black schooner" in the newspapers, and
knew at once that the end of the riddle was here. Ever since
early in August, orders had been given, to the U.S.S. *Fulton* and
to several revenue cutters, to chase the ship along its crazy
manoeuvering. Captain Green called together four or five of his
friends and went down to the beach. There she was, the
schooner, swinging at anchor just offshore, and eight or ten
black men were now waiting on the beach for the rest of their
party to return with water. As they saw this new group come
toward them ominously over the dunes, marching through the
stiff pale grass, they massed together in alarm, and Cinquez
whistled sharply—the prearranged signal for the others to run
back to the beach. Down from the house they came running,
the red and pink silks flying behind them. Captain Green's men
turned and fled. These blacks were unarmed, but the neighbors
with the Captain had thought to leave guns in the wagon standing on the shore road. When they came back, stepping gingerly,
they held their rifles ready. The Africans waited together; and,
seeing that the whites bore arms, the Africans sat down on the
beach, and Cinquez waved his arm in a sign of peace and an invitation to talk. Captain Green sat on the sand, and his men
gathered behind him, and there they held their parley, drawing
crude pictures in the sand and making the hand-signs by which
men understand each other's simple basic fears and wishes, even
when they have no words.

There were two questions the Africans first must have indicated. These were their two deepest dreads : Are there any
slaves in this country? Are there any Spaniards? And when these
two were answered, they were reassured, and sat smiling and
talking to one another in tones that anyone might have known
were those of congratulation. They were safe; they were free;
they were in a good country. But Captain Green destroyed their
moment. He drew the clumsy, thick-lined drawing of a ship
with his finger in the sand. Next to it he drew the heavy guns of
a vessel of war. They knew by these signs that they were being
pursued.

The parley on the beach lasted until late afternoon, four hours
of slow exchange, by signal and drawing, until the Africans had
turned over to Captain Green two guns, a knife, and a hat.
Besides these tokens of peace and friendship, they had given

their agreement to turn the schooner over to the Captain, who was to take them to another part of the island, and from there to sail with them to Sierra Leone.

And then another vessel came in sight, slowly, from the straits between Montauk and Gardner's Point. It was the U.S. brig *Washington*, Lieutenant Gedney in command, which was making soundings. It had sighted the strange ship lying inshore, and, as it watched, the small boat was seen crossing from the shore to the ship, and then back. Lieutenant Gedney had his career ahead of him, and he saw a prize in this black ship, riding so close to the beach. She looked like a pirate, he thought, as he squinted through the glass . . . and those people on the beach, with their carts and horses, and that boat crossing back and forth from land. He barked out his orders, and a boat was armed and dispatched with an officer.

As they rocked alongside the *Amistad*, riding in almost four fathoms of water, about three-quarters of a mile off free New York State, she seemed to them like some Flying Dutchman of dream, a derelict, impossible ship. Her rigging and her sails were torn and hung in shrouds and bandages down to the deck. The sides of the hull were bright green below the water-line, green and in motion, with the long, waving sea-grass that covered them and covered the crusting of barnacles on the wood. The sailors from the *Washington* swarmed up the green sides of the *Amistad* and for the first time saw the deck.

Stacked and coiled across the ship were the piles of goods they had captured : rice, silk, firearms, raisins, vermicelli, cotton goods. Everything seemed to be heaped here : bread and thin, sick Africans, emaciated almost to the skeleton, books and mirrors, hardware, olives, saddles and holsters, luxuries and fruit and jars of olive oil. The twenty men left to guard the ship waited for the first hostile move of the boarding-party; and over against the windlass, three little girls between eight and thirteen laughed at the strangers, who were prying into the cabin and the hold, uncovering still more fruits and silk, the calico heaped high, the crepe, the pictures, the entire rich cargo of the *Amistad*.

They came to a long bundle wrapped in black bombazine, lying on the forward hatch, and pulled back the black. There was a naked corpse, the last of the ten who had died on the passage. Kon-no-ma, who was watching over the body, pulled back the shroud, frowning at the intruders; he was the most ferocious-looking of the Africans, short, with a large, round head, a diamond-shaped tattoo mark on his forehead, and filed teeth that projected past his lips. The men from the *Washington* stepped back, and one said to another, "Cannibal!" But there was no reason for fear. The Africans had given up their guns—and, besides, they were in a free country. They offered no resistance.

Cinquez's boatload rowed up and boarded, and the Africans crowded around him, talking and pointing. There was still no reason for anxiety. But in that minute the entire situation changed forever : a breathless sailor climbed up from the cabin, yelling something about two white men, and in a moment Ruiz and Montez were brought up from below. Ruiz, who spoke English, demanded protection and the arrest of everyone on board. Cinquez could see what was coming, even before the officer started his quick and formal statement of possession. He rushed to the rail, stood balanced for a second, and then cut a swift arc in the air. Once in the water, while everyone on deck rushed to the side, the down-turned faces full of alarm and grief, he made a twisting motion, unbuckling the money belt around his waist. The doubloons—he had three hundred—sank, turning and seeming to darken and melt in the water. The faces watched, horrified; but he was already swimming back to the green side of the *Amistad*. They raised him, dripping, to the deck, and he gave himself up to the government of the United States.

The boat from the *Washington* rowed back with Ruiz, Montez, and Cinquez on it, leaving a guard mounted on the *Amistad*. Once on the *Washington*, however, Cinquez showed such distress that Lieutenant Gedney allowed him to return; the Africans clustered around him as he reached them, laughing, and wildly happy. He spoke to them in words the Americans had never heard, but the Africans seemed so roused by what he said that the officer in command saw to it that Cinquez was led away by force. On the following day, Cinquez signified by motions that if the sailors would take him aboard the *Amistad*, he would show them a handkerchief full of doubloons. They rowed him over once again; the irons, in which he had been manacled while he was on the *Washington*, were removed; he went below, and made another speech to his own people. They were even more

CINQUEZ
Leader of the *Amistad* mutiny. (From the portrait by Nathaniel Jocelyn.)

wildly excited than they had been the day before; when Cinquez looked at the white sailors who were with him, the Africans shouted, and talked to each other with the same determination his voice carried. The sailors found this terrifying : the strange tongue, the looks, the Africans leaping in the crowded cabin—these black men who had already killed and gone through a fearful voyage for their freedom! There was no further indication concerning doubloons. They locked the irons on Cinquez again and took him back to the *Washington*. This time he said nothing, but he kept his eye steadily fixed on the long, low, black schooner.

Lieutenant Gedney had sent an express to the U.S. Marshal at New Haven, and he in turn had given information to His Honor A. T. Judson, U.S. District Judge. He set sail that night for New London, and the *Amistad* followed. In the morning the two ships lay off the fort, and the gentlemen arrived to hold court on the deck of the *Washington*, a musket-shot away from the schooner. The cutter *Experiment* took the newspapermen, who had arrived, on board the *Washington* for the judicial investigation, and the New London *Gazette* published a complete report at once, which was reprinted immediately up and down the East. It began :

We have just returned from a visit to the *Washington* and her prize, which are riding at anchor in the bay, near the fort. On board the former we saw and conversed with the two Spanish gentlemen, who were passengers on board the schooner, as well as owners of the negroes and most of the cargo. One of them, Jose Ruiz, is a very gentlemanly and intelligent young man, and speaks English fluently. He was the owner of most of the slaves and cargo, which he was conveying to his estate on the Island of Cuba. The other, Pedro Montez, is about fifty years of age, and is the owner of four of the slaves. He was formerly a ship master, and has navigated the vessel since her seizure by the blacks. Both of them, as may be naturally supposed, are most unfeignedly thankful for their deliverance. Jose Pedro is the most striking instance of complacency and unalloyed delight we have ever witnessed, and it is not strange, since only yesterday his sentence was pronounced by the chief of the bucaniers, and his death song chanted by the grim crew, who gathered with uplifted sabres around his devoted head, which, as well as his arms, bear the scars of several wounds inflicted at the time of the murder of the ill-fated captain and crew. He sat smoking his Havana on the deck, and to judge from the martyr-like serenity of his countenance, his emotions are such as rarely stir the heart of man. When Mr. Porter, the prize master, assured him of his safety, he threw his arms around his neck, while gushing tears coursing down his furrowed cheek, bespoke the overflowing transport of his soul. Every now and then he clasped his hands, and with uplifted eyes, gave thanks to "the Holy Virgin" who had led him out of his troubles. Senor Ruiz has given us two letters for his agents, Messrs. Shelton, Brothers & Co. of Boston, and Peter A. Harmony & Co. of New York. It appears that the slaves, the greater portion of whom were his, were very much attached to him, and had determined after reaching the coast of Africa, to allow him to seek his home what way he could, while his poor companion was to be sacrificed.

After a description of the Africans on the *Amistad*, the reporter goes on :

We were glad to leave this vessel, as the exhalations from her hold and deck, were like any thing but "gales wafted over the gardens of Gul."

And then to the point of the entire incident :

There is a question for the laws of Admiralty to decide, whether captain Gedney and his fellow officers are entitled to prize or salvage money. To one or the other they are most surely entitled, and we hope they will get their just dues. Captain Gedney, when he first espied the Amistad, was running a line of sounding towards Montauk Point. He had heard nothing of this vessel being on the coast till after his arrival in this port.

The judicial investigation took place on the *Washington* on August 29, 1839. Complaints were lodged by Montez and Ruiz against Cinquez and the thirty-eight other Africans who were left alive, and the depositions of the two Spaniards were taken through interpreters. After they had gone to their cabins, the investigation adjourned to the schooner to inspect it and to allow Antonio, the cabin-boy, to identify the Africans according to their roles in the mutiny. The examination proceeded exactly as if Ruiz and Montez had owned the *Amistad*, and as if Connecticut and New York had been passionate slave states. At the end of the investigation, Ruiz and Montez caused a notice to be printed in all the city papers as a token of their thankfulness, and all the male Africans stood committed for trial before the next Circuit Court at Hartford. The three little girls and Antonio were held in $100 bond apiece, and being unable to produce the money, were sent along with the rest on board a sloop.

In charge of Lieutenant Holcomb, of the *Washington*, and Colonel Pendleton, keeper of the prison to which they were being taken, they sailed up the Sound, and arrived in New Haven on Sunday morning, September 1, 1839.

Living in the county jail was not too different from living on the *Amistad*. The great wooden room in which most of them lived together was not unlike the hold of the ship. It was larger, lighter, cleaner. Here thirty-six of them were kept, and the rest were in three smaller chambers, the three little girls in one, the sick in another. They could be together, could talk together in their own tongue, which none of these strangers seemed to understand. And once a day they were taken out of their confinement for exercise.

There was nothing in the lives of the Africans to prepare them for that scene. The glare of Sierra Leone, the sharp glimpse of angled Havana, was what they knew; and this was intensely different, this New England autumn of a century ago.

This color that they saw, these flickering delicate elms, the wide sweep of the Green, the profound sky—nothing in the tropics, nothing on the sea, could have predicted this! But there was more; for past the avenues of feathers gleamed a whiteness never seen before, in soft round pillars rising as marble never seen before, a new and enchanting whiteness, fluted intricately, and rising to support great shapes that floated like white reefs over these pale and columned porches, whose steps rose up to them in the whiteness of astounding sand; and beyond this, a warm red never seen before, warm walls taller than they had dreamed, with shining squares, the gleaming windows in the warm brick. More feathers, feathery trees in double and triple arches, fell into green shadows, green brilliance, wherever they looked. And under these walked tall, pale men in black; and through all these crowds women passed, swathed at the shoulders and thighs, bound tight at the waist, in the most voluptuous bindings and cascade and swirl of clothes they yet had seen. This field, these temples, these ox-carts moving among such fantastically dressed white men and women, these deep wild bells sounding from the pinnacles of the white steeples—this was the softest, most luxurious, most surrealist scene possible to dream. Even the grass was softer here, the leaves cut and curled into softness. The smells of farm-wagons, the fruit, the early fall vegetables, the oyster-booths at the corner of the Green, mixed with the grass-smells; and the rich shadows fell among this light more softly, more graciously, than shadows ever fell.

But, as far as the Africans were concerned, this was their prison-yard and their time of day for exercise—these minutes when they were brought out on the Green, while a crowd of these swathed women and men in clothes like tubes, and children in little clothes like the men's, came and watched their acrobatics.

Some of the white men even came into the jail. Many were beginning to visit the prison-rooms to stare, paying the admission price of twelve and a half cents; but some others arrived, making sounds at them, saying words not quite so strange as all the other words they had heard since the *Amistad* was boarded off Montauk. And then these gentlemen would turn to each other and talk for a long time.

In New York City, at a meeting of "a few friends of freedom," a committee was appointed to defend the Africans, and Lewis Tappan, Simeon S. Jocelyn, and Joshua Leavitt were now ready to receive donations, employ counsel, and act in any other ways as they saw fit for the conduct of the trial. The counsel that was engaged was Seth P. Staples and Theodore Sedgwick of New York, and, in New Haven, the rising and liberal lawyer, Roger S. Baldwin.

The main problem now was one of communication. The Africans spoke a language that was completely incomprehensible to anyone who had yet seen them; they were being tried, according to some, for a crime that included the worst, most anarchic list of separate crimes : mutiny, murder, theft of a ship on the high seas, abduction, piracy . . . but others, even while recognizing that the lack of speech might cover any sort of villainy, here saw these captives as people involved in a fight for their own freedom, against the strongest force possible : international business. For it was plain that, even at this early date, the Spanish government was going to make claims; the owners were demanding their rights; and Washington was rather ready to listen. By September 14th, the papers were noting that the

The "Amistad" Mutiny

Spanish Minister had asked for the ship, the cargo, and the slaves, and would probably get them. Most of the press sneered at the abolitionists, saying that if they were really friendly to the blacks, they would leave them alone. The abolitionists gave them clothes, but the prisoners would not keep them on, said the mocking articles. In the election campaign, the hostile newspapers poured out laughter, calling for Cinquez for President. But other newspapers answered, comparing democracy to the man's jack-knife—he had had it for years, though it had had nine new blades and thirteen new handles. And now the Spanish Minister, the Chevalier de Argaiz, was making new claims. He was asking for a trial at Havana, where the slave trade was wide open and the whole thing could be railroaded through. One thing was on the side of a speedy trial, however. It was going to be held in Connecticut. Mr. Holabird, the U.S. District Attorney, and Ralph I. Ingersoll, already prominent in New Haven law, were counsel for the prosecution.

Abolitionist feeling was high in New England. Case after case in Connecticut alone had laid open the structure of the country, the structure, indeed, of the country's will and feeling and economic existence. Sixty years before, Lafayette had been horrified at the spectacle of black and white Revolutionary soldiers eating together at the same mess; and during these years, the shape of the country was making itself plain. The South was farm country, breeding country, and it had become a breeding-farm for slaves; annually Virginia was exporting forty thousand Negroes southward; and New England, which stood by, watching with a certain horror and making steady profits out of the end-products of the cotton fields, had a shaky and equivocal position to maintain. The symptoms cropped up, in the small towns of New York and Massachusetts and Connecticut. All of the legalists involved in this new trial had been arguing one side of the slavery question in the courts for years, and the judge, Andrew Judson, had been prosecutor in the Prudence Crandall case, in 1833, which ended the persecution—her life had been threatened, her house attacked, her reputation smeared endlessly—of Prudence Crandall, a young schoolteacher who had admitted Negro children into her school at Canterbury.

The first trial, at Hartford, held on the habeas-corpus writ, served only to indicate how far-reaching the pressures were. A man named John Ferry, a native African, had been found in New York, who was able to speak freely with one or two of the prisoners, and imperfectly with the others, being a member of the Gissi tribe. Communication had become the most important objective for the defense. The Africans had at first been committed for murder, but the Circuit Court decided that it could take no legal cognizance of an act on board a Spanish vessel. Gedney, as master of the ship that took the *Amistad*, then filed a libel on the vessel and cargo. This cargo included the prisoners, whom he claimed as salvage. Montez claimed the three little girls, Teme, Kagne, and Margru, who were listed in the passports which had been whipped up at Havana as Joana, Josepha, and Francisca. But District Attorney Holabird, in filing two claims for the United States, spoke for the split country. The first claim and libel was on behalf of the United States at the instance of the Spanish Minister, and called for the restoration of the Africans to the Spaniards. The second, also on behalf of the United States, claimed that the Africans were free persons, wrongfully brought into the country, and to be returned to their native land. The court was adjourned after the session on Saturday afternoon, September 21st, and the Africans were sent back to the County house at New Haven.

The crowd gathering to watch them on the Green—the men in the long, black, tubed clothes, the swathed women—did not include one who could speak to them. In the courthouse, John Ferry had shown the long papers under which they had marked their signs. But they had not yet been heard once. People had stared at them, pointing and laughing, strange, busy men had come into the jail and drawn pictures of them; plaster casts had been made for Mr. Fowler; and Mr. Fletcher, the phrenologist, was measuring their heads and jotting down notes on the number of inches from the root of the nose to the occipital protuberance over the top of the head, to determine their temperaments. It was not until the day after they returned from Hartford that a tall, thin man all in black, with strikingly deepset eyes under a smooth bland forehead, its brown hair brushed in a wide swathe across—with lined and knotted cheeks, whose muscles of control tightened the jaw and mouth sternly together—came into the jail, walking in that day with his head down, in that stride they were to know well, brooding, remote, and careless. He came in, sat down among them, and with nods and thrustings of his fingers one after the other soon made them understand. He put out one finger, and nodded and smiled at them. "*E-ta,*" said one of the Africans, in recognition, and one of the little girls repeated it like a lesson—"*e-ta,*" she said, and held up one finger. The tall clerical man wrote down the letters for it. And held up two fingers this time. Now several of them were answering, caught up in the game. "*Fe-le,*" they said; and for three fingers, "*sau-wa,*" and four, "*na-ni,*" and so on, "*do-lu, we-ta, waw-fe-la, wai-ya-gba, ta-u,*" up to ten, "*pu.*" The white man took his page of notes and smiled at them, another smile with the beginning of knowledge and promise in it.

He strode off, filled with this new possibility, striding across the Green that they had seen as soft and voluptuous, that he saw scarcely at all, lost in his plans.

"Good day, Professor Gibbs," said a bonneted, mittened woman as he passed without seeing her. He turned and spoke, courteously, but with a distance in his voice.

Josiah Willard Gibbs, professor of theology and sacred literature at Yale, had devoted his forty-nine years to religion, to the language of religion, and to the new comparative study of languages which German scholarship, in the early years of the century, was illuminating as a study of the nature of man expressed in his words, the sounds and the structure of their various grammars. Born in Salem, he was the third son of Henry Gibbs, a merchant who had been in the class of 1766 at Harvard, and had then taught school at Rowley, at New Castle, N.H., and at Lynn, before he married Mercy Prescott of Salem and settled there. His father had died when he was four, and his mother had brought up the children, sending young Josiah to his uncle at New Haven—sending him to Yale rather than to Harvard, where the Gibbs family had always gone, and the Willards as well, as far back as Samuel Willard, acting president of the College from 1701 to 1707. Scholars and librarians, the family had handed down its qualities, unselfish scholarship, modesty, constitutional frailty, a single-minded pursuit of truth in son after son. And the women they married were the rare intellectual women of early New England whose spirits reach out still from the old portraits —fine, tempered, and thin. A merchant like Henry Gibbs in this family was almost an aberration. It was possible, perhaps, after many years of teaching. The tradition was one of withdrawal, of a canalízed passion given mainly to scholarship, of a remoteness among which this visit to the jail was a thunderclap.

But this was a combining occasion, one of those events that bring a life into focus, summoning qualities that until such a moment seem remote from each other, alien and useless. It was the first and only moment in Josiah Gibbs's career that could call into play his religious belief in the value of the human being, his skill in language and the reconstruction, as from fossils, of a grammar from the broken phrases set down in travel books, in the letters of missionaries, or on such a visit as he had just made—and the wish to affirm truth as he saw it that motivated a good section of the small faculty of Yale.

Walking home with his head down, almost looking behind him in the posture familiar to New Haven, he went from the College to Crown Street, where he lived in President Day's house, rented some time ago, with his wife—he had married when he was forty—the three small daughters, and the baby, his son and namesake who had just been born. He could be glad of his wife's understanding. For it was quite clear what he was to do. Communication—that was the problem here; and he held the key. Now he must find an interpreter. The abolitionists were eager for an adequate defense; his cousin, Roger Baldwin, would go to any length to give this trial its due, for it was now obvious that the deepest rights of the individual were concerned—and more, the deep rights of the inarticulate individual, the rights that must be fought for without the persuasion and argument that would move the Yankee mind. Tappan and Staples could be counted on to raise the money, at any sacrifice. But money and conviction were not enough without him. He, Gibbs, was the link. Communication was the link here.

Two days later he was on his way to New York. The port was the most likely place to find someone who could speak both Mendi, the dialect of the Africans, and English. The union stages left New Haven on Mondays at 3 A.M. and 11 A.M. and the early stage would take him through the morning darkness of Milford and Stratford to Bridgeport, from where the *Nimrod* and the *Fairfield* sailed for New York. For $1.75, the whole trip could be made, the hills rocking past the curtains of the stagecoach as the blackness lightened, and then the marvellous colored dawn over the farm-land of the valley, just beginning to turn metal and red in mid-September; then the clang and hurry at the dock, as the bales and casks were loaded on the packet, with its decks like the floors of a warehouse, its machinery showing as the connecting-rod and two tall black chimneys rose high above the wheelhouse, the whole thing standing high out of the water; and now the last-comers rustling up the gangway; and the still blue hours on the Sound. The orchard-lands and the drowned valleys slid by, and the turns of the river arrived—Hell's Gate, the Hog's Back, the Frying Pan; and at last the fenced-in island, behind its miles of masts and wooden piers, after the channels with their villas on the shore, the turf and trees, the lighthouse, the cheering inmates of the madhouse, and the jail. One could see from the deck as clear as water-color the Dutch houses, almost brick by brick, see the gables and the little steps to the roofs and the shining weathercocks that gleamed in the bright air. The crowded streets, with their carts and omnibuses. The buildings and the flags and the bells. A sunny, vivid city under an Italian sky, moving slowly as the boat pushed among the river-traffic, among all the red-and-black smokestacks of the ferries. And the New York sounds began, the puffing and churning of these boats, with their paddles, the clipped notes of the horses' hoofs as a carriage went by at the trot; until the last turn was made, and the slanting sails of the great packets at Sandy Hook began to fill the harbor. As he landed, he could hear the street-cries, "Ice," "Hot corn, *hot* corn," and he had the city before him, with a fantastic clue in his hand, the letters spelling out how the Africans had counted up to ten.

He made his way from ship to ship in the harbor, pausing to introduce himself and ask for a Negro boy who could understand his "*E-ta, fe-le, sau-wa,*" to be disappointed again and again. From the Battery, with the crickets chirping in the trees, he went farther uptown, to the elegant section of Waverley and Lafayette Places, with their cream-painted brick houses, white lines in the seams, the section of parasols and coaches, as against the bowling-saloons and oyster-cellars and general wretchedness of the Five Points. Offal was thrown into the streets, wherever one turned pigs ran wild, great brown, black-blotched hogs shunting their snouts along the curbs, nudging the walkers, feasting in the gutters at City Hall.

From boat to boat he went, until at last, on the *Buzzard*, a British armed brig under Captain Fitzgerald, he found, among the Africans employed there, two who he thought would do, Charles Pratt and James Covey. The brig was lying in the harbor with a number of vessels seized by her on the coast of Africa for being engaged in the slave trade, and when Captain Fitzgerald was shown the request of the committee, he gave his permission that the two interpreters be brought to New Haven. James Covey was about twenty years old; he was born in the Mendi country, and his mother was Gissi. Covey had been kidnapped when he was very young, and sold as a slave to the king of a neighboring tribe. He was used to plant the queen's rice-fields for three years, at the end of which he was sold to a Portuguese and taken to Lomboko. He and about three hundred others were put on a slave-ship to be sent to America; but, about four days out from Lomboko, the ship was captured by a British vessel, and Covey obtained his freedom in Sierra Leone, where he learned English at the Church Missionary Society. At the end of 1838, he enlisted as a sailor on the *Buzzard*. Pratt was a native Mendi, and had been rescued from a slave-ship about seven years before.

Gibbs and the two sailors started for New Haven at once.

There was "unspeakable joy" when they got to the jail. Professor Gibbs wrote to the committee about this meeting : "It would have done your heart good to witness the joy of the Africans at finding themselves able to converse with the men." And another witness added :

We called with the interpreters at the prison this morning, just as the African captives were at breakfast. The Marshal objected to the entrance of the interpreters until the breakfast was over, but one of the captives coming to the door and finding a fellow-countryman who could talk in their own language, took hold of him, and literally dragged him in. Such a scene ensued as you may better conceive than describe. Breakfast was forgotten, all crowded round the two men, and all talking as fast as possible. The children hugged one another with transport.

And now the trials began : a series of court session and newspaper debates, of international duplicity and intrigue on overlapping intrigue. The five sets of claims crossed a dozen ways : the Africans claimed freedom, charging Ruiz and Montez with assault, battery, and false imprisonment; Gedney (who had already earned prominence for supervising the dredging of the deep channel in New York Harbor which bears his name) claimed salvage on the vessel, the cargo, and the slaves; Captain Green and the Long Islanders who had met Cinquez at Montauk had filed a claim identical with Gedney's; the Spanish Minister, Calderón, and the new Minister, De Argaiz, claimed the boat and the Africans under the treaty of 1795, held that the trials should take place in Cuba, and objected that the effect of a "trial and execution" in Connecticut was not as good, and these Spanish demands were supported by a strong American pro-slavery press; and, finally, District Attorney Holabird claimed that the Africans should be held, according to the 1819 act, subject to the pleasure of the President. Acting according to the slavery interests, Holabird wrote to· John Forsyth, the Secretary of State, asking whether the Federal government could deliver the Africans up to Spain *before* the court had actually sat. He inquired about possible treaty stipulations covering such an act. The Secretary of State knew there were no such stipulations, but he instructed Holabird to see that the court proceedings did not put the Africans out of the Federal jurisdiction; and he turned the letter over to the pro-slavery Attorney General, Felix Grundy, who could see no reason to investigate the possibilities, and declared that they should be surrendered, together with the cargo, to persons designated by Calderón.

But President Van Buren, with all the sympathy in the world for the Spanish Minister, was unable to do this. There was no extradition treaty with Spain.

When the Circuit Court ruled that the *Amistad* had been found on the high seas, and the Africans were not to be held for such a murder, De Argaiz wrote another letter, denying the rights of the United States courts, and asked the President to send the Africans back to Cuba in a government boat. Van Buren, far from resenting this, sent an order to Lieutenants Gedney and Meade to stand ready to convey the Africans from New Haven. This order was sent *before* the court assembled at New Haven, on January 7, 1840.

At this trial the matter of the passports took on even greater weight. There was a distinction made in the terms for Africans newly landed in the New World, who were called *bozales*, and

Africans landed before the prohibition of the slave trade in 1820, who were called *ladinos*. The mass passports made out for these "slaves" were by owner—one passport for forty-nine slaves belonging to J. Ruiz, and one for three slaves belonging to P. Montez (the three little girls; for the little boy, Kale, whom Montez later demanded, there was no passport at all), and in these documents, the Africans are called *"cuerenta y nueva negros ladinos"* and *"tres negras ladinas."* Now, through the interpreters, it became possible to prove that the Africans had not been in Cuba and knew not a single word of Spanish. The stories of their kidnapping and sale became known, as they told their history, living and dying in the New Haven jail. Six more had died since the beginning of their captivity, and had been buried. Local clergymen, including Leonard Bacon, had spoken at the funerals. At the funeral of Kaperi, prayers were offered in the room, and the substance of his friends' remarks was, "Kaperi is dead. His body is still, and will be laid in the ground. The soul of Kaperi is alive. It will never die. Our souls will never die. They will live after our bodies are dead and cold. The Bible tells us how our souls may go to the good place. You must learn to read the Bible. Pray to God, become good, and then when your bodies die, God will take your souls to the good place, and make you happy forever." And then, with a great number of the New Haven people, they walked in procession to the grave. A hymn was sung and read there, and Mr. Bacon offered a prayer.

The Africans were learning to read and write. They could say "Merica," when asked where they were. They could make simple conversation. But the shadow over their religious and linguistic education was their anxiety, according to their teachers, Professor Gibbs and the "young gentlemen connected with Yale College." They had uncertainty in respect to the future. They dreaded going back to Havana, and would interrupt their prayers, in the middle of "*O ga-wa-wa* [O great God], *bi-a-bi yan-din-go* [Thou art good], *bi-a-bi ha-ni gbe-le ba-te-ni* [Thou hast made all things]", to speak of this. When the nature of an oath was explained to them, and it was added that God would visit the man who violated an oath with His displeasure, they asked, "What will be done to the people of the United States if they send us back to Havana?"

In a contemporary account, there is a description of the scene when they received the news of the decision of the District Court.

They were assembled and seated in a commodious room—they knew that their case was pending—some of them had been called to testify in court—they were of course deeply anxious for the event. All being present and quiet, they were informed that the judge had decreed their return, not to Havana, but to their native land. They leaped from their seats, rushed across the room, threw themselves prostrate at the feet of those who brought them the glad tidings, while "thank you, thank you" was the expression of every tongue.

The succeeding day Mr. Baldwin, one of their counsel, entered the jail. Cinquez was seated behind a table, and members of his class on either side of him. As Mr. B. approached, Cinquez was told that he pleaded his cause; said it would be wrong to send him to Havana. He dropped his book, rose from his seat, seeming for a moment deliberating whether he should leap the table. Seeing this to be attended with difficulty, he reached forward, and seizing the extended hand of Mr. B. with a firm grasp, and looking him in the face, his own countenance beaming with the most grateful emotion, exclaimed, "We thank you, we bless you, this is all we can do for you."

During this icy winter, the *Grampus* lay in New Haven Harbor. It had been sent up from the Brooklyn Navy Yard early in January, to the open dismay of most of New Haven, and a little later the anti-slavery group had stationed another schooner offshore, in the hope of running the Africans to Canada if any open attempt were made to ship them to Cuba or Spain. It was obvious that the verdict that they were freemen, not property—men who had fought to regain their lost freedom, not criminals —acquitted men, and not condemned slaves—it was obvious that any such verdict would not be allowed to stand. The case was appealed by order of the Secretary of State the moment the verdict was announced. The District Attorney rushed a special messenger through the icy mud of the road to Washington, so that the President might correct a clerical error in his order to hold the Africans. Van Buren sent a flagrant message to the Marshal—a message pandering at every point to the Spanish government, pandering in a manner so impossible for the Chief Executive of the United States that he was later forced to deny that it was his. But, with Justice Thompson on the bench, the decision of the District Court was affirmed pro forma, and the whole matter was left to the United States Supreme Court on appeal.

This was the end of April 1840. And now, with the addition of other members to the legal staff of the defense, the committee was prepared to go ahead without stint of time or money to the last appeal, before the Supreme Court. They needed a counsel whose argument would be brilliant and unquestioned in its honesty; they needed a defense that would set this case before history as a pivotal point in the climb towards freedom. They needed, not a lawyer, but an idealistic philosopher. The man they went to was John Quincy Adams.

He was ex-President, seventy-three years old, ill, tired, long ago defeated in a great and personal defeat. He was the "old man eloquent"; he was the President who had committed political suicide for the sake of science; and he had not been in a court for thirty-two years. He was one of the great peaks in democratic civilization, standing for law and human dignity, for science and faith. His standard was George Washington, and, as Brooks Adams says, "to him it was from the very outset clear that, if the democratic social system were capable of progression upward to a level at which it could hope to ameliorate the lot of men on earth, it must tend, at least, to produce an average which, if it did not attain to the eminent ability of the first President, might at least be capable of understanding and appreciating his moral altitude." He was at home in Quincy on October 27, 1840, when Ellis Loring and Lewis Tappan came to call, to enlist his sympathy in the case and to leave the two great scrapbooks of the *Amistad* captives—letters, press clippings, reports. As for his sympathy, that had been long ago enlisted. There was a sympathy in John Quincy Adams that must include these Africans. A year before, when he had had Loring's first letter about the case, just after the Hartford trial, he had begun to watch the developments; by that October he had been absorbed in their meaning; and only a few months ago, he had offered a resolution in the House, calling on the President for papers concerning the *Amistad*.

He pushed back the two huge scrapbooks. He could not possibly take this case. He was old, he was infirm, he had been away from these lists too long. They argued with him; this was a matter of life and death, but that was the least argument; the case was critical, it touched his interests, causes in which he had spent a lifetime. He alone was equal to this. And after long demurring, he pulled the scrapbooks across the table toward him. He would take the case. And he wrote in the diary which is only one of his monuments : "I implore the mercy of Almighty God so as to control my temper, to enlighten my soul, and to give me utterance, that I may prove myself in every respect equal to the task." And again, writing at night : "Oh, how shall I do justice to this case and to these men?"

Three weeks later, at five-thirty in the morning, he took the cars from Hartford to New Haven. At eight o'clock he arrived and went straight to the Tontine Hotel, the best in town, although the Quinnipiac was trying hard to equal it. He had a quiet breakfast there, and during breakfast Roger Baldwin called on him, talked for a while about the case, and invited him to his office to inspect the papers on the *Amistad* trials. They talked there for about two hours, and then Mr. Adams, with Baldwin, Marshal Wilcox, Deputy Pendleton, and a keeper, went through the rooms at the jail and met the Africans. He did not see the three little girls, who were in a separate chamber, but he met the men—of whom there were now thirty-two. They were sleeping double in crib beds, in a room thirty feet by twenty—"negro face, fleece, and form," he writes, "but varying in color from ebon black to dingy brown. 1 or 2 of them almost mulatto bright. Cinquez & Grabow, the 2 chief conspirators, have very remarkable countenances." They were put through their paces for him; while he listened politely, three of them took turns at reading part of a chapter in the English New Testament, "very indifferently." One boy writes, he noted. Mr. Ludlow was teaching them, but they learned slowly, huddled together as they were, with no one to talk to.

In lesser natures, there is always the danger in an issue of this sort that a lack of impressiveness in the prisoners themselves may make a possible champion lose faith. The public expects its martyrs to be saints, and it is only the defender who puts the cause above the man, the fight for life above the individual life, who can be reconciled to the fact that he is a martyr and part of a cause, and not too much more. Adams was not only passionately devoted to the cause under which the *Amistad* Africans were defended, he was committed to a future in which its justification would be taken for granted. He was concerned with the future—a future living in one's own time, whose origins are to be seen in the flowing present, a future that must daily be found and helped clear. "Besides anticipating by nearly a hundred years some of the most enlightened measures of conservation," say the Beards, "Adams foresaw in a livid flash the doom of slavery in a social war." Repudiated by his country, conscious of failure at every step of his effort toward the country's enlightenment, he knew the depth of the contemporary antagonism—the cleft in the republic, the great split in which he acted a firm and frightful role, prophetic, integrated, and hostile to a planted majority.

By the 30th he was in Washington, where he spoke to Attorney General Gilpin about the case, urging him to submit to the President to have the case dismissed by consent, without argument. The Africans were obviously *bozales*, newly imported; that fact destroyed the last Spanish claim, which rested upon their passports. In the documents, the term *ladino* had been wilfully mistranslated as "sound." Early December was spent in going over the translations, particularly of Document No. 185— and on December 11th, Gilpin's report came through. The President would not dismiss the case because of the Spanish Minister's claim. Adams records that he quarreled with Gilpin on the spot, and he writes on December 12, 1840, that he is preparing the case—

with deep anguish of heart, and a painful search of means to defeat and expose the abominable conspiracy, Executive and Judicial, of this Government against the lives of those wretched men. How shall the facts be brought out? How shall it be possible to comment upon them with becoming temper—with calmness, with moderation, with firmness, with address, to avoid being silenced, and to escape the imminent danger of giving the adversary the advantage in the argument by overheated zeal? Of all the dangers before me, that of losing my self-possession is the most formidable. I am yet unable to prepare the outline of the argument, which I must be ready to offer the second week in January. Let me not forget my duty.

December in Washington brought its bright sky and snow-chilled air, and the slush and mud for which the unfinished capi-

tal was notorious abroad. There were continual admissions and
exasperations : the proofreader confessed that the mistranslation
was his fault; Adams, in going over the records, fumes against
Gedney, raging for the Lieutenant's having taken the men on the
shore, without right, and the ship on the high seas, without right.
He wished the whole thing were over; talking to the President,
complaining about the difficulty and importance of correct
printing, putting through the new license for the *Amistad*. In
January, Gedney's sister-in-law arrived, pleading for the newly
made Captain. He was ill, she said, and not very sound in mind.
Adams answered her stream of appeal with the assurance that he
would have all due consideration for the condition of Captain
Gedney. And when Baldwin came in three days later, Adams
signed the brief, and sighed over his diary, "I know not yet how
to order my speech aright."

Francis Scott Key, the United States District Attorney who
wrote "The Star-Spangled Banner," came up to him, talking
pessimistically about the case—this case for which Mr. Adams'
heart was ready, while his unpreparedness more and more
rankled in him. Key had argued the *Antelope* case, which was
similar enough, and which Adams knew he would have to review
in his defense. Now document after document turned up—the
Chief Clerk's letter saying he had been sorry to see "the rascally
blacks fall into the hands of the abolitionists with whom Hartford is filled." The day after this came out into the open, a postponement was granted. Mr. Adams knew a momentary relief,
but his suspense was too real. He was immediately involved with
the British Minister, Henry Stephen Fox, who wished advice as
to what he might do in case of a judgment against the *Amistad*
captives. Adams advised him to write to the Secretary of State;
and with the new date pushed ahead to February 16th, and Baldwin's return to Connecticut until then, he plunged deep into the
House debate, which was furious at the moment. These were
desperate days for John Quincy Adams. Opposed by what were
to him the most malignant forces of evil in the country, the
reactionaries—the *popular* reactionaries—and by the slave oligarchy, he was fighting an isolated fight in the House, for free
speech, for scientific innovations, for the civilized application of
that education whose uncivilized use was creating the conflict
now gathering its storm. The furious, brainless, heartless debate

in the House could only be abandoned—he went back to read the old cases—he rose and went back to the House, to plunge into his savage feud with General Wise, attacking in this death-struggle. In the meantime, Fox had still had no answer to his letter. Time was growing short. Mr. Adams was deep in the demonic struggle in the House. He prayed. Praying for control, always more control, for he was swung from hell to hell in his passion, an immortal passion for America, for the mind of God in America, he raged against his "eccentric, wild, extravagant freaks of passion." Seeing this mind, this country, split, he remembered tragic Coriolanus and the Voices. He remembered the red and white roses in the Temple gardens.

And soon the trial itself was on him, among all the reading, the books of the *Antelope* record piled high, the pathetic death of the servant Jeremy Leary and his funeral, the last postponement to the 22nd ("I have yet to prepare a frame for my argument")—and now Baldwin begins, "sound and eloquent but exceedingly mild," carrying the legalistic burden in answer to Attorney General Gilpin. And on the 23rd, with the hour rushing on him, he is still writing, "The very skeleton of my argument is not yet put together." But that night it breaks; he begins to come through; he finds his form; and on the morning of the 24th, the scene.

The great hall of the Court, and on the bench, under the carvings and panellings, the nine among whom Adams might have taken his place. He saw other faces, the judges of his day, dead, all dead—he was standing, as he knew and said, for the last time, before this court, with its new judges, scanning the double image of the Declaration hanging on the wall opposite. He began, with his inflamed left eye still giving him pain, old, shaken with his palsy—his hand off the eagle rest on which it lay in the House—ill with the rheumy affection from which he suffered. He was old, he was old, and his eyes watery, his voice shrill, and he trembled with emotion as he gathered himself together for one of the greatest denunciations offered against the entire government of the United States. For he laid open the craft and hypocrisy he saw leading up to "the death-struggle now in continual operation between the spirit of liberty and the spirit of bondage on this continent of North America." In this great blast—"Justice!" he cried, "I stand before a Court of Justice.

The "Amistad" Mutiny

. . . I am obliged to take this ground, because, as I shall show, another Department of the Government of the United States has taken, with reference to this case, the ground of utter injustice, and these individuals for whom I appear, stand before this Court, awaiting their fate from its decision, under the array of the whole Executive power of this nation against them, in addition to that of a foreign nation."

He spoke of Shakespeare's Wolsey, and his virtue; of the Code Noir, the slave system, of the national sympathy with the slave-traders of the barracoons, officially declared to be the prime motive of action of the government. He spoke of the demands of the Spanish Ambassador on the President, marking how the Secretary of State should have called on the Ambassador to name another instance where such a demand had been made by any other government on an independent government. "He should have told him, that such a demand was treating the President of the United States, not as the head of a nation, but as a constable, a catchpole. . . ." He breaks down the charge that the two Spaniards, Ruiz and Montez, were "victims of an intrigue." After their cruelty, he says, that killed men on their boat, men in New York advised with the lawyers—"fanatics, perhaps, I must call them, according to the general application of language, but if I were to speak my own language in my own estimate of their character, so far as concerns this case, and confining my remarks exclusively to this present case, I should pronounce them the FRIENDS OF HUMAN NATURE. . . ." This was to be done : human beings were to be saved from slavery and death. In a careful analysis of the legal factors, with an interruption caused by the death of Judge Barbour in the middle of the trial, Adams goes ahead with his passionate insistence on personal liberty. "Is it possible that a President of the United States should be ignorant that the right of personal liberty is individual? That the right to it of every one, is *his own*—JUS SUUM . . ." He rages in praise of the Africans, in the face of "such a scene of Liliputian trickery enacted by the rulers of a great, magnanimous, and Christian nation." As for Cinquez and Grabeau, they "are not slaves. Let them bear in future history the names of Harmodius and Aristogiton." He swings around, trembling, the old man, the eagle voice, pointing to the Declaration on the wall, speaking of the Official Journal which gives the war-right of slavery—"Is that the principle on which these United States stand before the world?"

On March 8th the verdict was handed down. He wrote to Tappan and Baldwin that they had been confirmed. But he knew, he knew; and he wrote this in the diary, after the Africans went free:

I am yet to revise for publication my argument in the case of the Amistad Africans; and, in merely glancing over the slave-trade papers lent me by Mr. Fox, I find impulses of duty upon my own conscience which I cannot resist, while on the other hand are the magnitude, the danger, the insurmountable burden of labor to be encountered in the undertaking to touch upon the slave-trade. No one else will undertake it; no one but a spirit unconquerable by man, woman, or fiend can undertake it but with the heart of martyrdom. The world, the flesh, and all the devils in hell are arrayed against any man who now in this North American Union shall dare to join the standard of Almighty God to put down the African slave-trade; and what can I, upon the verge of my seventy-fourth birthday, with a shaking hand, a darkening eye, a drowsy brain, and with all my faculties dropping from me one by one, as the teeth are dropping from my head—what can I do for the cause of God and man, for the progress of human emancipation, for the suppression of the African slave-trade? Yet my conscience presses me on; let me but die upon the breach.

And after the prison, the plaster casts, the phrenologists, the tales of their African homes, the trials and appeals and final acquittal, the green fields of Westville, the Bible and the promise of return to Sierra Leone with the missionary society, Kinna— the young, the bright-countenanced, the good scholar—wrote to Professor Gibbs :

dear friend

I wish to write you a letter because you have been so kind to me and because you love Mendi people I think of you very often I shall pray for you Dear friend would you must pray for me If you love Jesus Christ and Christ will bless you and would you must come sometime to see Mendi people we must want to see you and I see you I am very Glad and Dear friend I pray for you My good love to your wife and all your family I love them very much I pray for them. . . .

CHAPTER THREE

New Haven Childhood

THE BELLS that to the Africans rang alien and deep spoke sacred commonplace to New Englanders. Their circles of sound fell over the entire town, from the Athenian State House over James Hillhouse's elms and up past the burial ground to Sachem's Wood: the speaking bells of the four churches, the Baptist ringing, "Come and be dipped," Trinity chiming, "Bishops, priests and deacons," North Church on the two notes of "Free grace, free grace," and Center passing grim syllabic judgment with "To-tal de-pravity."

The Green was the severe and beautiful center of the town, the colonial link with seventeenth-century England. When Adriaen Block discovered this river-mouth in 1614, he called it Rodeburg—Red Mount Place—for its rocks; when the Reverend John Davenport and Theophilus Eaton arrived at the place, it was settled as Quinnipiac, and in August of 1640, it was re-named for the Sussex seaport. It had been bought, together with the outlying districts, for 23 coats, 12 spoons, 24 knives, 12 hatchets, scissors, some hoes and porringers, and a "particular coat" for Montowese, the sachem. In 1700 Yale was founded, with a gift of a few books, as the third college in the country. Its dark stern buildings stood at the west of the Green, behind the hewn fence. It dominated the town, by a historical accident; standing at the center of New Haven, it was responsible for the growth of a village into a city. Even to the children playing in the foot-long grass, playing their games of "come away" and "snap the whip" in front of the State House, the College was as much the town as the blocks leading down to the station and the harbor. The grass grew long and fine here, and on the clear and breathless days of summer the Africans tumbled and bounded; they watched, and imitated them on State House Hill; and in the ringing cold of winter, coasted down, and skated on the ponds. These were the years of the Log Cabin and Hard Cider, of the delegations on the Green, and all the songs. The song that the New Haven poet, Percival, had just written, with its banging chorus,

> Old Tip is a coming from Ohi o,
> Old Tip is a coming from Ohi o,

and the children and women sang it with all the men, and followed it with the other, roaring louder than ever,

> Van, Van, a used-up man . . .

and the torchlight when Harrison won, and the silence when he died. These were the days before the Green was lit, when the little booths sparkled around it on fair-days, selling molasses and oysters, and the children could pitch pennies and shoot at cents stuck up on a pole with a bow and arrow. Days that could never end, in spite of William Miller, who arrived at the Methodist Church in 1842 to preach the destruction of the world out of the Book of Daniel. He could fix the date, yes, and tell what beasts would arrive. It was all right there, in the Book of Daniel, beasts and all, and it would happen in December 1843. The comet streamed across the sky that year; and in December, just as he had said, during a blazing white snowstorm, there was a red glare in the sky. The sky was lit up and lurid, during snow! And the people came out on the Green, to whisper, waiting, and some of them smiled nervously. They found out next morning, when the world rose, white and still, that it had been a paper-mill in Westville, burning; and they laughed.

It was good, this country of the saved world. Emerson was writing, "We walked this afternoon to Edmund Hosmer's and Walden Pond. . . . I said to my companion, I declare this world is so beautiful that I can hardly believe it exists."

There was the other side, the motion that Captain Marryat describes in his *Diary* : "All is energy and enterprise, everything is in a state of transition, but of rapid improvement—so rapid, indeed, that those who would describe America now would have to correct all in the short space of ten years; for ten years in America is almost equal to a century in the old continent. . . ."

Everything changed in a flash. The country was being transformed, people were moving West from all over these parts, and the West was unknown. Fifteen thousand people in New Haven, and more arriving, now that the panic had killed the watch-making trade, and the mills and factories were beginning. A price-cutting war on the Sound, and the boats bringing in people for twenty-five cents from New York, because Commodore Vanderbilt was forcing the New Haven steamboat company to operate at a loss. The banks had failed, whole States were bankrupt, and the East had been gripped by the worst panic yet.

But the Green did not seem to change; and the changes in the College came gently. Only the very old could note the large motions. They were visible in transportation, mostly. Old Noah Webster, now eighty-two and preparing the third edition of his dictionary, pioneering in terms of a national language for national unity, wrote in Reverend Leicester Sawyer's autograph book in 1840 :

When I entered Yale College in Sept. 1774, there were few conveniences for traveling. It was a rare thing to see a chaise or a gig; men & women rode on horseback, & in all our country villages, it was customary for a woman to ride behind a man, on a pillion. Boots were scarcely known in the country; & when I rode first to New Haven, I wore leggins, instead of boots. The price of a dinner at a public house was then nine pence, 12½ cents, & a bail of two quarts of oats for horse was two pence, three coppers.

At that time Yale College had only one brick building; the Old College, of wood, a long building of one room only in breadth, was standing on the South East corner of the College Yard. In this was the dining hall.

In April 1775, when the bells announced that blood was shed at Lexington, the alarm was great, the students left college, & as there were no public conveyances for travelers, we took our clothes on our backs, & walked home.

Webster's interest was in language and science, and in the rights of those who dealt with both; in common rights that he would fight for. He was putting thousands of new words into his dictionary, using, more and more, American illustration in his definitions with that fighting insistence that there be no more imitation of Europe. Emerson had published his intellectual Declaration of Independence, and, as Van Wyck Brooks says, Webster's dictionary was a Declaration. It has been compared to Willard Gibbs's great papers in its effect on its users. Anson Phelps Stokes, speaking of Gibbs, likens his work to Webster's Dictionary and to Kent's *Commentaries on Law*. Brooks says that Bowditch and Webster offered the two great "navigators"; Stokes finds the great spiritual influences, and in his remarks on Webster and Gibbs, goes on to say that Gibbs's influence on the leaders of the science of physics in the nineteenth century was like that of Edwards' *Freedom of the Will* in the eighteenth, and its permanent effect may be greater. Webster's concern with language was an immediate reflection of a national need. The country was becoming conscious that it had its own tongue, and, aware of its relation to other languages, was asserting its own.

Josiah Gibbs's interest in languages went back to his early years; back to his undergraduate years at Yale before 1809, and developing as he prepared himself for the ministry and began to work in sacred literature. He had heard of Professor Moses Stuart, who was Class of 1799—and after his oration on The Love of Truth and his graduation, his year of teaching school at Salem, and his four years of serving as a tutor at Yale, he had a chance to go to Andover and work with Professor Stuart in theology and linguistic research. He was very proficient in Hebrew, and the years in Professor Stuart's household gave him his opportunity to learn the methods and the results of the new German scholarship. In the meantime, he had been licensed to preach. But the work he cared most about was the preparation of Professor Stuart's edition of Gesenius' *Hebrew Grammar*, a text written according to the new principles, and the independent preparation of Gesenius' *Hebrew Lexicon*. He made a catalogue of the Seminary Library at the same time, and work on the *Lexicon* went ahead slowly. There were disappointments at every turn. Harvard and the Corporation of Yale had both expressed interest in the venture, and were prepared to act as its patrons, when in January 1819, Josiah Gibbs learned that Gesenius was publishing a Latin translation of the book, which had been written in Hebrew and German. He wrote to President Jeremiah Day, ruefully sending him the news, and adding that he did not expect the Corporation at Cambridge to stand by its offer (it had voted him "a very liberal patronage"), and that he would let Yale know if there were any reason for him to go ahead, now that this revised and cheaper edition had been announced. After a long delay, he went ahead with an abridged edition. He was now in New Haven again, serving as College Librarian and as Lecturer in Biblical Literature, with pupils from among the resident graduates and the students in the Divinity School. In 1826, he was promoted, and became Professor of Sacred Literature in the Divinity School, and in 1828, the first edition of the *Lexicon* appeared. This was followed by a second edition in 1832.

He was married, during this long work, to Mary Anna van Cleve, the daughter of a Princeton professor, on September 30, 1830. In 1831, the first daughter, Anna Louisa, was born. In 1833 a new version of Gesenius' original edition appeared, and he immediately undertook an English version of this. He worked steadily and cautiously, as he always did, through the birth of his second daughter, Eliza Phillips, on August 31, 1834, through '35 and into '36. About one-third of the work had been printed when a complete translation, by Dr. Edward Robinson, appeared. This was the keenest disappointment of his life. His long work, his devotion to the entire subject, which had reached its climax in the preparation of this book, was cut short.

He immediately went ahead with his other researches. He was the most thoroughly equipped scholar of his college generation; the habits that had made him devote his time to the most minute investigation might, if he had had that kind of imagination, have been used in constructive reasoning; but the two weapons on which he relied were accurate knowledge and precise statement. He loved this sorting, and tagging, and comparing—this detective work among the clues left by the words of man. He believed in it with the strength of a religious belief, for he had long since stopped preaching. What he said of his work stands : "There can be no exercise in the whole business of instruction more useful to the mind than the analysis of sentences in the concentrated light of grammar and logic. . . . It is here that every one who loves to think beholds the deep things of the human spirit, and learns to regard with holy reverence the sacred symbols of human thought."

Josiah Gibbs worked, through the birth of his one son, on February 11, 1839; through his most complete triumph, his work on the *Amistad* case, in which he was able to perceive the need, find the interpreter, compile not only a Mendi vocabulary but complete descriptions and biographies of the captives, and in the end see them go home free; through his protests about slavery and the Africans—"it is a shame to our courts, that the question could be tolerated a single moment," this reserved man wrote in the *Palladium*; worked on his glossaries and analyses and tributes to the new philology, with the slogan perpetually before him saying :

Language is a cast of the human mind.

It was the human mind that absorbed these men; and they stood or fell by that absorption. The mind of man, raised to its freedom; their passion was given to that. It ran through them, this passion, separating themselves, and setting them apart. One of them spoke for his generation when he cried out, in his failure and loneliness, for someone he could talk to. He was the least inhibited of all. Many of the others were not whipped by their loneliness; they could absorb it, as during battle one absorbs physical fear, saying as one might say after dinner, Now I am a person who has eaten, Now I am a person who is afraid. They were alone. They were recognized by their colleagues, one or two of them; by the town, one or two of them; even by the country. But mostly for the wrong things, if that was true. They crossed the Green, in a way cut off from the rest of the country, these New Haven ancestors, they read their papers advertising steel pens and bank failures, the abating of yellow fever, the news of the war in Spain, an exhibition of Sully's *Queen Victoria* (the famous slender-throated portrait of the young queen), the stories of the expulsion of the Mormons from Iowa and the wild experiment of Robert Dale Owen. They read their papers, and they went down the street to General Hezekiah Howe's book-shop, where they could see the latest books, perhaps see proofs of new Yale work, and certainly talk to someone.

New Haven Childhood

There were a few. There was John Trumbull, the painter of the Revolution; Benjamin Silliman, the most popular lecturer on science of his day, and the author of the standard *Chemistry;* Olmsted, who had written the *Philosophy;* President Day, and his book on mathematics; Ralph I. Ingersoll, the grandson of Ralph Isaacs, the Jewish Tory; Roger S. Baldwin, lawyer, governor, senator; Noah Webster himself, who was deep in work at the corner of Temple and Grove; Leonard Bacon, who was denouncing slavery from Center Church pulpit, as the other churches were denouncing the sinfulness of dancing and card-playing and novel-reading—it was from these sermons of Bacon, in print, that Abraham Lincoln said he first understood the range of evil under slavery; and James Gates Percival, poet and geologist, who had proof-read all the books of this group at Hezekiah Howe's printshop.

These were the lonely men, all in one way or another following one meaning, but in their way cut off, so that they lacked, as Van Wyck Brooks points out, the power of generalizing. They were cut off for varying reasons, and these reasons have been not at all apparent; for one was a successful, urbane, and attractive man, the source behind the Lyceum lectures that were already gathering young people in to learn about the natural sciences, art, and letters, all over New England; and one an official and recognized artist, backed by the government; and one the most popular poet of his day. When they kept their wish down, they could do what they set out to do, be successful and loved and bowed to on the street. It was when the great wishes arrived that they were marked as failures.

Benjamin Silliman was not a failure. Born three years after the Declaration, he was teaching chemistry at Yale in 1805, beginning a full and attractive career. He had graduated in law in '96, but when President Dwight asked him to become the first professor in chemistry he could not imagine a refusal, and set about preparing himself. He went to Edinburgh as the likely place. It was there that Hutton's theories were being taught; he learned, but his importance was not in his allegiance to theory. He brought back equipment from Europe, in these early years at the turn of the century, before the rediscovery of Europe and the subsequent enchantment were widespread here. And on his return, he founded the *American Journal of Science and Arts*, the most important scientific publication of the time. He was never given to speculation; he was an editor and a lecturer. He became the most important scientific figure in the country. Tall, erect, and elegant, he moved through the college and the town as a great man and a leading citizen. When Sir Charles Lyell visited New Haven in 1841, he stayed with the Sillimans, and his reception, it was noted, was proper and calm, not like all that running after Dickens on his visit, which had turned out to be such a fiasco, and had proved Dickens a "man of low and vulgar mind." If America was prepared for Lyell, when his work on the glacial epoch and the creative process appeared, Silliman was in great measure responsible. And he was firm in his belief. Slavery, for example, he saw as an enormous evil; concessions, however, should be made, he said, without sacrifice of principle or public welfare—early appeasement, in 1832. He started the scientific collections that Yale was to go ahead with, and countlessly to multiply. He was the great professor, the popular lecturer, the successful man.

John Trumbull belonged to an earlier generation. He was eighty-four in 1840, decrepit and with his honors wearing thin. The Revolution was his period, with the English influence on art that his master, Benjamin West, had so fully accepted. West had been a backwoods Quaker boy, with not a picture in the house, and no colors until the Indians gave him some red and yellow war-paint, and his mother added a stick of blueing to make the primary three. In the forests and in the Colonial towns, art was a luxury and sheer frivolity. It was not until he reached Europe with his wife, smuggled out of her father's house, that he saw what it might be in the lives of men; and even in Rome, the fair-haired young painter stood before the Apollo Belvedere, exclaiming, "How like a Mohawk warrior!" His heights were reached in England, after the trip on the Continent; his studio became the most famous in Britain, even in the days of Gainsborough, Romney, and Sir Joshua; and as president of the Royal Academy, the seal was set on him. He was startling the formalists, however; "The Death of Wolfe" horrified the critics, for it was the first painting in which soldiers were not dressed, arbitrarily, in Greek draperies, but wore their stained authentic uniforms. The quarrel, in England, centered here—as against the quarrel in France, to which Huet's dictum applied, "*Quiconque ne faisait pas des soldats de Marathon était romantique.*" But those soldiers were naked men in elaborate helmets. They looked like so many firemen, and the whole school was soon called *pompier*. This was a new direction. Here was the documentary method, arrived in English painting, and the young Americans, who flocked to West's studio, seized on it as their expression. The leaders of the next generation were here: Stuart, Copley, Washington Allston, and Trumbull.

The son of the governor of Connecticut, Trumbull had gone to Harvard, where he had been struck with Copley's work; and then, in his beginning twenties, joined the army. He was soon assigned to the craft he could best offer, and was set to drawing plans of the enemy works. He rose in the ranks until he became a colonel under Gates. Then, with growing dissatisfaction, he went abroad, going first to France, but soon gravitating to West's studio in London. West recognized him at once, and took good care of him. When Trumbull was put in jail after Major André was captured—he occupied the same position in the American army that André held in the British—it was West who got him out after almost eight months, on condition that he return to America at once. Trumbull came back, but the moment the peace was signed, he sailed for England. In 1794, he was secretary to John Jay, the American minister, and held that post during the signing of the treaty with Great Britain; and when he at last came home to stay, to paint the scenes of the Revolution which he worshipped, to found his Academy like his master, he became, more than any of the other painters with whom he is associated, the link between two epochs of American independence—the first, of political assertion and servile cultural dependence, and the second marked by Emerson's *American Scholar*, which in 1837 threw down its challenge: "Our day of dependence, our long apprenticeship to the learning of other lands, draws to a close. The millions that around us are rushing into life cannot always be fed on the sere remains of foreign harvests. Events, actions arise, that must be sung, that will sing themselves. . . ."

Willard Gibbs

That is the statement of a man haunted by the boundaries in art, boundaries that need not exist once the statement itself is followed. Trumbull brought back one method, but as he used it in his paintings he turned out great canvases full of literary composition and unapplied grandeur. His smaller work is purer in taste and color, and time has confirmed these miniatures. They have even escaped the destruction of decay which seems to have struck only at the larger paintings. These big scenes suffer from the same taste for the inappropriate that made such a tragedy of Washington Allston's life. Allston was born on the Waccamaw, in the Carolina country of moss and mysterious waters and bone-trees and legend, and he gave up America for the grandiose dream that used his years. Friend of Coleridge and Keats, Shelley, Byron, he was seduced by the power and grace of Italian painting and Biblical themes, and the twenty-six years that he gave to the unfinished painting, "Belshazzar's Feast," have become a parable for the artist's impotence of conception and execution. Trumbull turned again, however, and set himself to preserve and diffuse the memory of "the noblest series of actions which have ever presented themselves in the history of man."

He has been called a historian in paint, and that defines his shortcomings as an artist, and the shortcomings of his method. He painted "The Battle of Bunker Hill," "The Surrender of Lord Cornwallis," "The Signing of the Declaration of Independence," "The Surrender of Burgoyne." In 1817, Congress voted him $32,000 for the four paintings for the Rotunda of the Capitol—four giant canvases, certainly not murals and doubtful paintings. They are records. He recorded scenes and faces: Washington, in the crisis of the Revolution at Trenton, on the cold field of the evening before the Battle of Princeton—that battle in which Washington said, marking the peak of the war, "Give them plenty of grape!" There are portraits of Washington, Timothy Dwight, John Adams, Jefferson, Madison, even John Jacob Astor—many portraits, including the famous one of Hamilton, done from a bust, in which the bright, red-and-white face for once overcomes his hard, dark colors and his formal style. The portrait is cracked a thousand ways, like china, on the wall of the Metropolitan. The Capitol group still hangs; but the large collection is at Yale, in the Trumbull Gallery. In 1831, Yale voted him an annuity of $1,000 a year.

He was poor and old then, and it was painful. He had been the friend of the great: Jefferson, John Adams, Lafayette, West— all the great of the period he wished to honor and record. He had founded the American Academy of Fine Arts in 1808. He had tried to hold their great hours before the eyes of the States. But he had not had in him that greatness.

The most important among all of these, the man whom all of them saw with slight contempt, who lived among them and had gone to college with them, knew himself an outcast in that place. He was James Gates Percival. He was perhaps the best-known of them for a while, and now he is the most completely forgotten; or, if he is remembered, it is as he was popular—for the wrong reasons. In the '40s, he was translating for the newspapers, living at a boarding-house he hated, before he moved into rooms they gave him at the New Haven Hospital. Geologist, linguist, editor—he was all of these, also; but what he was, first, was a poet.

James Gates Percival was the most popular poet in the country before Bryant.

That is a shabby enough epitaph, if it were all; for there was no poetry in the country. Freneau, the Hartford Wits . . . there was nothing there that could express what the sailors' chanties sang, what the lullabies and street-cries told, what the sermons forespoke. Nothing in the country had found its proper expression; and the instincts of the versifiers seemed to be lost. The English Romantic poets swept New England, and the book-peddlers carried Byron and Burns; Keats and Southey were not only read well, but imitated badly. Literary creation had been subdued to the hacking out of a country and the killing of its enemy—and Revolutionary war was followed by Jacksonian turbulence.

And they remembered England, deeply; they seemed to crave the English decoration, even when the matter was native.

And the foreboding that later sprang to life as innately American was not yet possible.

Or seemed not yet possible. For it existed.

Percival lived in the business section of New Haven, on Chapel Street, over Sydney Babcock's bookstore, until 1843.

But his lounging-place was General Howe's, where he could meet his friends, Noah Porter, Silliman, Dana, and the circle of bachelors with whom he spent his time. A little while ago he had said, "I have lost ten years of my life"; but half his life was lost to him, in his headlong drive toward death that was checked by two forces only : poetry and science.

Born in Berlin, Connecticut, in 1795, his childhood had been sick and wild, and when his father—to stiffen him—set him on a horse and rode with him into sham battles among the trees, he had fallen into convulsions. He came to Yale when he was very young—fifteen was a good age to go to college—and he had a first book of poems ready in the middle of his freshman year. When he took the manuscript to Noah Webster, he was advised to wait awhile; when he took it over to Hezekiah Howe, the General would not even look at it. He went back to the mice-ridden dormitory, where his friends were waiting for the verdict on the poems, and burst into tears among them, crying, "I don't care, I *will* be a poet." They laughed at him for the rest of that year. He became the laughing-stock of the small college, which was in a high tide of prosperity under President Dwight, with Day, Silliman, and Kingsley as professors, and six tutors, including Josiah Gibbs. He wanted to stay on, but the laughter drove him out at the end of his sophomore year.

When he left, he turned to teaching. He was already interested in a range of knowledge that was to grow wider and wider, until he said that he sympathized with those who threw themselves into a single study, but as for himself, he felt equally attracted by the entire circle of nature. When he was a little boy, he had worked at dissecting the skeleton of a goose; and among the golden-flowered pastures and the rocks, the blue rye-fields and the brooks running on sand and pebbles, and barefoot on the ice at Hempstead, he had come to love natural science. He had read Thomson's *Seasons*, Bloomfield's *Farmer's Boy*, and the poems of Dr. Dwight and Joel Barlow. He was writing poems at twelve, when his father died.

And now he turned to teaching, until one day, to the horror of his village, he shut up school and never came back. He really wanted to finish college.

This second term was spent in hard work. He was a brilliant scholar, in spite of his shyness and his speech defect, which probably stemmed from that shyness; but Dr. Dwight was right when he told Percival that he must find some active employment, or he was a ruined man.

His drive to death was very strong. When he graduated and started to work in medicine, he fell in love with a clergyman's daughter, who turned him down at once, and his series of attempts at death began. He tried to kill himself, once with opium, once with a pistol, and he was known to run against trees in a fury of suicide. And then, suddenly, the impulse left him; he never tried again. But he was a man against himself; the destructive wish erupted continually and destroyed his chances.

On the surface, that was not always true. For a while, all went well. He learned prodigiously. He was working in medicine, however, during a fever epidemic, and all his patients died, until he could not bear to face his inadequacy; he went to Philadelphia as a tutor, and fell in love with Judge Chauncey's daughter. Fell in love!—he touched her hand one day, and fled to the New York boat. Later he proposed to her, and was refused. She married a clergyman; while he desperately went ahead with his writing, and his botanical studies, and applied for job after job. There was a chance for a while that Harvard would give him an appointment; that fell through; he was to go to Hampden-Sidney College, in Virginia, and at the last moment did not; he edited *Clio*, and later the *Atheneum* at $1,000 a year, until something went mysteriously wrong; he made an arrangement with a publisher to go abroad, for the sake of a European journal—$800 for six months and 600 pages of the British Isles, $500 for six months and 500 pages in France, and the same in Germany—and decided, at the last moment, that it was too many pages at too little pay.

During all of these psychic suicides, however, he was becoming immensely popular as a poet. The "P" with which his newspaper poems were signed was familiar in every town. These poems were commonplace, imitative, and flowery. He was unable to criticize or to rewrite; he was unable, also, it seems, to stop himself from writing these verses. They showered on the magazines. They flowed through the newspapers and into all the anthologies. This tall, shabby man, thin to the bone, this hermit in his glazed old sheepskin cap and his gray cloak, with his fine-cut head and its glaring obsessed eyes—this was the "purest and most mere man of genius possible to our race," according to his worshipper, the poet Willis.

It was this praise, for these reasons, that buried his real work.

He was acknowledged the best of the group of poets around James Fenimore Cooper in New York. Cooper had rescued Percival from the tenement in which he found him writing, plagued by the New York smoke, the clang of wagons, the shouting teamsters, and the little Frenchman who played his fiddle incessantly across the way. In Cooper's circle, Percival outshone all of them: Fitz-Greene Halleck, Pierpont, Irving, Pinckney, and the young Bryant. Again, for all the wrong reasons—and, certainly, for the wrong poems.

"Seneca Lake" is still to be found in the anthologies, and "New England," and more often than any of them, "The Coral Grove," which editors seem to include without bothering to read the rest of the works of such an obviously fifth-rate versifier. "The Coral Grove" begins in a flat imitation of every flat fault in English descriptive verse :

> Deep in the wave is a coral grove,
> Where the purple mullet and gold-fish rove,
> Where the sea-flower spreads its leaves of blue,
> That never are wet with falling dew,

and goes on for twenty-six more lines to the inevitable and symmetrically unbearable

> Then far below, in the peaceful sea,
> The purple mullet and gold-fish rove,
> Where the waters murmur tranquilly
> Through the bending twigs of the coral grove.

It was this sort of thing that was praised, when it was liked at all, and demolished later, by Whittier, who ignored the other qualities of Percival's poetry, and Lowell, who launched the most savage attack of his life on this poet and never again wrote a word about a contemporary American writer.

James Gates Percival was doing work of an altogether different nature, writing, during the same years he was turning out "The Wreck," "The Suicide," and "The Coral Grove," some of the most clairvoyant and certainly the first intellectual poetry of the country.

In 1822, he was asked to read the official Phi Beta Kappa poem before the Connecticut Alpha Chapter. He accepted, for he was working on his *Prometheus*. But when he faced the meeting, he confessed that he was discouraged with the poem, and refused to read it. It looked like one more of crazy Percival's gestures of suicide. There he stood, the mad rock-smasher, looking as though he were made of glass and would shatter if he were touched, refusing to read!

The poem he would not show begins in a rather usual way. It looks like a long, Spenserian jumble. You run rapidly over the first stanzas, seeing influence : here is some Shelley, here's Keats—and then, suddenly, after the tenth stanza, these lines follow :

> The whole machine of worlds before his eye
> Unfolded as a map, he glances through
> Systems in moments, sees the comet fly
> In its clear orbit through the fields of blue,
> And every instant gives him something new
> Whereon his ever-quenchless thirst he feeds;
> From star to insect, sun to falling dew,
> From atom to the immortal mind, he speeds,
> And in the glow of thought the boundless volume reads.
>
> Truth stands before him in a full, clear blaze
> An intellectual sunbeam . . .

and then the whole poem begins to take shape, in formed, magnificent praise of possible mastery, the spring of the world when mind was all on fire, praise of the new-born ancients, who leapt mind's barriers—while we drill and shave down the wall, in the old age of our fallen race. . . .

> The times are altered :—man is now no more
> The being of his capabilities;
> The days of all his energy are o'er.
> And will those fallen demigods arise . . .

He calls for spirits who can leave the lessons of their school, who can feel the beauty of simplicity and deal their blows. He praises newly freed Rome, calling for the renovation of the world in

the year of liberty, the radiant zodiac. Here are the mighty
months, the drunkenness of soul of a new-waked people. And,
in a strong revulsion against Europe, he goes on :

> Freedom can have no dwelling on that shore;
> She must away and cross the Atlantic flood.
> Why play the rude game over? you may pour
> In waves, like torrent rivers, your best blood,
> But it will end in "We have dared and stood
> In battle for our rights; we sink again
> Before an overwhelming weight, the food
> Of tyrants and their parasites, who drain
> Our tears like wine, and bind with doubled links our chain."

Here is the free spirit, the scientist and poet, the first poet in
America who dared to deal with these materials, the man who
worked for the progressive sciences, knowing himself in poetry,
but feeling that mathematical truth only could withstand modification, grasping in this poem at the science that Shelley had
only tentatively touched—writing lines that mount and mount,
suggesting the past of Newton, and the future of Clerk Maxwell
and Einstein.

> It is our pride to conquer Nature :—Mind
> Is an internal force, that oft can sway
> Things to its great dominion; 'tis designed
> As the one balance, which at least can stay
> Awhile the haste of causes, which convey
> All in their downward flood. . . .

and, in the burst after burst,

> I feel it,—though the flesh is weak, I feel
> The spirit has its energies untamed
> By all its fatal wanderings . . .

to this, on the journey of such spirits,

> Space is to them an ocean, where they rush
> Voyaging in an endless circle; light
> Comes from within. . . .

This deep foreshadowing of poems and sciences to come was
almost completely lost. Percival himself, with the house he designed on Park Street, a mausoleum having three windows in

front and an entrance in the back wall—with his geological surveys of Connecticut and Wisconsin, his years in the Hospital, shouting "Boo" to scare visitors (even Longfellow) away, his night excursions to Mount Carmel cave and the Hanging Hills of Meriden—lost. His papers, his translations from almost twenty languages, his lectures, his singsong hymns and rackety songs, and the fine work that nobody read and recognized—are lost, with his facility and torment. The little stories remain : the one of the woman who kept greeting him in the corridor of the Hospital, until he asked one of the doctors what he should do to stop her from bothering him. "Marry her," suggested the doctor, and Percival fled again. His fears, the sexual obstacles he must have tried to submerge in countless activities, in the compulsive obsessive activity that drove him to his hundreds of translations, his minute work on Webster's dictionary, his infinitely pains-taking work beyond work on the geological surveys—all these drives, and his wish for emancipation, his hatred of noise, his fear of fire, his fondness for turkey (and particularly for the pope's nose), the time when he followed a toast to the mechanics of New Haven as the right arm of the city with, "To Science, the right eye which directs the right arm of New Haven,"—all the rhetoric and personal quirks and passion, everything that is lost rises again, transformed and mastered, as he writes

> Farewell to the lost land,
> The world imagined, to the world we feel,
> Is glory and magnificence. . . .

He went on to Wisconsin as state geologist at last, to die, not of disease, but of some subtle wearing-away process which baffled his doctor. And, at the end, he reaches us, not as the eminent poet, the accomplished linguist, the learned scientist, the man without guile, that his tombstone at Hazel Green declares him. This was the man who walked back and forth between an evening party and his home at the Hospital, talking all the long shuttle with a friend, until they stopped dead to watch some rare phenomenon of light standing in the sky, not knowing it was sunrise. He was one of the first real philologists in the United States, quarrelling with Webster over his inaccuracies, introducing Bopp and Grimm from Germany. He was the geographer, and the literary lion of Bishop's Hotel, the grinning lecturer on Nosology in a time of fake sciences. He was the crank : G. P. R. James, the novelist, met him at the Berlin station, and talked to him for a while with all the airs of the man of society. Percival was particularly hesitant that day and made his worst impression. The two men did not get on at all, Percival showing repugnance, and James genteel contempt. When they got into their train, they took different seats, and James asked his companion who Percival was. He was described as a distinguished poet. James went on, "A little cracked, isn't he?" A few days later, the companion met Percival, who asked about James, answering "The popular novelist" with "A little drunk, wasn't he?"

Whittier praised the nature passages in Percival, writing for the *New England Magazine*. He later said that the apostrophe to the sun was "the most magnificent specimen of American poetry within our knowledge. The following stanza is of unrivalled excellence" :

> Thine are the mountains, where they purely lift
> Snows that have never wasted, in a sky
> Which hath no stain; below the storm may drift
> Its darkness, and the thunder-gust rear by. . . .

and it goes on like that. Of the rest of his work, that part that was not hackneyed description, he said, "It is wrought up in defiance, it would almost seem, of the natural laws of association and the common rules of composition."

Lowell tried to demolish Percival's work for all time in a review of his life and letters that has been called the only purely destructive piece of criticism he ever attempted. And the words of these two powerful critics have been accepted. Percival has been committed to footnotes; and the notes themselves have been based on the poems most easily available, the awful jargon of the anthology pieces.

Percival himself answers, in a passage that was condemned as an "infidel resolution" that would "excite sorrow in the breast of all his Christian friends," and bring down the *odium theologicum* that was so completely effective in New Haven :

> I ask no pity, nor will I incline
> Weakly before the cross, nor in the blood
> Of others wash away my crimes. . . .

New Haven Childhood

He called for clarity, for poetry—"another name for this innate philosophy"—and, for allegiance, wrote (one can see him, writing rapidly, biting his nails) :

> . . . and yet we will obey
> The intellectual *Numen* and will gaze
> In wondering awe upon it . . . the blaze
> Of mind is as a fount of fire, that upward plays . . .
> This is the electric spark sent down from Heaven,
> That woke to second life the man of clay. . . .

Deep in its central fire mind will burn, he wrote, praying for the strong gaze of Dante and a lightning conception.

He was the poet who ushered in the expression of Gibbs.

He was the outcast, even though he could be called a friend of professors, a friend of Josiah Gibbs—the man who haunted New Haven, living and working in his rooms, with two inches of dust on the floor, living on crackers and herring and dried beef, shutting out intruders and tying up his door with an end of rope. He thought of himself with the exiled, the jailed, and the refused. He spoke of himself as a reader of the woods, the waters, and the skies. But he came in sight of a binding link, wandering through his thousand changes; he cried for an ecstasy of mind, for new analogies—"All truth is sacred," said he, "sacred as the Bible," and wrote :

> How my heart trembles on so vast a theme!—
> The boundless source of energy and power.

These were the men whom the New Haven children saw. Their fathers knew them; the town was still small. It was an overgrown village, dominated by Yale.

And the mild, frail child growing up in the Gibbs home with its simple manners and its little Latin books—its primers and his father's Bible stories, and his mother's soft insistence on mildness and dignity—might see these men, all of whom his father knew. He wore the little jackets that children wore, played with them and his sisters, was like the rest, except that he was so delicate. He had forgotten the attack of scarlet fever that kept Josiah and Mary Gibbs awake and anxious during many nights, when he was two years old; but it marked him deeply, and his parents worried about the weakness it seemed to leave in him. They impressed on the child the need for regular habits when he was very little; they took solicitous care of his health, and trained him to pay close attention to his well-being.

The little boy sat on the floor while all his sisters read. He was playing with bits of string and wood. He would sit quietly for a long time, and then come around to them, his little, shallow-featured face alive with pleasure. That was what he liked to do best : build his mechanical toys, with the tiny parts that would move. It was not as if toys were the usual thing. But he was making them, and the parts did work. It was better to make these at home. Sometimes, when one of the big panoramas or periphaniscopes arrived in town, they could go and see the wonder; and soon he would be going to school a few blocks away, at High and Wall; but in the meantime there were Father's visitors, all the things in the world, and his mechanical toys.

CHAPTER FOUR

Science and the Imagination

Mrs. ADAMS HAD BEGGED him not to make this trip. His friends, who had been bringing the books he would need, from public libraries as well as from their own, had foreseen the long fatigue of the journey, the haste of preparation, the exhausting receptions and speeches. But John Quincy Adams had no thought of reconsidering, even when he admitted his friends' arguments. "I must go happen what may."

He felt as if he were incrusted in a bed of snow. He was old, he was shaken by his old man's cough, and Albany, at the end of October, was frozen. The hail rattling against his windows woke him to darkness at half-past four in the morning. He got up, trembling across the cold floor to the table, lit the lamp, and there, under the thick yellow light, wrote until six, when the hail had turned to a driving snow, and he thought he would go out to the barber-shop.

Of all English and American statesmen, says Brooks Adams, Bacon and Franklin were the only ones who "might have taken the view he took and chosen as he chose." But his choice had been made years before, when he identified learning and freedom, science and government, and imagination with all of these. There was, also, the historic paper on weights and measures, which related such views to commonplace practice. The trip itself had been suggested the summer before, in July 1843, when the Adamses had visited Niagara. This journey through New York had been a triumphal procession for the old man. After the *Amistad* case had been closed, after the long struggle against the gag rule had driven almost to the end, so that the majority against Mr. Adams in the House was now reduced to three, he had taken the summer for a vacation trip. The outing was converted into an official progress. Nothing like it had been seen since Lafayette. Crowds came out in all the upstate towns, cheering and waving, proving to the ex-President the contradictory forces at work and contributing to his defeat, and his immense popular love. On July 24th, he was at Niagara, and Professor Mitchell arrived from Cincinnati to ask him to deliver an oration. The cornerstone of the first American astronomical observatory was to be laid at Cincinnati, and the Society wanted Mr. Adams to speak.

He was profoundly excited. He had fought during his presidency, as well as during his long term in the House, for observatories, for astronomy as the best means to rouse public interest in science. He had met his most ironic defeats here; his enemies had turned his work against him. They made him a laughing-stock. "Lighthouses of the sky," he had called observatories, in his first message to Congress; the phrase became a catchword to express contempt for his notions. He had come to feel, in despair and hopeless anger, that the nation would be against astronomy now for no better reason than that *he* defended it.

He would always defend it, as he would champion any branch of science, as he fought for the uses of the money that Joseph Smithson, in protest against his bastardy, had left to the United States in the name of the Smithsonian Institution. He believed, on a higher conscious level than anyone since Franklin, in the relation of science to the growth of the nation and liberty. When the invitation came to him, he forgot his cough, the "tussis senilis" of all these days, his failing sight, his hoarseness, his disturbed unquiet sleep. He accepted, the next day. What he wanted was "to turn this transient gust of enthusiasm for the science of astronomy at Cincinnati into a permanent and persevering national pursuit, which may extend the bounds of human knowledge, and make my country instrumental in elevating the character and improving the condition of man upon earth."

The oration was barely ready. He had made his farewell to his constituents at Dedham, with the promise that in opening this first observatory, he was serving his own neighborhood as

Science and the Imagination

well as Ohio. He had lectured at Springfield on his way west. And here, at Albany, the journey was well begun.

After the comfortless night, and his usual early-morning work, it was pleasant to relax in the warmth, among the barbershop smells, covered and anonymous. The snow was still falling outside, the covering white snow—but now a man comes up, his face anonymous and covered with the white lather still on it, his hand out, recognizing Mr. Adams. There is to be no anonymity. The old man shakes hands all round, goes off to breakfast, and at eight o'clock he is at the Western cars.

The train is frozen, like everything else this morning—locked to the rails in ice. It takes a half-hour of scourging of horses and straining before the wheels are pulled loose, and another half-hour to get the steam up to an effective head, before the locomotive's yell sounds through the silent air. The snow has done, and the valley rings with the cry, over the locked river and the hills of the Hudson.

The train pushes and trembles, gathering speed. Its power is a new power in the country. Its shout announces the age of steam, its thrust answers the demand of the West, the boundless determination of the inland valley, with its pride of forests, its compulsive streams. This drive was opening up a nation of expectant capitalists. Under Jackson, picked up from the pebbles and thundered higher than a throne, the man of the people had come riding in; but '40 was a great reversal, like the defeat in a war; by that time of torchlight and "Jericho," there was a longing for a return of equilibrium, and what had seemed Biblical was now contemptible and very small; by then Jackson's party was living on the oysters of patronage, and the Whigs, the party of the landed gentry, had assumed the dress and manners of the farmers and plain people, exposing the Democrats as aristocrats and leeches. And now the rich were doing penance in this ant's nest of a country where everyone worked every minute—and there was self-made Girard running his Philadelphia banking business, self-made Astor his New York real estate, Lawrence his Massachusetts mills. Lawrence's mill-hands were falling into the defined groups of those underneath: factory-people, Negroes, women. But there was a transition, as Horace Bushnell pointed out, "from mother-and-daughter power to water and steam-power." The train yelled in the icy air; straight canals partitioned the states across the Appalachians; and on the tracks, on the quiet water, rose the midnight cry of a new energy.

The cry of Mr. Adams' train, riding over a hundred and eighty miles of marvellous country. The old man, whose fierce and bitter voice was now gentle as he spoke to the other passengers, stopped talking to watch the land pass at the windows. It was not as he had known it in the summertime, colored and flowering, but desolate. It lay, the most dreary sheet of snow "like Nova Zembla in January," broken occasionally by apple-loaded orchards. Crowds, last summer, had issued from these little depots. "My passage now is silent," he wrote in the journal.

In Buffalo, he was given a cold dark room, but this was changed, and he rested. On the morning of the 6th, he embarked on the lake steamer *General Wayne*. Snow was again falling, and on the lake the storm freshened, the small boat pitched on a savage Erie, until it took refuge with three or four other craft, at anchor under Point Abino on the Canadian side. The storm went on and on; the snow howled, the passengers were seasick, and Adams cursed the wind-bound imbecility of this voyage. He disapproved of everything: the ship's Bible had left the Apocryphal books out, and he put it aside. He read a life of Burr, and was pleased to find Burr as worthless as he had always believed. He passed the second day on the lake to better advantage, writing a seven-verse poem about the storm for Mary Foster, who was in "a deep decline."

Cleveland was reached on November 1st. It was here that he was to begin his four days on the Ohio Canal. But before he went on board the packet canal-boat, the Albany incident was repeated and magnified. Again, he was recognized in a barber-shop, and this time the town put him through the first of the receptions that were to make him say, "My catarrh, and excessive kindness, drive me to despair."

The next morning, feverish and with a sore throat, he went on the *Rob Roy*. It had been a huge reception, but he turned some of the boredom to account. After the official program, most of the audience had flocked up to shake his hand, and among the women, "a very pretty one, as I took her hand, kissed me on the cheek. I returned the salute on the lip, and kissed every woman that followed, at which some made faces, but none refused."

Once on the boat, Adams hoped for some peace in which to

catch up on his correspondence and his journal, and to go over the oration he was to make. But the packet was not designed for writers. Eighty feet long and fifteen wide, it was divided into six compartments for the twenty-five passengers—with two settee beds for the ladies, and the men sleeping feet to feet in the others, on the side settees. The windows were shut to bar the driving snow, and the little iron stove in the middle of the floor was raging hot, as the hands kept feeding it billets of wood. "So much humanity crowded into such a compass was a trial such as I had never before experienced," he wrote—and next door was the stable for the four horses. The boat bumped along at two and a half miles an hour, passing the muddy banks slowly, halting for the numberless locks—there were over two hundred of them—striking, grazing, staggering along "like a stumbling nag." Adams felt that he seemed surly, writing while the other passengers played whist and euchre. He took a hand at euchre, a game of which he had never before heard. He was grateful to reach Hebron; from there, he would be taking the stage to Cincinnati.

He marks the deep, rich soil of this beautiful country, but sorrowfully. He had always worked for conservation of natural resources : this is woodland, and the wood has been cut down; the stumps stand like the pins of a bowling-green.

In Columbus, a mulatto comes to his hotel, to thank him in the name of the colored people of the city for his efforts on their behalf. Outside of Dayton, an elegant barouche meets the party, and he rides in with a display, feeling the strangeness of the ovation and the crowd, acknowledging that the only comfort he has is in the recognition that these people are trying to show respect, not hatred. His bitterness and the sense of failure have been wildly alive in the old Adams, haunted by his attacks, and driven by illness that still falls behind his fanatic will. Now he is really worn out. Now he knows this trip may mean death to him.

However, the idea of death is not an unfamiliar one. He has been threatened by its many forms, seen it in the shapes of fever, heard death in his own cough, felt it in his shaking hand; the animal voices shouting against him in the House raved of it in another meaning, and in his darkest, most clear foreboding he has seen the fatal splitting of the Union. In rancor, he had accused Jackson of dying a long death, to his own advantage;

but then, he had received the engraved portrait of himself with a bullet-hole through the forehead, and had the letter beginning, "To that vile incendiary John Q. Adams . . ." and ending,

Is there no bold Virginian or chivalrick Carolinian ready to hurl you from the land of the living? I think there is—your craven spirit would quail before the menace of the outraged Southern man and nothing but a good horsewhip will serve you and you must & shall have it. You detested vindictive villain : Your motives are known it is revenge for your disappointment at the election in 1828. You are an insignificant imitator of Burr Arnold and O'Connell and deserve the gallows for your treason to your Country.

It will come sooner or later. It is not forgotten—your advocacy of Shays rebellion. The Devil will have his own when he gets your rascally soul.

Beware on the 4th July ***

⊔,⌞ > ⊔⌐

He had filed the letter under B, for Brutality.

And now he goes on to Cincinnati, until, on a fine day, he is welcomed to the city by the mayor, drives in past the shouts of greeting, and is notified that he is to give an additional address at the actual cornerstone laying. He sits up until one that night, writing his second speech; and wakes to the rainy morning of the 9th.

The ceremony at the cornerstone is held in a plain of umbrellas. Torrents have turned the raw ground into thick mud; the ink runs lavender down the sheets Mr. Adams is holding, defacing his script until he can barely read it, and the oration itself has to be postponed. It clears by evening, and there is a torchlight procession that night, Mr. Adams walking in the glare between two long rows of firemen.

On the next day, in the largest church in Cincinnati, before a packed and attentive audience, he reads his oration for two hours without finding a "symptom of impatience or inattention." In this speech, the connections between government and the laws of astronomical science are clearly affirmed. Starting with the tremendous axiom-breaking that the treason of the Colonies against the mother-country signified, Adams goes on to speak of the Declaration of Independence, and the meaning of the phrase, "the laws of Nature and of Nature's God." The republic we have here founded in a treason justified because of its appeal to the rights of man is, in the form of government it has assumed, the true republic of Montesquieu. It rests on natural faculties, and on the multiplying and sharpening of those faculties by education, which thrives on liberty. And its hope—its existence, indeed—rests on the fact that man is a curious and inquisitive being. What illustrates this with more vividness than the history of astronomy? Adams takes his audience through a compact history of the science, from the earliest times to Galileo and Tycho Brahe, and then step by step along the comparatively recent work of Newton and Herschel, and the development of the telescope, which has permitted us to perceive so much of law. At the cornerstone, the "old man eloquent" had repeated the phrase which had brought down ridicule on his head, "lighthouse of the sky"—with what justified triumph may be inferred. Europe was rich in observatories, but from border to border and sea to sea of the United States, this was the first. Adams had subscribed to one planned for Cambridge, but the Harvard committee had been unable to raise the money. And now, here was the first vindication in his long fight. He generalized meanings, he raised the naked fact, as he had raised the physical bare facts in the *Amistad* case from their primitive level—of struggle in which he shared belief—to the top spiritual line of affirmation. Now he quoted the Roman poet: "Happy the man who has been able to ascertain the *causes* of things." And continues, in his own voice, "To trace the causes of things is, of all the animal creation, the exclusive propensity, and faculty of man. . . ."

It was over, with the vote to name the observatory hill Mount Adams, with the ball that evening and its rushing sounds of music and the great fine skirts and the flattery. He wrote in his journal late that night: "Thus closes, blessed be God, one memorable day of my life."

And goes home, broken and near death, to reach an "aghast wife" two weeks later, and make the final entry on the trip:

I have performed my task. I have executed my undertaking, and am returned safe to my family and my home. It is not much in itself. It is nothing in the estimation of the world. In my motives and my hopes, it is considerable. The people of this country do not sufficiently estimate the importance of patronizing and promoting science as a principle of political action; and the slave oligarchy systematically struggle to suppress all public patronage or countenance to the progress of the mind.

The reception of work in science in this country has always been a reliable indication of the American attitude toward all creative effort. In the double and mixed reaction is our mirror of the acceptance and rejection of imagination. War and peace, times of intense effort and the rare periods when the country as a whole could be said to be resting on its achievement, have given us a curve of response that measures the "success" of the arts, of the combining and religious efforts, as well as science itself. For this country rests more than any other on scientific achievement and the application of scientific law to other fields.

Some of our scientists have recognized this; some statesmen; some poets.

The American genius has been the spirit of foreboding, of foreshadowing and combining. This foreboding casts its eye backward, it can deal with the future because it is aware of the past, it is indeed the faculty of which Mr. Adams spoke, "to trace the causes of things," and he was quoting Lucretius. The faculty is general; but here, on this continent, which at times lay coiled and secretive in its vast, terrible mysteries, and at times raged exultant up and down before the pioneers, like a stripper on a stage, throwing away its concealments part by part—on the American continent the inquisitive nature, turned loose, became recognizable as national man. With the foreboding, which was sometimes vague and not conscious, and sometimes tragic and at the tragic level most to be loved, as in Lincoln, went other essentially tragic qualities of waste and conquest and the application of these to a new earth. Fighting these went the rare men and women who could capture the clues and in their flashes of knowledge see combining grace, the virtue of form. So often formless, so often a chaos without shape, thought in this country—the wish of the country—has known a sunken tradition of one of the deepest desires : the wish to meet formlessness, evil, dissolution, and to find their place in form. Our greatest works as well as our greatest vulgarities have started here. Our giantism which is our disease is not only a reflection of a huge country and a huge effort, but of this; our immense expeditions and engineering achievements, the books and skyscrapers and flying fortresses, have some of this; and the pomp of acceptance as well as the smashing gestures of rejection perhaps all depend on hidden kinship with this chaos, and kinship in the wish to strike it down in thought.

There has been a long hooting all the way down our history.

There is no good in any tournament of pity for all those who suffered from mockery—the men at their workbenches and little laboratory cookstoves, the crazy fools who hung around the river-bank waiting for their steamships to move, their iron boats not to sink, who hung around the right of way swearing that their trains would run, who wandered in their own footprints on the lonely Atlantic beaches, watching the flight of gulls, obsessed with flying.

They knew the terrible strong common laughter, all the noises of shamemaking, the jeering, the little children with whom their work was intricately concerned running after them in the orange-lit streets.

Cranks and crackpots, the whole lot of them.

But any idiot could tell the difference between even them and the farthest lost: those who were seen stooped and abstracted on the way between the place where they worked and home, those who did nothing but write, on bits of paper, formulas and single concepts and poems, symptoms of an abstract burning of the brain that would in all probability not be vindicated within a lifetime.

For the little levers would go up and down, the black arms start, the wheels begin to turn, until the last skeptic might stand open-mouthed and confounded. The brain would go on burning, and the new influences working with the wind and the axe and the gun, the rider and the broadside in this country would be fuel.

The inventors were justified almost overnight. It takes a little longer for some of the others. America a hundred years ago was deeply engrossed with space; it cared rather less for time.

America, as the United States, had had only fifty years. It was avid for the instruments which would let it acquire and master the youth of riches given it by the new order. Machines and weapons and ideas would take this land. A fertility of detail in invention was springing up, as fifty years ago a fertility of invention about the details of liberty had shown. The ideas behind that growth came from oppression and the reaction of grief and anger which imagination brought to tyranny; they came from science and a new political theory which rose in interlocking structures, whose points meshed so cleanly that the meaning of that delicate triumphant gear was not mistakable in France; and in England, where Newton and Locke had touched the idea with fire, it could be plainly seen, even without action; and in Germany, among its wars, it was felt.

If we had assumed our full life in a gesture of treason, there were also many ways in which treason was impossible, in which we were bound forever. The bloodstream that proved our parentage and stamped its features on us was, more than any other, this double current of political theory and science which gushed up in two fountains : the Declaration and the Constitution.

Political thought had been bound to Newtonian science in the work of Newton himself, who evolved ideas of balance in nature that were already formulated in the ideas of government of his time. Natural bonds had been acknowledged, and the laws of society formulated, in pre-history; the mechanics of law and the *law* as Newton described it were "modern" ideas, indebted, as Crowther points out, to Whig or mercantile theories of government. "In the environment of such theories, and allied systems of thought," Newton "produced his mechanics. These, in turn, were adapted to give more precise expression to the theories of government suitable to trading classes. Thus there was a continual interaction between notions of government and scientific ideas."

When Adams, in his Cincinnati speech, referred to the republic of Montesquieu, he was tracing one of the sources of the Newtonian concepts in America. Montesquieu, born in 1689, published fourteen years of work in *L'Esprit des Lois*, in 1748— one of the first great works in which the scientific method which was still "new" was brought to government. In defining the republic, in predicting the rise of tyrannies, in condemning the corruption of the people in the times of the great tyrants, and also in offering a scheme of society which seemed like the scheme of a science, he cut a long road into the jungle. Many theories of history have entered the jungle along that road. And scientific theory has entered it as well.

In 1689, Newton had already finished the *Principia*. He was forty-seven, for the first time he was free of science, and he took his seat in the Convention Parliament. For the first time, living in London, he became a part of society, he renewed his friendship with Lord Halifax, he met Locke and Pepys, and he turned to the religious writing which he always considered far more important, to the world and himself, than his work in science.

Riding high on the wave of rationalism that a trade society produced, Newton and Montesquieu together influenced the laws of this country. Singly, their attitudes toward Church and State were conflicting : Montesquieu as a philosopher and parliamentarian held up a republic of regulated liberties and an equilibrium of powers, and was attacked by the Jansenists, the Jesuits, and by Rome itself. Newton's work was revered by the devout, who did not read it, and by the English Protestant divines, since it was clear that he believed that gravitational phenomena were the result of the direct will of God. He was not a profound philosopher, and indeed his questionings were reserved for his work in science. He was an ardent student of Boehme and Yworth, the great mystical writers, and at the same time a believer in the absolute space in which his entire system belongs, which our age rejects, and which is filled with the contrivances, the pulleys and balance-weights and checks, which are the parts of the mechanism of our State.

John Locke had taken Newton's attitudes—Blake says,

> . . . behold the Loom of Locke, whose Woof rages dire,
> Wash'd by the Water-Wheels of Newton : black the cloth
> In heavy wreaths folds over every Nation. . . .

The cloth folded over the United States with the framing of the Declaration and the Constitution. The dominant thinkers of the United States were influenced and possessed by this set of views. What Newton was to John Adams, Locke was to Thomas Jefferson. The Americans thought of the great Englishmen as law-givers, and the Declaration and Constitution are their Leviticus. And they were law-givers; the real danger was there. They were interested in structure and pure law, its analysis; what they handed down could be used for good or evil, as the specialists were good or evil. If they would take the methods, keep the creative flow, all would be well; if they accepted, and let the theories harden into form, there was all the danger. If they would be Levites, take this new science over and have its "legislation of the cosmos" reflected in the legislation of the states, harden and become holy, they would run into the fatal danger that all such thinking by hard analogy must meet.

This country was begun in treason and axiom-breaking. The church in New Haven, with the stones of the Regicides as corner-stones, is an image of its growth; for from the most violent denial of legitimacy, the form immediately hardened, until the hub building at the center of a new tradition could rest on the negation of the deepest tabu. There is a necessity, when a crime has been committed that so deeply shocks the spirit that a justification must be made at once, to set up another image as great as the dethroned one, and in the greatest haste possible, and irremediably, even if the promise is given that the image is only temporary. The new continuity that was set up in the small instance was Center Church; in the large instance, it was the Constitution, whose Convention made so many promises that what they promulgated was to be only temporary.

The working scientist of the Constitutional Convention was the man who most hoped that the instrument would be flexible enough so that its makers could experiment after the framework was set up. Benjamin Franklin, three years from death, interrupted the Convention again and again to dispute the notion of balances. When the seventh Section of Article One made it clear that the Senate was set off against the House like so many Newtonian particles, Franklin objected with a succinct parable. He was reminded, he said, of the habit of wagon-drivers who split their teams of four oxen when they reach a steep down-grade. A pair of oxen is taken out of harness, chained to the back of the wagon, and driven *uphill* to brake the down-rush. John Adams angrily got to his feet at this, and began to quote Newton against Franklin, whose knowledge of Newton was certainly second to nobody's in the country.

And it has been Newton who has been quoted ever since.

Woodrow Wilson, in his penetrating essay on constitutional government in the United States, says:

Science and the Imagination

The government of the United States was constructed upon the Whig theory of political dynamics, which was a sort of unconscious copy of the Newtonian theory of the universe. In our own day, however, whenever we discuss the structure or development of anything, whether in nature or in society, we consciously or unconsciously follow Mr. Darwin; but before Mr. Darwin, they followed Newton. Some single law, like the law of gravitation, swung each system of thought and gave it its principle of unity. Every sun, every planet, every free body in the space of the heavens, the world itself, is kept in its place and reined to its course by the attraction of bodies that swing with equal order and precision about it, themselves governed by the nice poise and balance of forces which give the whole system of the universe its symmetry and perfect adjustment. The Whigs had tried to give England a similar constitution. They had had no wish to destroy the throne, no conscious desire to reduce the king . . .

but what they wanted in the United States and England was, above all, to see to it that their highest ruling instruments would be *calculable*. It had recently been impressed upon them that it *was* possible to calculate the most obscure and overpowering forces. They would build a machine to be, as Crowther says, such a system of governors, safety-valves, and balanced mechanism that the people could safely be confined in it, and the positions of the interacting classes and interests would remain forever constant.

Wilson goes on with an analysis of Montesquieu and his tremendous influence, adding that Newton might easily have recognized this new system of counterpoises as suggestive of the mechanism of the heavens. Both Montesquieu and Madison's explanation in the *Federalist* are invoked, and Wilson says of the editors of the journal :

They quoted him always as a scientific standard in the field of politics. Politics is turned into mechanics under his touch. The theory of gravitation is supreme.

The trouble with the theory is that government is not a machine, but a living thing. It falls, not under the theory of the universe, but under the theory of organic life. It is accountable to Darwin, not to Newton. It is modified by its environment, necessitated by its tasks, shaped to its functions by the sheer pressure of life. No living thing can have its organs offset against each other as checks, and live. On the contrary, its life is dependent upon their quick cooperation, their ready response to the commands of instinct or intelligence, their amicable community of purpose. Government is not a body of blind forces; it is a body of men, with highly differentiated functions, no doubt, in our modern day of specialization, but with a common task and purpose. . . . Living political constitutions must be Darwinian in structure and in practice.

Franklin, who was philosophically and in the largeness of his nature opposed to the rather inhibited traits displayed in any system based on checks and balances—Crowther is very suggestive in his remarks about the Puritan psychology, and why the frustrations of an Adams are related to the Constitution, and the freedom of·a Franklin opposed to it—belonged to a new scientific generation. Franklin was for experimentation in every field.

Experimentation did not come into American politics on a large scale until the wide efforts of the last few years began to take shape. Above all other countries, we were fitted for a flexibility of life and method; and in three distinct periods, we were thwarted. After the Revolution, we might have expected such a flowering, but it did not come; after the Civil War, in the reaffirmation of unity, it might have come, but it did not— instead, the crudest setting of the forms followed; and after the first World War, in the safety of democracy, as the slogans had it, it should again have been upon us, this Age of Gold that never existed; but it did not come. In Wilson's passage, that is otherwise so fruitful and pertinent, there is the hint at one of the reasons for the long delay. Adams or Franklin might not have been expected to foresee the Industrial Revolution; they lived in an agricultural society and, as Laski says, they were interested in their checks and balances to the end of the diminution of authority rather than in its consolidation. Laski deals with the reactionaries who were resisting, standing by the ancient ways, and devoting all their ingenuity to preventing an increase of the new authority. The founders of the Constitution feared the masses, he says; liberty meant protection of vested interests, and they took precautions accordingly, keeping the presidential powers small; but Wilson had known intimately what all these things meant. He makes another mistake, which even Crowther does not pick up; and Crowther is quick to snap at the faults of a non-scientist dealing with scientific concepts.

The error that Wilson includes is the deep error that so many great writers have made in their dealings with scientific thought;

the error that is the weakest link in the marvellous chain of which science and imagination form the alloy. It is the error of a rigid analogy, of using the *discoveries* of science instead of the *methods* themselves in dealing with other material. Because Newtonian mechanics would not do, Wilson cast about, and found Darwin, who certainly occupied a similar place in relation to his century, but who would also not do, not because he has been disproved, but because the whole framework of one kind of thought cannot be brought over into another kind of thought without a terrible distortion and loss. Much of the distrust of the scientist for the rest of the world is academic narrowness, and the jealousy of petty specialization; but much, certainly, is due to the misuse to which scientific doctrine has been put in other fields, until a key formula becomes a basis for a hifalutin fortune-telling, or something as misleading. This fallacy is one of misplaced method, and produces grotesques when it is harmless. At its largest and most harmful, it may warp the history of the world.

"The imagination is the most scientific of the faculties, because it alone understands the universal analogy."

Intoxication of reason, the need for new unities! When one perceives that the liberty of the human being extends in all directions, and on every side discovers laws that define that liberty, one discloses only a margin of the possibilities. The freezing of the forms is unworthy of science, as the imaginary forms that fail to project life are unworthy of art. The schools are adept at fostering both of these; each has its jealousies, and makes them vocal. But there are relationships, and the point at which they are found is the dignity of the human spirit.

"The universal analogy," said Baudelaire. One hopes, not only for symbols that may be related to other symbols, but for meanings that are hieroglyphs of the world. The misuse of science has been in translating the law of gravitation, say, into the terms by which organisms breathe and recoil, and the law of evolution into the story of the adaptation of the family. The coherence of one is not the coherence of the other. We are dealing in different relationships, with their different passions.

We are machines of likeness. The brain is one; we spend most of our lives recognizing. We reason by the proportion of things. It is an easy step from recognition to seduction. The point is that there is very little uniformity.

There is some specific method behind this kind of understanding. If we cut it down, and cut it down again and again to the narrowest area, we are at the place where scientist and poet share the world, notably with each other, although many others join in the sharing. We reach an analogy with the creative process.

Science, according to D. L. Watson, is not only the discovery of facts, but always the finding of novel and appropriate combinations of existing knowledge to ends with human significance. That simplified; but the emphasis is where it must be, in spite of all specialization : on *combining*.

Creation is a delicate and experimental thing. The process of combining depends on experimentation. Knowledge and effective action here become one gesture; the gesture of understanding the world and changing it.

This combined power does not call for a knowledge of types alone, but for a search among deviations. The expression of turning-points, of new groupings and rhythms observed for the first time, leads to new analogies, new holy families.

And here the spirit's greatness is bound up with its expression.

Josiah Gibbs, talking with the captives by counting up to ten, thinking of language as a cast of the mind, dealing with unknown factors, became in a way a fresh man, reached a new relationship with the world. John Quincy Adams, so close to death, travelling on his dark journey through ice, and water, and steam, to say his word at a new event in America, made his gesture to change a continuity. These changes make history, these points at which the rules break down. We are concerned with them. We build our churches and our Constitutions on them, and it is here we must take care, and reaffirm our own wishes.

The parallels can be found often, and at all times, and depend on the same great energies abroad in the world. The imaginative act, in all its delicacy, in all its explosiveness, realizes these energies, and the continuity behind them—the continuity of force, and of the human spirit alive in many lives. The realization is expressed in the interruptions, however, at those dramatic points which disturb all balance, which flash and are gone as balance is made again. And in the flash we see the equilibrium, as in the work of a great artist we see his age.

In the human being, balance is reached in a search for unity.

There are analogies here. These analogies are universal.

CHAPTER FIVE

The Education

WHEN THE BOY WAS SEVEN, the Gibbs family moved into the house on High Street—that house which from the beginning was loved as a still center, whose garden was tended until the iris flourished, a pride of the neighborhood—the house which fixed for his lifetime the world-space of Willard Gibbs.

He was a child, he was a little boy in a house of women. The family was presided over by the long, sympathetic face of his mother and the teaching schedule of his father. Professor Gibbs's language and Bible students would stand on the front steps, looking up at the new cream-colored house, until one of the little girls or the boy opened the door and let them into the study, where the Professor met with some of his students. There was a decline in religious feeling all over New England during these years, and it was a thorn in the flesh of many of the divines. But Professor Gibbs was concerned more with the intellectual relations of religious truth than with observances. The language of the truth was his goad, his delight, his science. Murmurs of this came through the study door.

The children played in the new rooms of the High Street house, keeping quiet so as not to disturb their father, watching the puddings and cakes come out of the oven, the jellies being put up. Marketing was done early—at dawn, when the town woke, when the elms brightened again from black to complicated shadowy green, the port was full of the noises of exertion, and the young gentlemen of Yale were getting up for five-thirty chapel.

The Education

Colors and sounds, the first bright tastes of childhood, the dark wood of the furniture. The child first knows these things. The fever, with its days of delirium, its wasting furnace and red period, the long convalescence during which he could look slowly at things seen for the first time—a curtain blowing at the window, vivid leaves beyond, cattle in the street—that fever, faded into dim childhood, leaves its stamp of frailty and awareness on him.

He sees the rooms with their heavy dark tables, the ottomans, the sofa, the pattern on the stair, the leather books with their Latin names, the chairs with their cane seats and their hair seats. And his sisters, three of them older than himself—Anna, almost eight years his elder, the quiet, gentle one, who took care of them; Eliza; Julia, the lively one; and little Emily, who was born when he was two.

What marks the sickness left were not particular. Another child, born in Boston, spoke about the scarlet fever he had gone through as taking on greater and greater importance, from the point of view of education, as he grew up. He said he might through life puzzle himself to decide whether it had fitted or unfitted him for success; but Henry Adams, growing up through these years, was to be concerned with these things all his life. Young Willard Gibbs was not. Or, rather, Henry Adams has left all the traces. We know what landmarks he saw, what signposts he followed, as well as what roads he took.

The home of Willard Gibbs was not one of Presidents, but of divines, professors, librarians. His father stood at the window, watching the children at games; went back to his notes, and wrote down "handy-dandy, a play in which children change hands and places." He was absorbed in his work—after all, he was forty-nine when the boy was born—and intent on the studies in which he was a pioneer.

Henry Adams sat on a yellow kitchen floor and learned the color of sunlight. Young Willard Gibbs learned early what the arch of the elms was; snow, in its even quality of white; the strong kitchen lessons, how things were mixed, the salt in the stew, the chicken in the soup that could never again be what it was, as the chicken itself could never be taken out. That was the Puritan lesson : what was once done could never be undone.

Snatches and tags of conversation came out of the study, and echoes of those conversations went round the dinner-table. Words about religion—how the unity of science, whatever that was, could never be sacrificed to the harmony of revelation, whatever that was. The words were all household words, even though their sense was not yet clear. Then, too, there were words about words. Heaven, as Professor Gibbs pointed out with his smile, could be understood if you would look at what it said : *heaven*, from *heave*—something heaved over the earth.

The whole arch of heaven covered a small enough world. The Green; Crown Street, which they had left; the streets of the College, Chapel, Library, and Elm; and now High Street, where they lived, near Wall.

That half-block became the new circle of the world. For now he was ten, and it was time to go to school, to move out of this house of sisters during the daytime, away from his mother and his father—so distant, so firm, busy among the fine smells of the books and the cooking—and go to school.

Hopkins Grammar School stood diagonally across the street. You went up to the corner, under the young trees, to High and Wall, maybe a hundred steps from your front door; crossed the street one way, then across the other way; and you were at the building you had stared at for three years, even since the family moved into the High Street house. School.

Hopkins is the second oldest grammar school in America, the only older one being the Boston Latin School. Older than Yale itself, it had gone along with Yale in all its attitudes. Unendowed, carrying the rigid tradition of Ezekiel Cheever, it struggled for money, and invested in land when it did get money. Now it was in its new building, a one-story stucco house with a stone basement that was already a cave haunted by the short generations of schoolboys, where dust covered the papers and Latin schoolbooks. It was an explosive new world to a New Haven boy.

Sixty-three boys were in the school this fall. The yellow trees covered High Street with blown leaves, and the saplings that were set around the school grounds still looked frail in their wooden guards. They were almost as old as this youngest class, of whom one wrote home :

The Education

DEAR FATHER:

    Last Monday a week from tomorrow I began a boys school. I now like it pretty well. Willie Gibbs entered with me and I believe has formed pretty much the same opinion I have.

S. BALDWIN

That was Sim Baldwin, the son of the *Amistad* counsel for the defense. He was to grow up to be governor of Connecticut, and he kept all his papers. Willie Gibbs was quiet, however. He came in as the clear-toned bell in the cupola rang. He wrote his compositions, on "Thunderstorms," "Caves and Grottoes of the World," and "Water," and historical papers on "Nineveh" and "Yale College." English had recently been added to Latin and Greek as a respectable subject for boys to study, and one afternoon each week there was a recitation. All the classes recited together in one room, as classes were reciting all over the settled parts of the country. Most of them were using the text the Hopkins boys read from—Ezekiel Cheever's *Accidence*. Willie Gibbs's father had that book; there was no need to get another. They had all the texts at home : Cheever, Adam's *Grammar*, Aesop's *Fables*, the *Colloqui* of Erasmus. Incidental expenses at school could be cut down, living at home as he did, and not having to get new books. The normal expenses for a year of forty-four weeks was ten dollars per quarter for tuition, and two or three dollars for incidentals. These extra dollars would cover some of the oyster and cider suppers that the secret societies gave.

    Once during these years, the whole school had whooping-cough together, and Willie Gibbs and Sim Baldwin were the only ones who did not catch it. They visited a lot back and forth between the Gibbs house and the Baldwin house on Church Street, and Sim's sister helped them keep up with their reading, writing, and arithmetic. "And in after years it was her proud boast that she had laid the foundations of Willard Gibbs's mathematical career."

    It was a sharp distinction to be a quiet child; school was for extroverts. The century was for extroverts. One could have another kind of "quietness"; the mock, hilarious secrecy of the societies that flourished at Yale and that were imitated at Hopkins, with Clio, the fraternity organized just after Gibbs entered, complete with rites, suppers, and noisy meetings. Then there was

The Club, which had been started for the purpose of debating, but was mostly for fun, and petered out in '50. That year Polymnia was founded as soon as school opened after the September vacation. Polymnia was a literary society that came to an untimely end. One of its members wrote a long poem on the landing of the Pilgrims—a poem that the fraternity at once decided was the most inspired verse that had yet been written. In an access of admiration, the Hopkins boys voted to print the poem and sell it from door to door in New Haven. The boys, in their tight jackets and flowing ties, or in the plaids that all children wore after Queen Victoria's trip to Scotland, their trousers carefully creased, knocked on the doors and waited on the steps; and over them, the long sad faces of New Haven shook from side to side : no, no. The society went bankrupt, owing tremendous sums to the printer.

Willie Gibbs does not seem to have belonged to these groups; or, if he did, he left no mark on them. It was too easy to go home after classes; and he cared most of all about classes, and rapidly went to the head there. One verse, written in 1850 under the pen-name of Gregory Grinwigg, sets him down forever at the scarred school desk :

> ... Next to him Gibbs, with visage grave
> Sits in the seat our Rector to him gave.
> A student he—and one who seldom looks
> With playful countenance from off his books.

Once, that spring, Edward F. Blake got out of his usual composition by writing instead a letter to Sim Baldwin which began :

Dear Sim
    It is now Tuesday afternoon and I am in school at my desk, we have just recited our lesson and Gibbs class is reciting. . . .

If the boy Gibbs did not belong to the societies, he did "belong" to a part of young New Haven which included the Blakes and the Whites, the Bacons, the Bennets, the Trowbridges and Whitneys and others whose names appear in the letters which the Baldwin family kept. They went camping, fishing, picnicking; or sometimes the boys went, and the little girls consoled themselves in the Baldwins' cherry tree. Mrs. Baldwin wrote to her son that Martha Greene had done that, one June afternoon. ". . . Julia and Emily Gibbs and Addie Bowen and Martha were all up in the tree together—eating by the hour, and they are coming again this afternoon. The tree is so full there is plenty for all, birds included, to whom your Father gives the freest welcome. . . ."

In one letter, Tom White tells Sim Baldwin in a hushed tone of respect how Rog Day had his arm broken while he was being initiated into their society, Clio; how he never told anyone, but went to a doctor when he got home to have it set. And Tom goes on to say that two tents are to be pitched in August at the head of Saltonstall Lake—"Let's have Gibby go on our camping out if his parents will let him go."

In the flourishing correspondence between Ed Blake and Sim Baldwin, one letter tells of a picnic that Gibbs went on when he was fifteen. Ed writes:

DEAR SIM

I received your letter just as we were starting on a pic-nic to Saltonstall and I read it on the way. The pic-nic was composed of boys and girls and was a glorious one—not like the one's we used to have—walk out of town about two miles and then sit down and talk sentimental nonsense or chase "Marthy Ann" through the bushes;— nothing like those but a real pleasant jovial pic-nic. This is the way that it was planned and carried out. Wednesday afternoon I started off trouting at one o'clock. I had capital luck (which I will tell you elsewhere) and got home about 6½ o'clock, tired, dirty, sunburnt, wet and hungry. When I reached home I found that the Whites i.e. Tom &c were going to have some company in the evening and wanted me to come. Tim and Eliza had gone already. I "rigged" and went down. We had a very pleasant time. During the evening Freddy and Fanny got up the pic-nic in behalf of the girls and Tom and I in behalf of the boys. We boys Rogs Dies, Rogo Albus, Tom White, Gibbs, Tim and I, hired a pic-nic wagon for 5 dollars and took the girls consisting of Freddie, Fanny, Julia, Emmie, Amy Armstrong, Miss Barrett and a Mary Wright from Miss Duttons school. As Miss Dutton would not permit her scholars to go out in a boat and Mrs. Gibbs did not want Julia to and as Freddy had been interdicted from it and above all as when we got out there were no boats in sight we had to walk up the side of the lake. We stopped round the first promontory just out of sight of the ice-houses. We boys then went off bathing while the girls got the dinner ready. After dinner Freddie and I fished. I brought out a little line for her. You never saw any body so delighted as she was when she caught a fish. She went into perfect ecstasies over two miserable little roaches which she caught and which I carried round with us in an old tea-pot we found there. We got safely home just about sunset having had a delightful trip. . . .

All that summer, young Gibbs had been coming to see Fanny Storer. At Presentation Day, he and Fanny had gone with Freddie and Ed Blake to the chapel, to hear the oration, the poem, and the letters of old boys. They had been horribly embarrassed —one lady had even left, saying indignantly that she would hear no more—at the reading of one letter from out West, which said that the writer was unable to attend because of the interesting condition of his wife, but that if he had known sooner about the date of the occasion, he might have made different arrangements. That night there was a torchlight parade, with transparencies in the streets, and people in disguises running through the crowd. School was better; the new head-master was letting the boys do just as they pleased, and they could send down to the pie-bakery for pies and cakes, beer and ginger-pop, and draw them up into the window by a string. Gibbs seems to have been included on all their picnics; he is listed on the picnic and camping lists—on one with a little map of the meal, the oranges and white grapes surrounded by mottoes and candies, with an outer ring of custard and lemonade and cream cakes and almonds. But people must have felt his reticence—now, at fifteen, he is being called "a universal bugbear" by one of the friends who was on all the trips. Some hint of the mixed attitude toward him was in his relations already. The strongest picture of it is in this letter from Tom White :

Sunday, New Haven, July 30th, 1854.

DEAR SIM,

I received your letter last week, and was right glad to hear from you.

I should have opened a correspondence before, but as you began it with Ed Blake by writing to him first, I thought I would wait for you to begin it with me, and I was much disappointed that you did not write sooner. You will doubtless soon meet Freddie at Trumansburgh, for I believe (if nothing prevents) she intends returning home in about a week.

The Education

Ed is as much in love with her as he ever was, but alas she does not return his affections, any more than a kind of friendship for him, for she likes Mr. Taylor a senior, or rather a graduate better, or rather she is cracked with him, and Ed whenever he sees her, always instead of talking sensibly, carries on a kind of silly bantering with her, about other people or young gentlemen, for he is dreadfully jealous. Rog White and myself launched our boat yesterday upon the lake she sits very prettyly upon the water and looks very well with the exception that she has a square bow. Ed said she had got on too much pitch but she had not, for he does not know how to scull though, he says he does, and Capt. Brooks says he does not, he has turned up his nose and laughed at us all the time we were building it. Ed feels dreadfully grand now that he has got into college, he has joined the brothers society. Willy Gibbs whom I detest has got into college, and sports a tail as also I do.

He is as much in love with Fanny as ever, and is forever bringing her flowers, why only yesterday he brought her a most beautiful bunch of pond lillies which look very handsome on the parlor table in one of those old fashioned punch bowls, but Fanny does not like him at all, and we teaze her about him, she likes his flowers much better than she does him, even Freddie & Fanny Perkins dislike him, (for Fanny is here now at your house I suppose you know) for the other night they were at our house in the evening, and Willy came down, nobody knows what for, and Freddie and Fanny Storer ran into the privy, while Fanny Perkins and I ran into the house to escape from him, a universal bugbear. . . .

Lost days. The river he knew, the faces he first saw against the sky, the pier he sat on and watched break the circles and waves of the Sound, the leaf he picked up and broke brittle yellow in his hand, the little sisters whom he loved. And the autumn-colored books, the scrawls of childhood, the cliffs he grew to know : red precipice of East Rock, West Rock which ends in a basalt cliff of columns. Lost. To see it as it once was seen by him; to know that it was these colors and qualities into whose nature he first inquired; and to know that they are lost. When did he realize the snow and ice, and their fine kinship with the rain that fell over the streets of snow? When did the stars spell a meaning to him? And the steam of the harbor ships, the screaming train? The words his father spoke, of words and meaning? And the simple, irreversible soup, that can never again be what went into it—the water, colored forever by one drop of ink that winds in the clear air-bright bowl and is lost to the eye, but hangs forever there? The numbers written on slate in the schoolroom? The story of his father learning to talk to the African captives because he could count up to ten in their tongue? Lost, with the lost days, and the little boy lost.

He is tall now. He is the son of the family. Now there is only one thing to do. And he enters Yale.

The rowdies, the townies, bang around Chapel Street, and smash windows, and swarm up the trees, and drive the young gentlemen in retreating waves down the length of the Fence that marks the College. The waves bear down on the town toughs, and the long battle is joined again.

New Haven is so sharply divided an organism that its entire character is based on the gap between the physical and the intellectual life. Half of the town is concrete and industrial; the other half is Yale. In other towns, one or the other half takes precedence : the Cambridge factories swarmed and engulfed Harvard, and Oxford kept its little town in hand. The location of Yale in the middle of the city is, as has often been remarked, a historical accident. But more than any other single factor, it has been the College that was responsible for the growth of the city. When Willie Gibbs entered in the fall of 1854, the balance was almost perfect : the place was indeed half New Haven and half Yale. This house was already divided. This civil war need not ever be declared; it existed.

There were 20,000 people in the city, and ten years doubled the number. The railroads, the harbor, the factories were doing that. Immigrants streamed in; the newspapers grew, and their paragraphs were the only reflection in this town of the seething country, of such continental issues as the Missouri Compromise and the Dred Scott case. The town grew and fought; and the undergraduates fought, and slaved over the books, but stayed remote, a world to themselves. In the decade, only one essay on any political subject was published, and that was an abstruse discussion of the fugitive-slave law, in the one Yale publication, the *Lit.* The world of Yale had other laws, which it followed, and according to which it thrived.

The Education

Most of the students lived at the College, in the Old Brick Row. One-fifth of the entire number lived in private houses, but it was understood that if there were vacant dormitory room, these students would be taxed to make up the rent. There was a new era, however. The office of the butler, who sold food and beer and tobacco to the students in Gibbs's father's time, had been abolished, and the fagging system was deep in the past. Those were echoes of the English school system; but all the rest remained. German scholarship was coming in—philology attested to that; French thought had shaped the early years of the United States; but the colleges reflected Oxford and Cambridge, and not the Continent. Chemistry and the three learned languages constituted the secular course, along with a few lectures in law. Brilliance in literature was admired; a boy who was bright at math was likely to get nothing but a certain kind of laughter. There was a Medical Department, a professorship in natural history was established while Willie Gibbs was working under Rector Olmstead at Hopkins, and other departments and new subdivisions marked the growth as accurately as a tree's rings.

Riots were the actual mark of these years. Gibbs came from a quiet house, made even more still now by the onset of illness. Death had already entered. Eliza died when Willie was ten, and she was buried a block away, in Grove Street cemetery, with a spray of lilies and her age, fifteen, on her headstone, and the four words : "No More to Die." And now his mother was ill, with a long, slow illness in which she seemed to ebb farther and farther. Anna more and more took her place as she grew weak; and the boy grew up rapidly as the relations of the family shifted. His long face looks out from the early daguerreotypes, with its strange eyes, hostile one moment, and then suddenly soft and perceptive. He takes stillness with him, and "takes" is a suggestion of too great motion. This is not like going to college, with its journey, its adventure and explosive promise. Yale is like home; the classroom is like the study of the High Street house. This only adds a few rooms to young Willard Gibbs's home.

But if the classrooms are like the room in which his father now holds Bible class, the streets are vastly different. They are changed, actually changed, with the new inventions that seem to be taking hold. Although the city pigpens still are here, and the swine are still used to scavenge the streets, gas lamps have been installed, and the Green is lit at night. This new light arrives the same year that the railroad is finished which connects New Haven and New York, so that the town is now a metropolis joined to the metropolis. Laws suitable to its dignity are passed : now there are to be no more horses and cows pasturing in the streets, a volunteer fire department is established, graded schools are set up. There is some talk of paving the sidewalks, but when this innovation is made there is strong opposition.

Violence seems to be everywhere, and growing. Boys are drowned training for the Yale-Harvard meet; students are advised that it is a good idea to keep a pistol; as Gibbs enters Yale, there is one of the fiercest fights the students and townies ever had. On a fine evening in spring, just as the curtain goes down on the play being performed in the Exchange Building, and the crowd flows out into the street, bricks and stones fly in the air, and there are suddenly two hostile crowds struggling in Chapel Street. Pistols are fired, and a rowdy seizes a student. The town man falls instantly, and when they turn him over, it is at once clear that he has not been shot at all, but stabbed through the heart "by a dirk in the hand, it was said, of a Senior from Mississippi." His body is carried bleeding into the Glebe building, but the riot does not stop. The students fight a retreat toward the campus. There is no way of stopping the battle, and a mob darkens the Green as the fire-alarm bells ring. A few of the town mob drag a cannon up and set it opposite South College. Some of this mob, ready for a long siege, load the cannon with powder and missiles; but Captain Bissel of the police force is the hero of this occasion. While the cannon was being loaded, he was "quietly plugging up the vent with a sharpened stick." The mayor arrives on the scene before things go any farther, and order is somehow restored. The college boys are questioned closely, but nobody is ever identified, and nobody can be held.

If the questioning is as casual but effective as Gibbs's entrance examination is said to have been, somebody should be held. That kind of deduction would have found the undergraduate who killed Patrick O'Neil. There is a story that Gibbs's father confessed, when he was interviewed by President Day in 1805, that he was nervous about the entrance examination, and they talked for a long time about preparation for Yale, Day (who was then still professor) asking long and searching questions. At the end of the time, he stood up and told Josiah Gibbs that he was admitted. When Willard Gibbs entered, he consulted Professor Thacher, a friend of the family's. The faculty was small enough to be well aware of Josiah Gibbs's son, and to know that he was entering the college, and Professor Thacher informed Willard Gibbs at the end of the interview that he had passed his entrance examination.

Freshman year means tragedy. After three years of unbroken illness, Gibbs's mother dies, and the family is bitterly changed at first. Little by little, it takes on a new balance : the sisters move into their mother's domain, as indeed they have been doing since she took to her bed; the two servants have more responsibilities; the whole household is now responsible for the Professor's well-being and quiet, the calm routine of his schedule, and young Willard, involved in his new studies, begins again to give himself to his work.

New Haven is shaken by excitement and premonition. The children of the town have a Fourth of July procession of singing emblematical groups, with tableaux and a patriotic concert given by six hundred children of the town on the north steps of the State House. Refreshments are set out on a long table. The shaky pageant affirms a strong Union. But only a few months pass before, in Center Church, an appeal is made that rouses the whole section. The story of John Brown is told with renewed passion. Volunteers are needed in Kansas. Henry Ward Beecher speaks, burning with the pressure behind his words, and then Professor Silliman gets up. He suggests that the town present the volunteers with adequate arms, and the meeting shouts its agreement. The monuments of the Regicides are cornerstones of this church. Money for Sharpe breech-loading rifles is raised, and the arms are presented, in a full ceremony. Ten days after the first appeal, there is a farewell meeting, with a letter from Beecher, a song by Whittier sung, another song by the Reverend Hiram Bingham, and the volunteers are escorted to the New York boat. Two months later, Sumner speaks of the portents of Civil War, which "hang on all the arches of the horizon."

Gibbs does not do well in class the year of his mother's final illness and death. His solutions of the Freshman Prize Problems, a month after her death, show that only six problems out of ten were solved at all. This paper is notable for a phrase that echoes through all his work. "Substituting (for simplicity)" he writes. . . .

Freshman year had its festivals : the Statement of Facts, freshman Pow-wow, Thanksgiving Jubilee. But sophomore year had a curious celebration, dedicated to the murder of mathematics, a tradition handed down by a hundred classes who had hated their two years of pushing through page after page of geometrical proof. This pageant was called the Burial of Euclid.

On an evening near the end of the term, the class was called together by the magnificent announcement of Euclid's death, and the news of his funeral was sent out. When the sophomores reached the big hall, they found it decorated with revenge. Clusters and streamers made the wooden beams glorious, and on the wall was a cartoon roaring in reds and blacks, the fire and furious smoke fuming over a sea of tar, with demon stokers industriously in charge of Euclid's remains. These remains were painted in with loving detail, filling most of the foreground. Over them stood Jupiter, with whose sanction this took place. There, in the corner, stood the edge of a dark forest, with struggling demons seen—writhing legs here, here a diabolical face—in all the postures of battle to the death. And at the edge of it all, a weeping student accompanied and confirmed by a weeping crocodile.

Under the panorama the ritual unrolled. An upper-classman held out the Law that was being defiled—a volume of Euclid, the hated book complete except for the round and black-rimmed hole that stared from the middle—and another initiate offered the sophomore a glowing poker. The threefold rite began : the sophomore thrust the poker through the hole, so that the book burned red, and a little shower of sparks rose as he pulled the poker out. The chant rejoiced; he had gone through Euclid. Then the book was held over his head. He had understood Euclid. And finally, the book was passed under his foot. He had gone over Euclid. When the whole class had shared the mysteries, the funeral cortege of undergraduates in grotesque and mythological costume filed out in the torchlight to the burial place. Sometimes Euclid would be buried as a man in classic dress, book pressed to breast. Sometimes the symbol was enough, and the book itself would be shrouded and carried to the pyre and, after lamentations, burned.

The Education

The orations were a chance for heresy at last, after the two years of lip-service. The dirges sang :

> No more we gaze upon that board
> Where oft our knowledge failed,
> As we its mystic lines ignored,
> On cruel points impaled. . . .
> We're free! Hurrah! We've got him fast,
> Old Euk is nicely caged at last. . . .
> Black curls the smoke above the pile
> And snaps the crackling fire:
> The joyful shouts of Merry Sophs
> With wails and groans conspire.
> May yells more fiendish greet thy ears,
> And flames yet hotter glow;
> May fiercer torments rack thy soul
> In Pluto's realms below.

How strange this firelight and singing must have been to the boy who had here found what he had been looking for, to whom the hours spent over these diagrams were beginning to mean something more, even, than the most intimate, the hopeful times, when the meaning of his life opened. If Euclid was to die, it was going to be a far different death. The flames went up; the voices grew louder, and hoarse.

He stayed with his books. This year he won the Berkeley Premium for Latin Composition, and his prize paper in algebra and geometry contained only one mistake. The problems went from :

1. Given $4x^3 + 30x^2 + 75x = 302$, find x

to

10. To find the length of that arc whose cosine is to its versed sine as the secant to the tangent.

The only error he made was in 1, and it was a simple error : he multiplied 38×4 and got as a result 272.

This examination became famous for the extraordinary case of cheating that went on during its writing. The "skinning" that was epidemic at the time became more and more inventive, until one particularly ingenious boy noticed that the floor of the examination was directly over a cellar, and worked out his own system. It was possible to learn the seating plan for the examination, and when he found out where he was to sit, he bored a hole through the floor next to his chair. A friend with a complete set of reference books sat in the cellar under the hole, waiting for the question to be lowered to him. When the slip of paper came dangling down through the darkness at the end of a long black thread, he tore off the question, looked up the answer, and sent it back up with plenty of time left to copy it out.

During junior year, Gibbs won the Berkeley Premium again, and the Third Prize for Latin Examination, as well as the Bristed Scholarship, which carried a prize of ninety-five dollars. This year he wrote the best examinations in his class in Greek, Latin, and mathematics, and was chosen to give the Latin Oration. He also won a set of Shakespeare, a prize given for English composition.

He ended his senior year as a member of Phi Beta Kappa, with another Latin Oration, the De Forest Mathematical Prize, and the Clark Scholarship, whose $120 was given for the best examination of the entire college course, with the proviso that the winner continue with one or two years of graduate work in non-professional studies. The prize problems of the senior year were done in a concrete example : to find a factory located somewhere between A, B, and C, if the haulage distance to all points was equal.

During Gibbs's last undergraduate year, another man was killed in a fight between students, members of the Crocodile Club, and the town fire brigade. The Crocodile Club, one of the most popular of the secret societies, had been meeting, and when the students passed the firehouse a block down from Gibbs's house, on their way back to the College, a fight started with the firemen who were loafing there. When the fight was at its height, there was a cry, "Shoot! Shoot!" and shots were fired from both sides. The fight stopped immediately when a fireman fell. He was shot in the back, and died next day. Again, the man who fired this shot was never identified. Five hundred dollars compensation was raised and paid to the fireman's widow and children, but the coroner's jury was unable to indict anyone. Three students of the class of '59, who were known to be handy with firearms, were held. Edmund Carrington was down on the books as having fired a pistol within the college buildings the October before, and it was known not only that he kept firearms in his room—which would not in itself be enough, as freshmen used to keep sophomores out of their rooms when they arrived on hazing parties by firing through the door after due warning—but that he had been seen with a pistol the day before, preparing for the fight, which had been coming for a long time. Two other men were suspended for about three months; Carrington, who was later killed in the Civil War, was suspended for three weeks longer, and that was that.

Students could not walk in New Haven with any assurance of safety. There were likely to be riots after the theatre, and the fact that there were few plays made these riots seem inevitable. Outside the Woodcock Inn, an extremely popular tavern with no heating facilities, no plumbing, and dim lights, a good fight could always be started. And if all else failed, you could always beat up the freshmen, or paint them with indelible ink, or subject them to indignities "which cannot be named," according to the records. The most complete account of these tortures is also the best account of classroom procedure and the cheating that was as ingenious as the methods of hazing, as crafty, and as prevalent. The examination in mathematics of Gibbs's sophomore year was the one that made history, but there are other tales. The whole system turned out a unique type, less literary than a Harvard man, less religious than a Princeton man.

The Yale system of the 1850's and 1860's was a powerful machine for giving young men certain social characteristics. It was particularly suitable for training men of an active, extrovert disposition for executive positions in politics, law, the Church, and commerce. If the United States had not been growing and changing rapidly, and the number of Yale graduates had been larger, their history would have been different. They would have been governed by a type of politician even more thoroughly trained in clique management, and more undemocratic, than that produced by Oxford. The United States was too large, and the number of Yale men too small, for their government to pass entirely under the control of that group-loyal type. Students who passed through the system could not evade its profound influence.

Crowther goes on to say:

Gibbs absorbed the Yale spirit completely. He accepted a set of social ideas of high value to a politician, but unsuited to a scientific discoverer. It increased his tendency to intellectual isolation, and at the same time, made that tendency seem natural.

He seemed, at any rate, to absorb Yale. What he really did was to wall himself about with the most convenient armor—the Yale attitude—and to live within that wall, dedicated and alone. He lived in his home and in his head.

There were resistances to this society—to both sides of its split. Power of every sort was the country's obsession : slave power, mechanical power, political power, the cleavage of the West by the railroad pioneers—until those people who were set against power seemed to be the obsessed. There is a whole line of resistance in New England. Every little township has its crank, whose one wild floating gesture has often made the place a name in history. These are the fools of protest, whose tantrum stops nothing, but who, with an actor's precision, express their age as much as the obvious leaders against whose forms they shut their doors. Think of Edward Dickinson, the father of the poet Emily Dickinson, who saw the September sunset in 1851, when Gibbs, eleven years old, played in the rich fields under its bannering orange. That father ran gasping up the steeple stairs of the Baptist Church in Amherst, and pulled and pulled on the bell-rope until the clanging startled the whole town, who turned to look, and saw the sunset. That was the gesture of a poet who does what his daughter was later to do : uses the old forms, pulls on the churchbell-rope, to call attention to the vivid and changing moment in an unheard-of way.

Unheard-of ways. Lord Timothy Dexter knew, but he was dead. He had taken the name of Lord to impress his neighbors in Newburyport, and they had been impressed. He had held his mock funeral in his own drawing-room, and stood, spyglass in hand, at an upper window, while his own funeral procession wound down the path, and he could watch them winding and diminishing all the way to the graveyard. When his wife came home, he thrashed her; she had not mourned enough. And then he hated the business rules. He would get rich on the first ship that entered the harbor. He bought that first ship, and its cargo —of cats. He sailed away, and came home a rich man. He had landed at Malta, where there was plague, and sold the cats at marvellous prices to kill the plague-carrying rats. It was easy; he could do anything. He bought the next cargo. Warming-pans; he would take them to Cuba! And sailed down the coast, on a leisurely voyage into the hot South, ripping off the lids of the warming-pans on the way to Havana, where he sold them for molasses ladles. Well, the whole set of rules was wrong, that was clear—rules, and proverbs, all of a piece. The proverbs were crazy. He would take coals to Newcastle and prove them all liars, the proverb-mongers. And Lord Timothy Dexter sailed away again, and the people came to the dock to jeer. He sailed back with a fortune. There had been a strike in Newcastle, and he had broken it with his coal.

That was the active protest. New Haven had another way. It had Milton J. Seward. Early in the '40s, William Miller had been only one of many predicting the end of the world; by 1855, Seward was convinced. He bought the top of East Rock, over the town and river, built a house to live in during operations, and started work on his real project. This Noah was working scientifically : he was building a forty-foot steamboat. It was his way of rising to the occasion. When the end of the world came, it would come in flood; and Seward was ready; his steamboat would be floated off the Rock, and he would triumph in steam over a sea of waters.

There were other, more real triumphs. These were the years that have been called the American Renaissance; the years of greatness, of *Moby Dick*, of *Leaves of Grass*, of *Walden, The House of the Seven Gables, Representative Men*. John Brown at Ossawatomie, in one fierce crazy gesture, dramatized the wish of half a country. There were triumphs. Emerson gave his lecture, "Poetry and Imagination," in 1854, saying:

The magnificent hotel and inconveniency we call Nature is not final . . . nothing stands still in nature but death . . . creation is on wheels in transit. . . . Thin or solid everything is in flight . . . everything undressing and stealing away from its old into new form, and nothing fast but those invisible cords which we call laws on which all is strung. . . . All multiplicity rushes to be resolved into unity.

These were the victories. And the sea knew two great triumphs of the imagination : one which created a world in hazard

and madness, facing the forces of evil abroad and fighting—
Moby Dick. The other was done in an accepted framework,
to link two actual worlds together. In clumsiness and bungling,
the efforts to lay an Atlantic cable were successful. William
Thomson, later Lord Kelvin, met Helmholtz in 1855 and started
work on the cable, whose first painful trials and failures took up
the years Gibbs spent at Yale.

On July 25, 1858, Gibbs's class graduated. Gibbs gave the
salutatory speech in Latin; Addison Van Name, a first-rate student in Hebrew, one of the best of Professor Gibbs's students,
a quiet, shy boy from Binghamton who was quickly becoming
at home in the High Street house, gave the Valedictory, a speech
on the Influence of Feeling on Thought; and Theodore D. Woolsey preached the Baccalaureate sermon, exhorting, like the verse
in Titus, the young men to be sober-minded. He warned them
that the spirit of the times was opposite, that feeling had become
more intense, action more hurried. He drew an image of action :
"Freedom of intercourse, and diffusion of knowledge, circulate
feeling with electric speed : we move in masses, and intensify
each other's feeling by sympathy," he warned. He spoke of the
recent commercial disasters, the desire of wealth which was high
in the country, and which had led to the bankruptcy of millions.
He mentioned with respect the religious revival which had taken
the place of the irreligiousness of five years ago. And he ended,
"With such voices urging you to a life of religious sobriety, you
are going forth into a fascinating world."

Diffusion of knowledge, and the fascinating world. New
Haven celebrated them a month later, and young Gibbs and
young Van Name, the only members of their class who lived in
New Haven, stayed up with the town on the night of August
17th, waiting for the three cannon shots that would announce
the success of the Atlantic cable. The evening wore on, and the
jokes went around about a new failure; but at one-thirty in the
morning, the cannon went off, and in a trumpet voice, a leading
citizen read the Queen's message to the President, and the President's message to the Queen, those links of time and space. The
Green was lit up. All the fire companies were out, the whole
town was out, cheering and laughing and celebrating the new
age. There were huge bonfires set all down Church and Chapel
Streets, and the red-lit people standing around them talked of

other cities where the bonfires burned tonight for the same reason. Processions toured the town all night, beating their drums, and the horns blared. The steam calliope tootled all night; nobody wanted to sleep; here was the new age! All next day was holiday; and the hundred-gun salute that had been promised was duly fired in the evening. There were fireworks far into the country, and the town glittered with illuminations, lighting the transparencies hung across the streets. From the Green, you could see the bonfires high up on East Rock, where the silhouette of crazy Seward's steamboat tried hopelessly to say that the old age was dead and deny that the new had begun. But here was the new age—the bands, the rockets, the roman candles proved it; and the bells, the howling calliope that could be heard from Mount Carmel in dying wails to Long Island. It did not matter that the cable died. It had swung from world to world. It would swing again.

Very little in that year was appropriate to Willard Gibbs. The year was part of him; he lived here; but his time was to come, and he lived very lightly in these seasons. He was preparing himself.

CHAPTER SIX

Father and Son

VERY LITTLE seemed appropriate to him. The Connecticut Academy, perhaps; but that was little more than an extension of the study at home, a group of men known to young Gibbs, seen by him almost daily, that from time to time met in each other's homes, and on those evenings became the Connecticut Academy of Arts and Sciences. The institution was largely made up of members of the Yale faculty. The Sillimans were extremely active here, organizing, publishing, lecturing, and young Hubert Anson Newton, his tutor at college, his neighbor at home, was on the board. Hubert Anson Newton saw his promise. It was showing itself then, although he had written nothing but his college papers. He was nineteen and only just out of Yale when a letter came to the High Street house, addressed to Josiah W. Gibbs, Esq., care of Professor Gibbs. He opened the letter. It was dated Nov. 26, 1858, and written on the third page of the printed constitution of the Academy. He read :

MY DEAR SIR,

It is my duty and pleasure to inform you, that, at its last meeting, you were elected a member of the Connecticut Academy of Arts and Sciences. Full membership being, as in all cases, conditioned upon the payment . . . and signing . . .

His eye travelled down the closely written page, to

Next meeting will be at the house of Dr. E. H. Bishop on Wednesday evening, Dec 15th at 7 o'clk.

LEONARD J. SANFORD

[*104*]

Father and Son

His father had been a member for years. Early in his own life, Josiah Gibbs had been aware of his aptitude for mathematics, and had been drawn towards a life in science instead of theology. His feeling for analysis provides a structure for all of his work, is the bones of his study of language. As he went further along in his field, he found excitements that opened up new ranges. The work that was being done, particularly in Germany, illuminated the new understanding of language and its forms. This new philology was used, along with the advances in science, to clarify Biblical criticism and religious thought itself; it was used as our contemporaries are using the study of semantics to light up their philosophy. But Josiah Gibbs was not a divine, he was an intellectual. His concern was with the intellectual relations of religious truth.

He was a clear and logical man, working in a field which he recognized as scientific throughout. In his most important work, *Philological Studies,* he begins by saying, "Language is a cast of the human mind"; by speaking of the inquiry of the new students of the science of language in this "new field for investigation . . . known to the grammarian only in dark surmises." But he complains in his first paragraph that while we in our nation pursue every branch of the natural sciences, while every literature is brought to us and our writers are neither few nor small, we neglect the subject of language as a scientific study. We teach language as a mechanical art for practical purposes, he says. The study of language has had more and more commercial value to this country, and it has been seen to throw light on the history of our race and the origin and relationship of nations; and so it is of interest to the literary and scientific world.

But now comparative philology is regarded as of high importance in itself, as embodying, as it were, the philosophy of man. Since the commencement of the present century, and especially within the last fifteen years, the philosophy of language has been pursued with great ardor, and the learned on the continent of Europe, by following the grand Baconian principle of induction, have placed this science on a solid basis, and are in the way of most important discoveries.

This teacher, for almost twenty-four years Librarian of Yale, this preacher who hardly ever preached—or, when he did, analyzed his subject with a surgeon's care, as in his discourse on the Sermon on the Mount—Josiah Gibbs was above all a passionate scientist of language, a man who loved words as symbols, who worked in the comparison and grouping of symbols, in the relation of physical to intellectual ideas. He saw language in its literal and physical sense first; he saw imagination coming to the aid of man as he moved between worlds. He wrote :

Man is a citizen of two worlds, *the world of sense*, in which he is surrounded by physical objects, which operate on his sense variously, and awaken the corresponding sensations and perceptions; and *the world of intellect*, in which he rises above the physical world, and becomes aware of objects, operations, and relations, which do not strike the external senses. Whether we regard man in his individual or social capacity, he is first introduced to the physical world, and, even when introduced to the higher spiritual world, still continues, as to a large portion of his existence, a citizen of the former world, and subject to its laws.

He speaks in this section, which is called "Language of the Intellectual World, or Faded Metaphors," of the necessity of the metaphor. The fading is in its passage into use so that we no longer see the image. We do not think of *sin* in its root-meaning, as a missing the mark; we forget that *heaven* is something *heaved* over the world.

The new philology makes possible "a sort of natural system," in which words are only the rude material, and more is necessary to make "an organic whole."

A very strange, a very beautiful pattern makes itself clear as one comes across these words on the brown-stained pages—a pattern of father and son. Here, in these preludes, these foreshadowings, are the immense suggestions. The energies of the mind . . . activity is motion—relations of activity are directions of motion . . . the infinite relations expressed by a small number of signs . . . Here in the little purple textbook of this pioneer of language are the calls and stirrings that were reflected with vast and different meaning much later by his son.

The study of language was to the elder Gibbs a religious work, a work of loneliness. He felt closest to the men working in Germany—Gesenius, Becker, Harris—and to Noah Webster, revising his dictionary with Percival in New Haven according to American usage and his ideas of the basis of speech. Crowther points

JOSIAH W. GIBBS
Father of Willard Gibbs. (From a portrait by F. B. Carpenter.)

out that the elder Gibbs had the ability of pursuing researches without intellectual companionship. All through his son's childhood, the boy must have been aware of the increasingly lonely work of his father—the silence in the house must have added to his own loneliness, as well as his ability to stand intellectual loneliness all his life long. It must, too, have added to his respect for his father, and his distance from him.

Young Gibbs's religious feeling went in channels very different from the line of divines and theologians behind him. Whatever the recurrent Bible classes meant to him, as they met in his home—whatever the stacks of reference to Scripture and commentary—these paled in his life before his main relation to his father. This was a subtle and great reflection of minds. The son, born into a household of women, brought up to think in terms of the relations of symbols one to another and the causes behind symbols, the basic terms of meaning, was bound in some way to be tied to language, to be engrossed in this kind of thought. Father and son deal with two facets of one theme : words as symbols, symbols as words, and the system in which they live.

The list of works by the elder Gibbs is a catalogue of point-by-point investigation into one thing. *Characteristics of the Peshito Syriac Version of the New Testament, the Ante-Mosaic Origin of the Sabbath, The Historical Sense of the New Testament, Teutonic Etymology, Philological Studies, Latin Analyst,* articles in the *New Englander,* the *American Journal of Science and the Arts,* the *Journal of the American Oriental Society,* the *Theological and Literary Journal,* the *Massachusetts Teacher*—his compiled vocabularies, American Indian, Greek, Arabic, Hebrew, Gissi, Vai, Mendi (that was part of the result of the *Amistad* years)—his list is like Percival's lists of languages, until it could be said, of both Percival and the elder Gibbs, that language unlocked philosophy and the recesses of the human heart. New analogies entered. Percival said, "All truth is sacred, sacred as the Bible." Gibbs had not the recklessness to say that. What was sacred to him was also secret, in many ways. His son must have seen that in his father's life. Percival said,

And therefore Poetry, another name
For this innate Philosophy . . .

and he claimed allegiance,

> . . . and yet we will obey
> The intellectual *Numen* and will gaze
> In wondering awe upon it . . .

Percival spoke, too,

> Of all who bear
> Their forms in motion, when the spirit tends
> Instinctive, in their common good to share . . .

Motion was the key. It was as clear in language as it was in science. Noah Webster had made a list of the thirty-four primary or cardinal ideas, and all of them expressed motion. Gibbs lists the twelve that Becker had given. They are :

> *to go, to flow, to blow; to shine, to sound, to grow;*
> *to give,* and *to take; to bind,* and *to separate;*
> *to injure,* and *to defend.*

All the ideas of physical activity are here contained. And all of these may be reduced to the idea of motion.

The relations of these cardinal ideas will be seen in the work of the son.

This reflection between the minds of father and son from generation to generation is, of course, the deepest pattern of education; training being what it has been, and the place of women being what it has been. When the aggressive mind matures, one of the first important objects in its struggle is the image of the father, in all its potency, its protectiveness, and its own aggression. It is basic, totemic; and if it means a reservoir of strength, it means also the severe burden of the past, with whatever guilt the past may convey to the imagination of the child. When the intellectual values are in the fathers and sons in such a way as to reflect sum after sum to succeeding generations, and when the women in the family are chosen for intellectual qualities, the intellectual products sometimes reach a final greatness which is not one great fact so much as a final translation in a series of translated statements. The Gibbs family appears to have been one of these families. Generation after generation sometimes seeks expression for one truth in modality after modality, as if a small race had an utterance to make, and tried to make it until it found its form. The constraints of New England a hundred years ago emphasized the father-and-son drama, and in three families particularly the imagination is seized. We can see the links of this chain in a line of portraits of the same statement. The three families have made profound contributions to imagination, and in such a way as to illuminate many of the meanings of this country for imagination. They are the Gibbs family, the Adams family, the James family.

In 1824, a group of schoolboys were playing in the park in front of the Albany Academy, where Herman Melville would in a few years go to school. At the time, the school had four teachers to its 130 boys. A group of the boys used to play games in the park—and one game in particular, that was half a game of ball, half experiment. The ball that was used started as a balloon, tied to another ball of tow soaked in turpentine. The big ball would be lit, would rise, and the boys would follow it as it soared above their heads, heat-driven, until the ball fell and the real game of football started. Henry James, the affectionate religious boy who was to grow up to be the father of two distinguished sons, William James, the great psychologist, and the novelist, Henry James, was one of the boys playing balloon-football this day—and he had sprinkled his trousers with the turpentine as the ball was lit. The big burning globe rose, dropping its straws of flame, and floated turning over the field, heading for the open window of a stable. Up to the last moment it seemed as though a breeze might turn it, but it cleared the window, and thin black ribbons of smoke began to ride out of the hayloft. The boy rushed up to the hayloft, stamping and stamping among the flames. He put out the fire; but his trousers, which were saturated, caught.

The boy's leg had to undergo a double amputation above the knee. He spent the next two years in bed. He did not go on with the Academy work, but prepared for college with a tutor. William James says that the tutor under whom the half-game, half-experiment was conducted was Joseph Henry. This has been contradicted for rather arbitrary reasons, but in any event,

Joseph Henry was young James's tutor during the four years this active and gifted boy, deprived of all activity, spent at home. Joseph Henry went on to Princeton and to be the first head of the Smithsonian Institution; but it was in Albany that his first impetus toward experimental science had been aroused, and it was in these years that his appetites were feeding on all the material he could find. He himself had been given a gift during illness. He was staying in bed in his Albany boardinghouse one day when he was sixteen. Lying on the table beside him was a new book, which a young Scotchman, Robert Boyle, had brought with him from London. It was entitled *Lectures on Experimental Philosophy, Astronomy, and Chemistry*, by G. Gregory, D.D., Vicar of West-Ham. The boy picked it up in idleness, "read it with avidity," says William James, "and thereupon dedicated his life to experimental science."

As the tutor of the boy Henry James, he found the qualities of avidity for material, religious insight, and interest in science which could seize on whatever he would teach. The boy hardly needed stimulus; he was quickened in an unconquerable joy which even the frightful physical loss did not kill. James later wrote of his own childhood, "I had always had the keenest savor and relish of whatsoever came to me by nature's frank inspiration or free gift. The common ore of existence perpetually converted itself into the gold of life in the glowing fire of my animal spirits. I lived in every fibre of my body."

The boy grew up, reared in an extremely wealthy and decorous household, craving larger sympathies, vistas of belief. Two beliefs especially were close to him, close to what he wished of life, at any rate—the unity or personality of race, and the human innocence. When the elder Henry James went abroad after Princeton, he wanted to find Faraday in London. Joseph Henry was in Europe at that time, traveling with Dr. A. D. Bache, Benjamin Franklin's grandson; there was great sympathy between Faraday and Joseph Henry, who used to love to talk of the hours he and Bache had spent with Faraday; and it was simple to get a letter of introduction. Henry James, however, did not wish to talk to the scientist about science; he wanted to talk about religion. Much later, the English Swedenborgian White wrote to him, asking about the curious intercourse he had had with Faraday, begging that it be recorded, either by

Henry James himself or by "your son who writes for the press."

The answer to this letter has been lost; young Harry James, the novelist, never wrote an account of the meeting; actually, the elder Henry James never mentioned the name of Sandeman in any of his own work. But White's second letter says, "What you write about Faraday quite confirms the conception I had formed of his intellectual religious condition." James quite clearly was led by Faraday to Sandeman, the leader of a cult which professed primitive Christianity, the return to Christian Socialism, a solution to the problems which James had been arguing with his professors at Princeton. There was an equivalence here that pleased him, and resolved his attitude toward faith; this group believed that faith was equivalent to belief; and as one of the relations of Sandeman's practice observes, "there is no difference between believing any common testimony and believing the apostolic testimony, except that which results from the testimony itself, and the divine authority on which it rests." The relations between religion and morality, and religion and science, were what James most cared to understand. He brought his children up according to his beliefs. He became a shrewd, strong, heavy man, who would turn the great flood of his love toward anyone who followed truth, as he saw truth. When he met Emerson, he found himself pouring his spirit out in gratitude, for here was a man who, as he himself in his way was doing, hunted the realities of things, the love of which underlies and vivifies all the seeming barrenness of our most unloving world. He never believed in barrenness; that was his open secret. He believed in the spiritual flowering, and did not see it possible to limit that spring; in a letter written from Washington Place to Joseph Henry, he once wrote: "Again and again I am forced by scriptural philosophy to the conviction that all the phenomena of physics are to be explained and grouped under laws *exclusively spiritual*—that they are in fact only the material expression of spiritual truth—or as Paul says the visible forms of invisible substance."

His children were encouraged to laugh and talk. The family was wealthy, and its members were able to choose their own education, as Henry Adams could also consciously choose, and the family also had a wealth of nature that freed them from restraints and discouragement at home. The James children were brought up among questions of religion and profession as other children are given riddles and little wooden puzzles. His daughter tells how, after a thirty-six-hour absence, the father returned. He could not bear to be away the fortnight he had planned. His wife and the five children met him at the door, "pressing close 'round him, as if he had just been saved from drowning, and he pouring out as he alone could the agonies of desolation through which he had come!" He poured himself out, in the deepest, most helpless generosity. Ideas were presented to his children without the camouflage of tradition—his family was brought up on "the strong meat of the Word."

He took them around the East—Manchester, Newport, New York, the progressive school that Frank Sanborn ran in Concord, left his sons there as he agonized about this country—America, this fastness, this forest of savage paths down which the drumbeat fell. His eyes grew fiery and he cried out, "What a world! But once we get rid of Slavery the new heavens and the new earth will swim into reality!"

These years were the years of precipitance—John Brown appeared in Concord in 1859—the tall, lean, withered man, with his "big scornful eyes and the fanatic's lipless mouth."

In New Haven shortly before, a meeting of private gentlemen had enthusiastically voted him a contribution of a thousand dollars. The money was never raised. And within a few months after he spoke at Concord, they were singing for him at a Martyr Service, and the preacher was scribbling on the cover of his prayer-book:

> Not any spot six feet by two
> Will hold a man like thee;
> John Brown will tramp the shaking earth
> From Blue Ridge to the sea.

It was that tramp, that drumbeat that Mr. James had felt in his mind's forest, which he might recognize as one emblem of America. His children felt it, and they acted as his children. Two of his sons rushed to the war; but William, with his illness and his eye-trouble, was definitely out; and Harry, who had said the world was peopled by "the busy, the tipsy, and Daniel Webster," was torn and silenced between the injury he suffered at the time of the war's beginning, and relief that he could go on with his own work. These children were their father's; the reflection of his nature would be taken right down the century with them; they loved him, and learned, and grew up, while he criticized "as caustically as if his name had been Adams."

These legacies are great—the literary heritage, the gifts of belief and passion and expression, the travels, the laughter, the revelation that arrives at the red day's end, or in the night over a book, or suddenly at a word and the flicker of a face that one has always and will always love. But the children of such families, all of them, with their heritages that open them in childhood to a great tradition—these children, like the James children, grow up so often inheriting most of all the loneliness, unable to be at home in the world which has placed so many unreal values on what they know as the currency and not the thing itself, the menu and not the meal. Many of them grow up, at home only at home.

The Adamses criticized, yes. But they could, for their family had suddenly turned into greatness, and was holding the great line. Presidents, statesmen, scholars. . . . "Without warning," James Truslow Adams says in wonder, "like a 'fault' in the geologic record, there is a sudden and immense rise recorded in the psychical energy of the family. For a couple of generations this new energy finds itself in harmony with the greater lines of force acting upon human society. . . ." Now there are the three sons, grandsons of John Quincy Adams, who was called, in contempt for the monarchy the family seemed to be setting up, John the Second of Braintree. These three sons, Charles Francis, Brooks, and Henry, bore the burden; lived in a gallery of august portraits, handled the silver service of presidents. But they have left to us the record of their uneasiness, their effort (on a level even higher than their ancestors, perhaps) to meet the furious complexity of their own age, their uneasy regard for power and acceptability, and their emotional knowledge of power as *the father*.

Their own father was John Quincy Adams' son. He was editing his father's papers, and writing letters to his sons—to Henry, at his labors of education, as the boy left for Germany —letters full of common sense, advising him not to delude himself into believing that Germany, his first door of escape, led to the education the boy was after. All the Adamses owed a debt to European life; a certain degree of their breadth, like that of the Jameses, was European, but Europe, as this Adams insisted to his son, "unfitted Americans for America."

The boy wrote later, "A fourth child has the strength of his weakness. Being of no great value, he may throw himself away if he likes, and never be missed." This was pure wish, pure folly for any Adams, who could no more throw himself away than he could throw away the memory of Quincy, and its meaning to the nation. Oppressed by the Berlin heaviness as well as by Heine's laughter, with Sumner (who was recovering from the attack made on him by the South Carolinian), drunk on his emotion and away to Italy, his heart singing like a bird in Thuringen, in lost, seductive Rome, he thought of Pumpelly and Clarence King, finding their equivalents in Indian diggings, and said, "All experience is an arch, to build upon."

Whatever would be built upon would belong in part to his father, and to his father power, building to the split in the country and in him. He had to a large degree the equipment and the restraint to know how uncommercial its value was; he had the words. The inheritance in each of these families was a language.

Young Willard Gibbs was a fourth child, too. He was in a different position during this last illness of his father. This was a slow illness; the man was dying of frail old age. He was seventy-one, his wife was dead, the household was full of girls and this one silent son, with his own frailties and the sadness in his face, but with endurance and burning with his own beginnings. The son was coming into his power. It was a power that would not be shown. It would not show itself. He was at home only when he was at home, speaking the family code to his sisters, working for his degree—or out walking, or on one of his long rides.

Gibbs wrote to his friend Sim Baldwin, asking him to join his party for two weeks of riding to the Catskills. The invitation, phrased so stiffly, expresses the diffidence which must have kept young Gibbs away from some of the circle. But he was, nevertheless, accepted here; there were many camping trips, with their last-minute changes of plan :

Father and Son

DEAR SIMEON

When I last saw you I was intending to go to N. Conway, but stopping here on my way I have been persuaded to join my cousin's party to the Catskills. We are very anxious to have you join us if you can give up your other engagements. The party is small Hinckley, Ed B. & myself on horseback & two Northampton young men Warriner & Warner in a carriage. The first three will probably leave here on Friday afternoon next, the others on Monday afternoon next, probably. We expect to unite at Pittsfield on Tuesday evening.

You might meet us at any of the three times and places. We shall not be gone more than a fortnight probably less,—ride 25 or 30 miles per day on an average.

You would have been urged to come before if the arrangements had not been unsettled, but hearing that your plan for spending the vacation might be given up, we thought that it might not yet be too late.

Please answer as soon as possible that we may be able to give you notice of any change of programme.

Very truly your friend
J. W. GIBBS

His sisters knew him; he was very close to all three of them, Anna, Julia, and Emily; he could have his silences with them, or his brief gaiety, his tenderness that others scarcely knew. And now these two deaths of the heart would bring him into a full quiet power. This one meant even more than his mother's death, this the father of his mind, whose words were reflected in his own self, to issue years later. He was different from this religious father. He was more ready to break down the walls of the mind, less ready and ever less ready to touch the walls of the world. The tools he had, in mathematics and in language, were his father's; and while Dr. Gibbs could understand the linkages of language, he had also said that all this had to do with common sense, common intelligence—it was not to be judged of or restricted by scientific definitions, or subsequent scientific discoveries. It is concerned with actualities rather than realities.

Willard Gibbs could see how he was going to be cut off. He was young, he was twenty-one, and this old man, this old father, must have been in many ways a challenge, a burden and the closest person to his heart, in love and conflict. Like Kierkegaard, like many whose fathers have been much older than they and conventionally religious, he seems to have felt the complicated tyranny of a parent's life which has penetrated deeply, binding the son to the house, to whatever love the house offers. He was being cut off. Illness was making the dying man more abstract, and he had himself classified together in his grammars the dead, the absent, and the abstract. The darkness of the deep eyes was growing in these winter months, the cheeks falling sharply away from the fine high cheekbones. A change, too, was coming over his attitude, which had been so rigorous and pure, or so he told his minister in regret or remorse. He had spent a long life in intellectual labor, wrapped in the discoveries of thought, and now in age and illness he fell away from these, or said he did, in this slow final weakness. He had always taken low views of himself, and now he partly recanted, with the partial gestures of an exhausted man.

Now he was saying, "The simplest verities . . . they are the only truth."

He spoke often of his ancestry. The pride of family runs high in many healthy men, but illness and exasperation, the consciousness that flesh itself is a burden, and that that burden is dying, will remind any invalid of the fathers of his flesh. Now Dr. Gibbs lingered, in the pale winter sunlight, on the memory of Massachusetts forebears—his father Henry, the long line of scholars (the Willard family emphasized that line), the Gibbses far back to English Warwickshire—shadows that for their moment offered comfort, the shadowy dead divines, the motto on the old coat of arms, with its three battle-axes on a silver field : Tenax Propositi. "In his last illness he adverted, with deep satisfaction, to his connection with a godly ancestry, among whom were several ministers of the Gospel." This is an old man sitting at a window, watching the blue snow-shadows turn deeper blue, feeling his life ebb into abstraction and the past.

He had mocked mildly at lineage, saying that the present participle had a parentage which is clear and undoubted; no princely family in Europe can boast equal antiquity. But this was in the days when he was declaring firmly the correlation between the intellectual and physical world. That correlation was dissolving for him. He was slipping down the hill of time, in the pale winter sun. He was dying.

Father and Son

Young Willard Gibbs rode out into the hills, torn by the tearing of his world. His horse reared on the crisp snow; the black branches shook, and his heart shook in him. In the town, he could hear daily the rumors. South Carolina had seceded, other states were following, in early spring it was clear that the whole South would form a nation, and that nation was built for war. For most of the "young gentlemen" of Yale College, the restlessness of the eve was eating into their time, war was becoming a sad and terrible appetite, filling their dreams at night. Willard Gibbs was older than they were in many ways. One of the few graduate students, quiet, diffident, withdrawn, he knew this thorn of curiosity that was being driven deeper into him as he read, as the stirrings of invention, the questions, the premonitions of immense knowledge, burned into his brain. As he read, as he rode into the country, as he took his long walks in the snow, he was older, and taller. But in many ways he was not grown. There was no release about him. He was set and proud, and he could resist pressure by strength of will and intellectual force; but his home was across the street, he had never left his home, his emotional life had never been fought for.

That life, the life of his emotions, had known little but attack. This last, the death of his father, would give him authority. It was a challenge, for his father's attitude and work was stamped deep on him, and he knew all of its meanings : whatever force it had in the lives of his mother and sisters gained additional force in him, for he was learning new terms, the pioneering mathematics that had not cleared a space in this country, but was felt abroad. Benjamin Franklin, Count Rumford, Joseph Henry, were almost the total of the background in America. Harvard had produced nothing; the Lyceum lectures dealt with popular, down-to-the-ground fact; so did Silliman's public lectures. But the Connecticut Academy, to which his father had belonged for years before he was accepted, provided as much as he could find anywhere. After all, none of the three—Franklin, Rumford, Henry—were really college men, and he felt himself a college man by heritage, with that particular academic emotion which has its iceberg seventh above the water as snobbishness, and its six-sevenths submerged as a wish for security in a world which is an undeciphered welter of fact and relationship. Yale, and the

Connecticut Academy, and High Street, were a well-rationalized home for him. They became appropriate.

His father lived into the spring : February, the first windy days of March. And then, as March turned mild, the early false warmth came. These first days kill the winter invalids : the old seem to wait for the fine day, the threatened young seem to believe in summer now, relax their hold that fought off the ice, and die. The sphinx that guarded this year held silence and menace. Lincoln was made president on the 4th, and Whitman was writing:

I welcome this menace—I welcome thee with joy
Why now I shall know whether there is anything in you, Libertad,
I shall see how much you can stand
Perhaps I shall see the crash—is all lost?

To Willard Gibbs the menace was war, the death of his father, his own majority. His father finally died on a soft Monday, March 25, 1861. And on the Sunday, the three daughters and the son sat alone in black on the front pew of the College Chapel, with the faculty of Yale behind them, and in the pulpit, Dr. Fisher preaching the funeral sermon :

"In his last illness he adverted with deep satisfaction . . ."

Young Willard Gibbs stiffened against this, hard, young; burning with pride and curiosity, fear and sorrow and his new freedom.

Dr. Fisher went through the long list of his father's virtues, recalled the extempore examination of anxious Josiah Gibbs, his modest deportment, his painstaking industry, his aptitude for mathematics. He summed up the theological history of the end of the eighteenth century, when learning in that field was giving way to the classics, to mathematics, natural sciences, English literature, and praised the dead man for fighting the Unitarian heresy with all the exegetical and historical learning he could command. He mentioned the translations, the frustration of the Gesenius venture, his posts as lecturer, librarian, professor. He acknowledged the minuteness and limitation of his work. . . . "Yet, with these fragmentary notes, a man of less modesty and more tact, might have won a distinguished reputation." He spoke of the dry orthodoxy of Michaelis, of aesthetic Eichhorn, discarding the prophetic in Scripture, and Gibbs's attitude toward these. Of his life in the classroom, where there was no way for a student to shift responsibility, where the teacher was always there to point out shades of feeling and meaning, where he was always "a deep fountain of feeling." Of his respect for the word, and what he had said about analysis of sentences: "It is here that every one who loves to think, beholds the deep things of the human spirit, and learns to regard with holy reverence, the sacred symbols of human thought."

The children in the front pew . . . Man is a citizen of two worlds . . . The spirit, which is breath . . . Prose may contain the elements of rhythm; just as chaos may contain the elements of a world, and yet not be part of a world. . . .

The sermon went on. Young Gibbs heard again, moved and with deep love for the lost, the holy, how his father had written, for the most part anonymously, or with no signature, other than a single initial under his newspaper articles. "So little effort was made to call attention to these essays, that it almost seemed as if his main end was to record and have for himself in print his ideas upon the topics which they handled."

From the pulpit, restored for a moment, since all these people and the preacher had known his father well, the Delphic answers in the lecture-room, the courtesy and humility, the quick answers about the one subject he was always willing to argue with anger: the Negro problem. He was not fanatical, but he always expected the wrath of Heaven to fall on the country in judgment. How he fell back on the simplest verities at the end, his head drooping upon his attenuated body. . . . He has done a great and useful work . . . his children's grief will be softened . . . and then the great challenge, that must have rung forever in the ears of the son:

Mr. Gibbs loved system, and was never satisfied until he had cast his material into the proper form. His essays on special topics are marked by the nicest logical arrangement. It was in the treatment, however, of special topics, that his power was spent. Had he possessed, in a degree proportional to his other intellectual faculties, the wider grasp, the power of more extended combination, the architectonic quality, through which multiform fragments of truth are organized and fused into a consistent whole, he would have done a still greater service to the cause of learning. The separate stones are chiseled with a master's hand, but the temple remained unbuilt.

That was the true note. The deep and accusing charge of limitation, made at the end of an old man's life, leaping from the pulpit straight to the youth of his son, so like him in many ways, so resistant, timorous, and intellectually pure. And the old cry that followed, Biblical sorrow with its pride and echo :

O my father, my father, the chariot of Israel, and the horsemen thereof!

When the inventory was made, it was clear that they were provided for, for life. Josiah Gibbs had been a sound business man. He had invested in three banks in Boston, one in Middlebury, two in New Haven, and had bonds in three Middle Western railroads. Over $29,000 had been loaned on mortgages, and the list of household items is as clear a catalogue of that vanished house as we might hope for. Here are the stacks of unsold *Philological Studies*, 550 copies of the *Teutonic Etymology*, one hundred of the *Latin Analyst*, the easy chairs and sofas, the lamps and candlesticks and snuffers, the footstools and secretaries and tables, the inkstands, oilcloth, stair carpet, umbrella stand, chairs and more chairs, looking glasses, bedsteads, washstands, bookshelves, feather beds, chests, silverware, crockery and glass, all the way down to a set of Oriental type and wearing apparel, the twelve hundred volumes of the library and a silver watch. Josiah Gibbs had worked hard, married well, and invested carefully; he left the house, the lot, the burial plot, and $37,759, with claims of over $14,000 against that sum.

The shaft was put up in the Grove Street cemetery, where Henry Gibbs and Mary Anna had been buried in 1855, and Eliza had been buried as a little girl. It was a tall monument, listing his posts and qualities, his birth in Salem and his death. But the line that speaks with Josiah Gibbs's voice runs across the bottom of the monument's front face; it issues from the mind that works and tortures itself to be stripped, but cannot while it wears flesh; it speaks to its son :

NOW I KNOW IN PART, BUT THEN SHALL I KNOW EVEN AS ALSO I AM KNOWN.

CHAPTER SEVEN
The Civil War

JOHN QUINCY ADAMS had stood up in the House, his piercing voice cracked with age, the tears of weakness streaming in mockery from his eyes as he cried—and this was in 1836 : "Mr. Chairman, are you ready for all these wars? A Mexican war? A war with Great Britain if not with France? A general Indian war? A servile war? And, as an inevitable consequence of them all, a civil war?"

This war was seen as it began, years before the early guns at Fort Sumter. It was seen as all wars may be seen in their inception, as indeed all human expression is visible to those who will notice things at the time of their happening, as poets notice them and mark them according to their image, rather than as the journalists who mark them when they finally happen. The images and symptoms of these expressions—these arts, these wars, all imprints of the decisive conflicts—are apparent to anyone who looks for the truth as it appears, and does not wait until it has finally proved itself in irreversible action. The farmer knows winter by the frost's quickening and by October's red, as well as by experience of previous Decembers; the landlubber at sea for the first time knows the fume of spray, the unique standing fountain, recognizing a whale before the lift of the dark skull; in grief we may see the fears and shiverings and obsessions before the statesmen to our doom confer, we may smell blood on the air before the final insecurity overtakes countries, and the wars come.

John Quincy Adams, used to looking for logical results, was aware of the competition rising around him, of the spread of this

country to the West by rail and canal, of science in its application as we produced a race of inventors, of education which had
lost dimension and, acquiring edge, was now nothing more than
a goad toward social ambition, the terrible climb for wealth. He
was aware, more than of anything else, of the equilibrium of this
country, shifted by growing energies, and shifted most abruptly
by inventions which pointed toward great power and every sort
of slavery.

Each loss of equilibrium meant further insecurity. The drain
of men and women from New England to the West had gone
so far that by 1850 a good part of the population had set out,
by wagon, in the magnificent clippers that were the peak and
perfection of sailing ships, and brought the square-drawn, simple
lines of the wharves of Canton home in silk and teak and china
to the drawing-rooms of Boston, Portsmouth, New Bedford,
New Haven. If all the slaves in the South were reckoned at $200
a head—if all the slaves in the South were sold away at that price,
you would have the price on all the runaway New Englanders,
reckoned at $200 a head. It was hard for New England, left with
its students, its whittling boys, its weaker sons, and its new factories and mills, impoverished for people and cheap labor, to
think of the necessities which Virginians, for example, believed
their rich produce-bearing, slave-bearing land to have.

And the slaves sang :

> Massa bin an sol yeh, O!
> To go up in de kentry
> Fo de link o day—
> Run yeh! Run yeh!
> Fo de link o day. . . .

And the slaves sang:

> O death!
> Can't you spare me over for another year?

Before morning of April 12, 1861, Charleston Harbor lay dark
in the spring blackness. The sentry patrolling the Battery could
not see the islands as they lay, past the sand, past the palmettoes
whose fans spread in faint outline against the rocking water.
The warning had been given at three-thirty in the morning.

The Civil War

The forces of South Carolina, speaking under General Beauregard from Fort Moultrie, Morris Island, and Sullivan's Island, had given the United States troops in the newly constructed Fort on the shoal in Charleston Harbor one hour's notice that their batteries would open. The report reads :

At 4:30 A.M. a signal shell was thrown from the mortar battery on James Island; after which the fire soon became general from all the hostile batteries. . . .

At 7 A.M. the guns of Fort Sumter replied, the first shot being fired from the battery at the right gorge angle, in charge of Captain Doubleday. . . .

The fire of our batteries continued steadily until dark. . . .

The night was very stormy, with high wind and tide. . . . The enemy threw shells every ten or fifteen minutes during the night. . . . At daybreak no material alteration was observed in the enemy's batteries. . . . The last of the rice was cooked this morning, and served with the pork. . . . The aim of the enemy's gunners was better than yesterday. . . .

It soon became evident that they were firing hot shot from a large number of their guns. . . . From the exposed position it was utterly impossible to extinguish the flames. . . . The men then withdrew to the casemates on the faces of the fort. . . . The small stock of cartridges now only allowed a gun to be fired at intervals of ten minutes. . . .

At 1 o'clock the flagstaff, having been struck twice before this morning, fell.

This was a social war depending on "the defeat of American political democracy," as Ralph Gabriel has pointed out. The shells at Sumter spoke for a large minority of the American people. Free people, they had withdrawn their support from a central government which was no longer able to influence them, to convince them, or indeed to govern them. The people were not governing themselves, as they had set out to do. They were resorting to war and the ingenuities of war. They would invent all the machinery of war they needed; the machinery of peace was the government in Washington, and it had been abandoned. Gabriel goes on : "Responsibility for the disaster rested with the American people. No outside nation was involved. No foreign ideologies played any part in causing the tragedy. . . . Partisans on both sides, moreover, looked upon the war as a battle for the doctrine of the free individual, a war for liberty."

The South had lost its security, and with it its loyalty. Without loyalty to it, the federal government loses its reality in the minds of the citizens of a democracy. The North, canny and abandoned, saw its security vanish before the crumbling South and the rising and airy West. It was not only Calhoun who wished to protect the vital interests of all groups within the nation, so that the interests of each would be merged in the common interest. Calhoun—as Gabriel compares him—enlarged Thoreau's individual to a section, an interest group, separated government from nation as Thoreau did, and saw, as Thoreau saw, the possibility of the destruction of the individual in the unrestrained power of government. Now the parts were falling away, the interests of the rich South hated and feared the North, and secession was the order of the day.

General Winfield Scott said to the seceded states, "Wayward Sisters, depart in peace," and outlined four possible divisions of the United States. Horace Greeley wrote in the New York *Tribune* that the Southern States had an absolute moral right to leave the Union. Wendell Phillips denied Lincoln's right to "a soldier in Fort Sumter"; and Senator Henry Wilson of Massachusetts had long ago spoken in a way that seemed to indicate that the best thing to do was to cut loose from the slave states.

In July 1861, the armies were equally unequipped, lacking uniforms, variously armed, unfitted for marching and fighting. Washington was full of soldiers and diplomats, and if great cities are great sores, the muddy, impossible capital was the greatest sore. Its avenues were rocky prairies infested with hacks; insolvent, without commerce, without manufactures, the city can be seen in an *Atlantic Monthly* article of the moment, which says of it, "If the beggars of Dublin, the cripples of Constantinople, and the lepers of Damascus should assemble in Baden-Baden during a Congress of Kings, then Baden-Baden would resemble Washington." And again, "It has a Monument that will never be finished, a Capitol that is to have a dome, a Scientific Institute which does nothing but report the rise and fall of the thermometer, and two pieces of Equestrian Statuary which it would be a waste of time to criticize." But the article ends with the realization that was giving the North its center, here where Lincoln was : "Its destiny is that of the Union."

All over the North, that Fourth of July, the pageants proclaimed, in their feeble and garish manner, the nature of the local loyalty. Willard Gibbs watched the New Haven children go by, the little, embarrassed children, stiff and excited, sitting on the floats—the daughters of Columbia, the Goddess of Liberty supported by Loyal States.

In the Hundred Days after Sumter, there was little beside hysteria—the unprepared and incapable time full of surprise and recrimination, the impotence of unready defense. When the middle of July arrived and nothing had been done except the building of some fortifications along the Potomac and a lot of marching, a plan to take Richmond was advanced.

"Suppose you go to war, you cannot fight always," Lincoln said sadly in his first inaugural; and here, at the beginning of the war, the images of loss and tearing. "Physically speaking, we cannot separate," he said; but separation was deep in American life. We had cried "Liberty!" as a drowning man cries "Help!" when there was no news in the term, when it was already our responsibility to have liberty; and with the cry, we separated from England. Now, invoking the mystic cords of memory, we were breaking them once more. Only yesterday we had left home; we were splitting the new bed. The terrible image that sat covered in loss and tears was again a mother-image.

The soldiers that went out to war sang songs of home. "Mother, When the War is Over" and "Bear This Gently to My Mother" were at the top of the list of songs about family, which followed the first songs about the flag. It has been pointed out that during the French Revolution, love songs were popular. "The Girl I Left Behind Me" had been sung and, like "Yankee Doodle," was sung again and again; but there were hardly any love songs for this war. There was grief, and disgrace, and the rally and tragedy after, and the final peace; but the level of emotion, permitting these songs, shut out the others. In the national character the cleavage deepened. The first Battle of Bull Run was a defeat to drive panic into the most cool.

It was the first great defeat in this battle for an identity.

The Northern troops had crossed the Potomac, and the march

was accompanied by Congressmen, reporters, spectators of all sorts. The morning of July 21st was noisy with McDowell's infantry and artillery attacks; but in the afternoon the attack was changed into a stampede. The soldiers turned, rushing through the corn, leaving their firelocks and cooking-tins behind them; the wagon-drivers pulled at their horses' heads, turning the four-wheeled tilt wagons against the advance; baggage-carts, ambulances, horses cut out of harness; regiments turned and doubled on other Northern regiments; drivers lashed at their horses, or abandoned them in the press, as the army abandoned its artillery, its muskets, its stores and baggage.

When "Bull Run Russell's" story of the battle appeared in the London *Times*, Henry Adams, serving as secretary to his father—now Lincoln's Minister to England—wrote to his brother, Charles Francis, who was still in Boston:

After studying over the accounts of the battle . . . I hardly know whether to laugh or cry. Of all the ridiculous battles that ever were fought, this seems to me the most so. To a foreigner or to any one not interested in it, the account must be laughable in the extreme. But the disgrace is frightful. The expose of the condition of our army is not calculated to do us anything but the most unmixed harm here, though it may have the good effect at home of causing these evils to be corrected. If this happens again, farewell to our country for many a day. Bull's Run will be a by-word of ridicule for all time. Our honor will be utterly gone. But yesterday we might have stood against the world. Now none so base to do us reverence. Let us stop our bragging now and hence-forward. Throw Bull's Run in the teeth of any man who dares to talk large.

The *Times*, devoted to the Southern cause, was only one of the reasons for a private secretary in London to control his feelings.

In the rout at Bull Run, there were two men hurrying to the rear, among all the others, who were using equipment to match the times. Better-armed than the soldiers who threw away their muskets, one was a young correspondent on a fast horse, galloping to beat his rivals to the Washington telegraph line, to wire the story to his New York paper. He was Henry Villard. The other was a stocky little Irishman trudging back from Centreville, his equipment for the moment lost like the rest—

wearing, however, a sword given to him in the woods by a company of Fire Zouaves. He was the photographer Mathew Brady.

The history of American union has been to a great extent a history of people's pressure, political thought, and mechanical invention. The history of imagination in America to the time of the Civil War is largely a matter of aggressive ingenuity. The resourcefulness of the early settler; the tragic sense of destiny of the pioneer; the split ego of the fantastic American still aware of the mysteries of the will that had not yet met recognition here; the wide-minded man, breathing in the promise of these states, the tears, the radiance, the powerful scene—these might be raised to the level of genius, as Jefferson, as Franklin, as Jackson, as Lincoln, as Poe, as Whitman. But to produce and cohere—to make, as Washington and Rush had wished, and as John Quincy Adams wished, a national center where the new learning might be given, where indeed the imagination of America might govern. In Massachusetts alone had there flourished a group.

The idea of schools and movements in imagination is one of the happiest and most fanciful of the Utopian notions. In poetry it can be seen most clearly. The term "school of poetry" pre-supposes a level of civilization, a centralization of forces, a benevolence of rule, and an expansion of the state in which it occurs, that rarely happen. The material of, say, six people ready with their ideas, just short of their creative height of power, and drawn together by some community of belief or passion, active enough so that they will be stimulated and reinforced by the contact, and not have their energies drawn off into conversation, comes very close to the Olympian standard. But, more important than the gearing of personalities, the climate of belief necessary to a group-stand takes first place. The history of poetry provides excellent examples, since exploration, perception, and expression come so closely together. There are two periods in English history when the motion was made freely, full tide, in gestures that had no object—no label—that permitted the imagination to exercise its range, and provided a climate of belief. One was the Elizabethan period, when at a flash, or so it seems at this distance, many people saw human capacities that had not until then been guessed at in their richness; the other was the time of that group which revolved about Coleridge and Wordsworth and their further intuition about the capacity of the human spirit. The parallel in this country is that time which has been rightly seen as flowering and springtime and frontier, which gave us the Concord group. And these artists had liberated themselves from formula—they guessed, they guessed continually in an expanding age, their guesses turned on greatness, and they moved in an air of unboundaried belief.

But there must be an exchange of such belief.

In the war years there has been no belief. Faith in the gifts of the imagination is most likely to be suspended when death rips open the body and the brain. Terror deals deviously; when the excitement of war, with its common purpose, its sudden general inclusion, nerves the body until all physical fear seems absorbed, the acute fear of the imagination is most ready.

Here are the movements of causes; squadrons of victory seem the first necessity; whole peoples become aware, like a man burning with mortal fever, of the immediacy of life, and the immediate gift becomes the only good. It in a flash appears, to a nation that has just declared war, that the gifts are the gifts of invention, the gifts of fact and not the gifts of law.

The reactionaries of the imagination—those who have acquired insuperable prejudices about the nature of thought—suspend their prejudices for the moment. All the walls are down. People again are willing to say that there are no limits to invention. But they say this at the moment at which they are obsessed with war —the news of battles, disaster of maps, infinity of horror thickens their air—the only infinity they will recognize is an infinity of invention as applied to ways of killing. New weapons are accredited, and new defenses against them; new means of transport to make them effective; new methods of recording their efficacy. Until the world behind the lines may improve these gifts for their own uses; until the war begins to pass, and it becomes clear that many of the technical innovations of the society of that moment have been the real means of the war itself.

It is that mechanical belief, a belief that depends less than any other on a constructive faith, that grows in wartime. The wish to win a war has always been a tremendous impetus to invention. Not that the last step in invention was made during wartime, but that the acceptance was there. In agony, in destruction, the devices were accepted. The promoters ran shouting about the country with them, and the country was ready for them, rushed to accept them. Invention is the currency of wartime, as it is of national expansion. For our country it is also a historic means toward unity.

In America, the history of imagination and the acceptance of its gifts may be summarized in the history of invention. Making, communicating, recording—these have been speeded to a complication terribly multiplied over the complication of process, decade to decade, since the Civil War. And in the years just before the war, inventions were pouring through the Patent Office. The interdependence of the parts of the act of invention, the relations of the figures who carry any perfected instrument step by step closer to its perfection, are so close that there are few machines to which the single name of an inventor may be assigned, and few processes that bear the stamp of one person. The social nature of mechanical invention has been analyzed competently. The nature of the act of perception, the act of the individual imagination which precedes invention and expression, is essentially different, and misleading in its place in history. If one traces the history of any years merely through the series of points of the great perceptive acts of that time, one plots a course that is as omissive as a film reconstructed from the close-ups alone. The pressures are missing, the backgrounds, the forces themselves. But it is possible to draw from such a chart certain conclusions as to the nature of progress which are not visible if one considers the larger view.

The notion of progress, over-simplified, smug, unimaginative in all of its broader aspects, belongs as clearly to the nineteenth century as does the idea of energy. The middle class of that period often appears as a dark, undeveloped engine, running on the tracks of those two ideas with a great hooting and fuming, brakeless and terrifyingly incapable of choice. The middle class, and the governments based on its ascendancy, was ready for inventions; it was thinking of energy in terms of labor, and of progress in terms of labor-saving devices.

The history of invention balances the two hundred years of clearing America. There is nothing national about most inventions; but the eighteenth and nineteenth centuries have their wild strokes of war and pioneering and the great sweeping crossings of the continent, while at home, in the cities and in the wintry villages, those who remained whittled and forged and worked over the retorts, piecing together a future for that intense and furious effort of taking a country. Franklin is the archetype of the early culture; challenging, hard-headed, generous, producing his many proofs and demonstrations and devices, from muscular and tireless boyhood to his profound and civilized old age. The Revolution produced the first technical spurt : weapons, from the submarine of David Bushnell (of Yale) to the iron chain stretched across the Hudson River; clothing machines, these last two stimulating two great industries. Just after the crisis, the cotton gin was invented by Eli Whitney (of Yale); reaper, steamship, metal clock, railroad, and telegraph drew the farm-lands in, brought Europe closer, insisted that the day was for production from minute to rapid minute, and at last leaped the continent. And all the time the people coming on. And all the time the power growing, and then the giantism that must be a result of power incompletely absorbed and incompletely used. Until the Civil War, with Lincoln's rough and tragic power; and the fanatic hatred for him, the contempt and half-support and hysteria of the first hundred days, topped by the scramble at Bull Run of soldiers running through the forest and screaming on the roads; and the two men, one galloping, one panting back to Washington without his camera.

Mathew Brady returned to the battlefields to make the record of the Civil War. His cameras, his plateholders, his darkened wagon which bumped over the furrows and muddy roads of the battlefields until it was known throughout both armies as the What-Is-It-Wagon—his glass plates and collodion have kept the clear and precise scenes for us. The bodies thrown down, the rolling country and wagon-trains, death with a flowering twig, dead horses, dead soldiers. The tired and heroic faces, the firm lips, the calculating eyes, the empty looks of loss—recorded in 7,000 prints.

He had set out to do what Trumbull required of himself : to preserve and diffuse the memory of these moments. But Brady had the instrument which that requirement demands when the record is wished and the only selection involved is in the choice of the subject itself.

Born in upstate New York of an Irish father and a mother whom he never in mature life mentioned, Mathew B. Brady was in his teens a portrait painter. The likeness was what he wanted. First in Saratoga, and later in New York City, he painted and studied. When he was about eighteen, he met Samuel F. B. Morse, whose life had just suffered its great change as he gave up his deeply satisfying years as a painter to become a promoter of the invention he had recently brought to a new degree of completion, the telegraph. Morse had been to Yale, had painted abroad and in the South, and had moved in the most brilliant drawing-rooms; his conversation as he walked the deck of the *Sully* on his return from Europe had introduced the idea of the communication of intelligence over distance by means of wire, an idea on which Joseph Henry, among at least five or six others, had worked. Roger Burlingame points out that it was the fact that Morse had an *unscientific* mind that allowed him to feel surprise, delight, and the belief in his own originality that would not be found in a scientist conscious of the work of others; but the nature of that surprise and delight led him to use every possible channel to communicate his invention. In 1838, he gave a private exhibition; in 1839, he was home again from Europe, this time as a disappointed scientist who had seen a railway telegraph already in use in England; and in 1840, he received his American patent. These years were the first years of the camera, as Daguerre and Niepce used it; and Morse was fired, as an artist and as a scientist, by this portrait-machine. He introduced Brady —the little-educated, the boy who did not even know what the "B." in his name stood for—to the camera.

By 1842, Brady was a portrait photographer. He was nineteen, he had a studio at Broadway and Fulton Street, he was beginning to make his portraits of the rich and fashionable that in the next twenty years won him a rain of medals, publications, and customers. When the war began, he was famous and prosperous, there were two branch studios as well as the original, and his *Gallery of Illustrious Americans* was well-known and well-respected. He went to Washington at the news of war. He had only been married for a year; he was trim, square-shouldered, well set up in his broad flat hat and duster, a cross between a stocky Irish business man and a Paris art student. He had one wish : to photograph the war. Lincoln and Allen Pinkerton, the head of the secret service department, were at once interested, and Brady set out, with official permission but at his own expense, with his equipment, his assistants, and his wagon, to record these moments. He counted on the war's lasting about a year.

It is through these pictures that we know those terrible four years. The earthworks, the breastworks, and fascine trenches, the ruins of Galligo Mills, Richmond layer on layer of shelled walls, each brick outlined in a freezing clarity, the field hospitals, the tents along the railroad tracks, Petersburg, Atlanta, the poles at the second Battle of Bull Run carrying the life-lines of the telegraph wire, the military railroad, the boats and supply carts, the wharves and stony shore of City Point. And the men, the anonymous dead, the staff meetings, Grant leaning against the tree, worn and tired with the terrible, shabby look of war, Whitman with the sustained and moving look not seen in any other portrait, and that last picture of Lincoln taken on March 6, 1865. And the fearful picture after the hanging, when we see swung from the rope the three bound men and the woman in her voluminous bound robes, and all four with the white, frightening hoods slanting over the noose—the accomplices to Lincoln's assassination.

In an article on motion and rest, published in 1861 in the *Atlantic Monthly*, these words appear : "The modern world is all battle-field; the smoke, the dust, the din fill every eye and ear; and the hill-top of Lucretius, where is it?" From his far hill, the Roman had seen motion as rest; Brady's camera answered the question for the Civil War.

The railroad tracks and the military railway, the telegraph, the balloon ascension of Thaddeus Lowe—which was sponsored by Joseph Henry—who went aloft with a telegraphic apparatus which transmitted to Lincoln at the Executive Mansion, "The city, with its girdle of encampments, presents a superb scene"— these were symptoms of national unity, and certain symptoms of the defeat of the South. Slave-substitutes, they outdid slavery, produced new forms of serfdom, and fought the war as surely as the soldiers who rallied after Bull Run and fought pitilessly through to '65. And of these, the railroad was the farthest advanced, most intimately allied with the fortunes of the West, and closest to the life of Willard Gibbs.

New Haven was violently involved in the war. Three months before Fort Sumter, during early-morning chapel, undergraduates raised the palmetto flag of South Carolina to fly from the tower of Alumni Hall. It was discovered as the College came out after service. There was a free-for-all before the flag finally came down.

The eve of the war marked the presentation by Joseph E. Sheffield of $100,000 towards the founding of Sheffield Scientific School, and plans for the new departments were being made as the college began to dissolve for wartime. All the Southern students went home as their states seceded. There were thirty-three Southerners in all. Yale, the largest college in the country during these years, sent 183 undergraduates and 574 graduates to the Army during the war. When a particularly popular man enlisted, there was the ceremonial of a sword presentation; more than twenty of these rituals were undergone in the one College generation. And, officially, the baseball games, boat races, and commencements included army leaders. Rear Admiral Foote and Major Anderson attended one commencement; in 1864, General Terry, Charles Sumner, and Secretary Seward received honorary degrees.

The College was thriving and the town was thriving. Six factories went up; a College boathouse was built; although teachers' salaries suffered from the war, New Haven teachers' salaries had, by 1865, gone up. The men were raised $150, the women $50. Woollen mills were going full blast. There was a drive to patronize home industry, particularly home clothing industry. The shoddy that was manufactured during the Civil War corrupted the meaning of the word from its respectable origin. Northern soldiers shot at each other's different-colored uniforms; the guns that they were sold often went off in their faces because they were rusty and of faulty manufacture; the food was often half-putrid. Fortunes were made; and lost, as money and stocks went down. Railroad stock, however, stock that had been low before the war, rose quickly; the railroads were knowing unprecedented seasons of traffic and activity; they were loaded beyond capacity with produce and soldiers; interest in railroad transportation was general; in '61 it was remarkable that the value of railroad property went up, when everything else went down; in '62, the roads announced that they had had a very prosperous year, '63 was the most prosperous in railroad history, and '64 was a capacity year. New England, farthest away from the grain and the Army, was the most backward section. But the Gibbses' small investment in railway stock was Middle Western; and it went up.

Willard Gibbs was working towards his Master's degree when the war broke out. Always considered frail, supposing himself threatened with tuberculosis, there would have been no reason for him to be deeply involved in war other than his own wish. His wish did not point toward the front. He needed to do his work, he was needed at home, he was the only man. His final prize carried the stipulation that he go on with graduate work.

Families were split as the country was. Two of the James sons went to the front, but neither William nor Henry was physically qualified to serve; Charles Francis Adams served in South Carolina, Virginia, and Maryland, for three years as colonel of the 5th Massachusetts Cavalry, while Henry was in London with his father.

The little New Haven group was broken up by the war. Their expeditions had continued into August of '61. His wife wrote to Roger Baldwin :

New Haven Aug. 2ᵈ, /61

DEAR HUSBAND,

. . . Charles Tomlinson went to Lyme yesterday to meet "the boys" as they arrived at the mouth of the River —.

They left New Haven on Tuesday about ten o'clock —. The rain of Monday detained them over that day.

These were some of them Two Whites—Two Blakes—Higgins, Gibbs & Simeon. All in blue flannel shirts and pantaloons and with havelocks.

They wanted a flag, which has since been made, and sent them by Tomlinson. They arrived at Lyme at eleven o'clock on Thursday, having rowed fifteen miles the first day, past the Thimble Islands and camping at or near Sachem's Head.

The next day eight miles, and Thursday morning to Lyme—there they called at Mrs Hardy and at Judge McCurdy's,—dined at the Hotel, and started up the River in the afternoon when the tide was right, expecting to stop for the night at Essex —. Their intention was to reach Hartford on Saturday, and remain there over the Sabbath.

I hope they will arrive in time for you to see them. But I shall write to Sim tomorrow, and have a letter in office there waiting for him. . . .

Five days later, Mrs. Baldwin had a report from Sim himself :

> Camp Buckingham
> near Long Meadow
> Wednesday afternoon, Aug. 7, 1861

DEAR MOTHER,

You see that we have not made very wonderful progress since you heard from us at Hartford. That night we camped near Windsor, and before going to sleep engaged breakfast for six at a neighboring farmhouse for the next morning. This breakfast, being the first civilized home-like meal that we had had for a week, and being furthermore topped off with gooseberry pie and green apples made us a little sick and grim. Blake quite sick, so that at evening we left him at a tavern at Windsor Locks, along with Ed., and the rest of us went on & camped beyond the village.

In the morning (this morning) Ed rejoined us, and Jim expects to meet us to-morrow at Springfield. Owing to Jim's sickness we went only seven or eight miles yesterday. The current also near Windsor we found very strong against us, and the bed of the river so shallow that for a mile or so we all got out and dragged the boat along after us, wading in true Mississippi flatboat style. In buying milk and eggs up at the village this noon, I inquired about the Coltons here, and was surprised to hear that there were so many families of them—one sister of Dr. Simeon Colton, one nephew, &c. You see I date from "Camp Buckingham." We name every camping place after some young lady, and give three cheers as we leave it. Just now, at six o'clock we have finished our dinner, (or breakfast, or supper, as you please, for we have had before, only at 8 A.M. some tea without milk and bread without butter and some red herrings, and at 11 A.M. some bread and milk) and I am writing this letter on the cover of a tin kettle. Ed. Blake is greasing his boots, Tom White washing the dishes, Rog. crooning over the fire, and all are gathered about a cheerful fire, for this is the first cold day since we left home. Higgins has gone into Springfield to visit some friends and stay with them over night.

Friday, we expect to spend at Northampton. Farther than that we don't plan yet. If we find the current strong against us, and the canals round the rapids out of repair, as we hear they are, we may take the cars for Albany and row down the Hudson to New York, & come home on the Elm City, boat & all, or we may keep on "regardless," and see how the Olympia can stand being dragged over the rocks of the Connecticut rapids. Tom is calling for somebody to wipe the dishes, and so, Good evening.

SIM

But by Christmas of that year, their trips were over and the group was broken forever. Ed Blake was in Maryland, with the Army, and he wrote to Simeon from near Hancock :

Dec. 26, 1861

. . . I have been telegraphing back and forth to Kelley & Banks to find out who owns us, and what he proposes to do with us. If we are going to stay here any length of time we must move or we will all die of fever in this hole—but yet it will not pay for us to locate the camp elsewhere with all the attendant fuss & work if (as is probable) we shall be ordered off that night—

I saw some boys skating today & it brought up Saltonstall & its joys in vivid colors. Have you had any excursions out there yet? Ah! I *long* for my new "Murphies."—The Potomac would suffer.

Gibbs took the pressure of the time directly, in these years. His graduate work was with Benjamin Silliman, Jr., in chemistry, with Dennison Olmsted in natural philosophy, and with Hubert Anson Newton in astronomy. The thesis which he presented for his degree, according to two professors asked to pass on its authenticity, is entitled, "On the Form of the Teeth of Wheels in Spur Gearing."

With his degree, he received his first appointment, to begin at once. He was to serve the College as a tutor, of Latin at first, and then of Natural Philosophy. This was not an easy assignment for Gibbs. He was not completely formed, but it was plain even then that he was not suited temperamentally to teaching. He was going on with mechanical problems. During his free time, on the back of the corrected Latin papers, he wrote his paper on the turbine—a pencilled paper, emphasizing economy of construction, simplicity, the possibilities of "fanciful regulations of velocity" and the need, finally, for all of his statements to be "in no danger of ambiguity."

In these semesters, too, he was working hard on an invention. The railroads of the early period had no brakes at first, and then had only spikes for additional friction. According to one contemporary, "When the steam brake was put on, the folks were unpleasantly jostled together, first ahead and then back; and the concussion was not in any way adapted to induce people to patronize the lines." These brakes were hand brakes, operated by brakemen who would begin at the head of the train while it was still a half-mile from the station; they would throw the brake of the first car, run to the second and throw that, and rush from car to car, in wild and guesswork timing. Inaccurate and unsafe, the primitive brakes were responsible for many piled-up trains, and head-on collisions were not rare enough.

Willard Gibbs started to make notes for his brake on the back of some work on optics by H. B. Barnes. There are three pages of notes, drawings, and computations; and then he opened his correspondence with Munn & Co., applying for a patent on his brake from the *Scientific American* and the Patent Office. Late in 1865, he received the rejected models by John Lahaye and Edward Amsden, who had submitted designs in 1854 and '55. He then sent five dollars and asked for all other rejected models. This letter went astray, to his disappointment, but before the end of the year he had turned in his patent design and description, and received the old models with a bill for eleven dollars. He sent sixteen dollars, and inquired about the drawing "which I left at your office in October." He enclosed a statement of the object of his invention—"to dispense with the brakeman for RR cars and to secure prompt action of the brakes." On February 28, 1866, he sent forty-five dollars with his patent application. The Department of the Interior Patent Office granted him Patent No. 53,971 on March 24th. Four days later the *Scientific American* notified him, with an incidental plug for the magazine, to which he immediately subscribed. This was the beginning and end of Gibbs's dealings with the Patent Office, although at least two other inventions of his exist.

He knew that, although his age wished for power through machines, his power was elsewhere.

Hubert Anson Newton had gone abroad while Gibbs was an undergraduate. Newton's appointment carried with it a year's leave of absence, that he might study in Europe. As Gibbs wrote :

It was but natural that he should be attracted to Paris, where Chasles was expounding at the Sorbonne that modern higher geometry of which he was to so large an extent the creator, and which appeals so strongly to the sense of the beautiful.

This is the indication of Gibbs's own way. But he goes on :

Nevertheless, although for many years the higher geometry was with him a favorite subject of instruction for his more advanced students, either his own preferences, or perhaps rather the influence of his environment, was destined to lead him into a very different field of research. In the attention which has been paid to astronomy in this country we may recognize the history of the world repeating itself in a new country in respect to the order of the development of the sciences, or it may be enough to say that the questions which nature forces on us are likely to get more attention in a new country and a bustling age, than those which a reflective mind puts to itself, and that the love of abstract truth which prompts to the construction of a system of doctrine, and the refined taste which is a critic of methods of demonstration, are matters of slow growth. At all events, when Professor Newton was entering upon his professorship, the study of the higher geometry was less consonant with the spirit of the age in this country than the pursuit of astronomical knowledge, and the latter sphere of activity soon engrossed his best efforts.

Yet it was not in any of the beaten paths of astronomers that Professor Newton was to move. It was rather in the wilds of a *terra incognita*, which astronomers had hardly troubled themselves to claim as belonging to their domain, that he first labored to establish law and order. . . .

The *terra incognita* was the subject of shooting stars.

When John Quincy Adams had spoken of the "lighthouse of the sky," he heard years of fierce laughter. Now Whitman spoke of the moment. He had said of a locomotive :

Type of the modern—emblem of motion and power—pulse of the
      continent. . . .
Fierce-throated beauty!

and of other deeds and signs :

Nor forget I to sing of the wonder, the ship as she swam up my bay,
Well-shaped and stately the Great Eastern swam up my bay, she was
      600 feet long,
Her moving swiftly surrounded by myriads of small craft I forget
      not to sing;
Nor the comet that came unannounced out of the north flaring in
      heaven,

Nor the strange huge meteor-procession dazzling and clear shooting
    over our heads,
(A moment, a moment long it sail'd its balls of unearthly light over
    our heads,
Then departed, dropt in the night, and was gone;)
Of such, and fitful as they, I sing—with gleams from them would I
    gleam and patch these chants,
Your chants, O year all mottled with evil and good—year of fore-
    bodings!
Year of comets and meteors transient and strange—lo! even here one
    equally transient and strange!
As I flit through you hastily, soon to fall and be gone, what is this
    chant,
What am I myself but one of your meteors?

Now Newton and Gibbs watched in the observatory. Newton was serving actively on the committee to observe meteors
which had been set up by the Connecticut Academy, as well as
the publications committee. He was presenting a paper to the
new National Academy of Sciences, which had been set up in
Washington because the government needed technical scientific
advice in connection with the conduct of the Civil War. Senator
Wilson of Massachusetts, Agassiz, Bache, and Benjamin Peirce
helped draw up plans that were passed and signed by Lincoln in
March 1863. Newton's paper was read in 1864, and another
paper was read to the Connecticut Academy on the paths of
more than one hundred meteors which showered down and were
observed on August 10 and November 13, 1863. Newton was
also associate editor of the *American Journal of Science* from
1864.

His work and thought and friendship deeply influenced young
Willard Gibbs. Apart from the work on meteors, in which Gibbs
joined, Newton's activity in the agitation during the Civil War
to legalize the use of the metric system enlisted Gibbs's help.
John Quincy Adams, as Secretary of State, had prepared a report
to the Senate on weights and measures, which has been called
unprecedented. Dealing with history and philosophy as much as
with physics, it challenged the scientific world, which, Brooks
Adams says, likes interlopers least of all the trades or professions,
and cannot believe that a work may be sound and yet literary,
artistic, and historical. "His work of weights and measures is

monumental and has, since his death, been so recognized by a younger generation who did not feel themselves to be in competition with him." There had been resentment against "John the Second of the House of Braintree." This report provoked more. Adams traces the history of measurement, by hand and foot, through the Bible, Greek and Roman history, "multiplied by the abuses incident to the poverty, imperfections, and deceptions of human language." He goes through their career to our two influences in modern Europe, France and England, and speaks of the long history of English usage in pursuit of uniformity. And he makes a final argument for the metric system, that child of the French Revolution : "If man be an improveable being; if that universal peace, which was the object of a Saviour's mission, which is the desire of the philosopher, the longing of the philanthropist, the trembling hope of the Christian, is a blessing to which the futurity of mortal man has a claim of more than mortal promise; if the Spirit of Evil is, before the final consummation of things, to be cast down . . ." the race needs a system of common instruments to form the links of sympathy.

Gibbs went on with the argument. He stood before the Connecticut Academy on March 21, 1866, while he was still waiting to hear about his brake patent, and began :

A uniform system of weights and measures, adapted alike to the wants of practical life and to those of Science, is an acknowledged desideratum. . . .

He went on to speak of the French contribution, of the four quantities under consideration, time, length, force, and mass. In speaking of the intensities with which either of two properties, attraction and resistance, manifests itself in different bodies, he foreshadowed his coming years. The little group of Academy members heard young Gibbs say :

Now this is certainly a very convenient way to state the case, and will answer for all practical purposes. Yet it is evident, that when the matter of the bodies compared is different in kind, we cannot strictly speaking say that the quantity of matter of one is equal, greater, or less than that of the other. All that we have a right to say, except when the matter is the same in kind, is that the gravity is proportional to the inertia. To say *that*, is to express a great law of nature—a law, by the way, of that class which we learn by experience and not by a priori reasoning. It might have been otherwise, but its truth is abundantly attested by experience. But to say that the intensities of these two properties are both proportioned to the quantity of matter, is to bring in an element of which we know *nothing*. And yet something may be said in apology for such a statement. Not only is the intensity of either of these properties always proportioned to the quantity of matter, when the matter is of the same kind and under the same form, but the same is true for matter of the same kind under however different forms it may appear. Thus if we compare different bodies of ice, of water, and of steam, the quantity of matter in the bodies will be proportioned to the degree of these properties. The same might also be shown in the case of chemical composition. The rule is true then in all cases in which it can be put to the test, as results from two experimental truths or laws of nature; 1st, the law already mentioned, that the properties of gravity and inertia exist in different bodies with intensities proportioned to each other; 2nd, that changes of whatever kind in the form or state of matter do not in any degree alter these two properties.

He was following in a great tradition. He was going to move through it and out of it. He needed to wait and work. Young Gibbs met with his class at reunion time. He told them he would remain at Yale a little longer, and then he had his plans. And he sang with the rest of them, now that the peace had come, "almost as suddenly as had the war" :

The cruel war is over, and the boys are marching home,
And so to dear old Mother Yale her soldier children come;
And some of them have brought along their shoulder straps to show,
While valiant soldiers sing the song of Alma Mater O!
Of Alma Mater O!

He had no shoulder strap. He had nothing to show. He belonged in the last line :

Some have gone to York or Hartford,
Some to Paris or to Rome;
Some to Idaho's gold mountains—
More, perhaps, did stay at home.

But he had plans. The others had come home. He would not stay much longer.

CHAPTER EIGHT

The Years Abroad

H<small>E WAS</small>, in several degrees, free. As head of the family, he had lived in High Street through the war years. Emily died in 1864; she was the youngest, two years younger than Willard, and they cut her name into her father's monument, now raised behind the squat red Egyptian gate of the Grove Street cemetery, with its pagan golden butterfly—symbol of immortality— inside, among all the New England divines. The monument to Josiah Gibbs had cost eight hundred and fifty dollars. Entered in the long sheets of the estate, among the household expenses and the careful investments, it is the only entry to signify pride. The others speak of paid notes, U.S. Bonds, library books, stock in banks and railroads, an allowance to each of the four children of $1,057.37 for the period before March 4, 1864, and between that date and August 22, 1866, to Anna, Julia, and Josiah Willard, each $1,606.07.

There was that freedom. The panic of 1873 need not touch a young Yale tutor, whose inheritance is safely committed to real estate, government bonds, and a few sound banks. The promoters were collapsing, and only the bankruptcy courts seemed to thrive. But a college community is likely to be untouched, and Yale had grown during the war years. His father's inheritance promised Willard Gibbs that he would be able to go on with his work.

His real work was not in invention. That had been clear from the beginning, even when he was occupied through the last winter of the war in securing a patent for his airbrake—even when he saved another kind of promise for himself. During these years, he had been having trouble with his eyes, and no one in New Haven could help him.

My eyes! he thought, in that possessive panic. An end to this beginning, the work all unentered, the plans not yet mature. It looked in these moments as if there were no help. There was no one to help him, for a double reason. He refused to speak of his distress. Slowly he turned to the methods he knew best : silence and work. He looked for treatises on the defect of vision he found in himself. He had tested his eyes, and he recognized astigmatism. Airy had understood this error of refraction in 1827, and ground corrective lenses to focus the rays as they pass through the unequally curved meridians of the cornea; but there were only one or two lens-grinders in Europe who were aware of the proper correction, and none in America. As Franklin had solved his own problem and invented bifocal glasses, so Gibbs now worked toward his own solution, quietly, under the strain of this threat as well as the new strain upon his eyes. Working in secrecy, he had to depend on his own skill. His future was at stake this time. Slowly, he worked out the proper formula for lenses.

The praise that followed these inventive bursts was, he felt, a false praise. To those working in imagination, the nature of invention is quite clear, given any honesty and any self-consciousness. A New Englander as thorough as Willard Gibbs will have both of these qualities, and as he grew older, they developed. Living at home, studying through a time of war and strain, preparing himself for the future he began to realize—certain elements of secrecy in his own nature rose to trouble him when he met praise. One part of this secrecy was intellectually earned, clear and consistent and a fit response for the slippery compliments that ignorance would pay; the other part was a penalty, the burden both of his background and of the life that he was choosing for himself.

At the class meeting in the summer of '65, after all the business had been finished, there was a supper at Tremont House. All during that July night the old class talked and sang. War had separated them; many had gone abroad, or West. Bacon, who was chairman, spoke of Addison Van Name, who two months ago had received his license to preach. Like Josiah Gibbs, he was not using that right. He was more deeply interested in philology. He was working in the Creole language, and during these July days he received his appointment as Librarian of Yale College, to succeed Professor Gilman. He and Willard Gibbs were the only members of their class who lived in New Haven, and Gibbs was saying that he thought he would be in town another year.

His plan was to go abroad as soon as the estate was settled, to learn at those universities which had held philosophy and science as a prize for the Americans who had been leaving the Atlantic seaboard for the last twenty-five years, in more and more steady streams toward Berlin and Paris, Rome and Heidelberg and London. Van Name had travelled in Germany for a year and a half, studying at Tübingen before he returned to Yale. His course had been parallel to Willard Gibbs's, as far as his work at the College went : the same class, the same formula of gradu-ate work and degree, tutorship leading toward a more important post. After four years, he was Librarian. By the following spring, he was an instructor of Hebrew in the Theological Seminary. And he was courting Julia Gibbs.

The Gibbs children—Anna, Julia, Willard—seemed to be, from the beginning, a close and unbreakable household group. The two sisters were what the women of their lines had been : keen, firm-willed, intellectual. Julia, in comparison with her sister and brother, was lively and social, gay and talkative in the front of their family silences. But Anna and Willard seemed, early and late, to have achieved a complete understanding. These two sisters, and friends like Hubert Newton, supply the whole tex-ture of his emotional life, as we know it now.

New Haven supplied him the materials of his life, but he knew where he must go. His final invention during these years, a new type of governor, brought his name forward in the community. This governor, constructed in the shops at Sheff, was, according to Kraus, of a higher order of approximation to astaticism than any before it. It is in the collection of the Department of Physics. Kraus says :

Until we have come to know that Gibbs was endowed with a mind which possessed a keen appreciation of and interest in things physical and practical, his life and works remain a profound mystery. Possessing intellectual powers of the highest order, as much at home in pure mathematics as in physics and chemistry, Gibbs constantly exercised his will to direct his thoughts along lines that lay within the framework of material phenomena.

These inventions were exercises of the will. They led up to his prime interest, as yet unnamed.

He had his freedom, within limits. His preparation was well on its way. He regarded the period as preparation : his background, his facility in ancient languages, the modern languages he and his sisters were practicing at home against the day of their voyage—the work in Yale graduate school, the first school of its kind here—the painstaking work in applied mechanics—the lonely work, like his father's loneliness, which is the only discipline for isolation—these prepared him. As for the undergraduate work, the tutorship, any parts of his prescribed life—they can at best be said not to have unfitted him for the life which lay ahead.

As soon as they received their money, they sailed for Europe.

The two great territories which lay before this war generation, in their twenties in 1865, were Europe and the West. The continent was to be filled; it was this tremendous fertilization to which the country, wounded in a war agonizing beyond anything it had dreamed, was given. Warfare against the Indians actually prolonged the Civil War for thirty years; viewed in one way, it was a continuation of war for a single country with a single economic system, from the Atlantic to the Pacific, with accompanying victimization. More wounds; ending, in neither war, with extermination, but with a spreading powerlessness, a shifting of equilibrium until industrial power, steam power, city power—power, the big Power of the nineteenth century—spread over the country like a stain.

The West was still open and colored, extravagant, generous, beautiful, and poor—as it would be while its space still signified. Mark Twain, Bret Harte, Ambrose Bierce, were beginning to write down this country, and the young men who were invading it would be the railroad men, the scientists of railroads—geologists, mining engineers—who would build fortunes and the waste of fortunes across the country to Pasadena, San Diego, Sacramento. Later, there was a wave of return, when the writers came back, and the sons of the fortune-makers entered Yale and Harvard. But the adventurous, the practical, the grasping—they went West.

Europe had had its first wave of Americans, hunting scholarship as others went out with their drills and pans. Josiah Gibbs had felt that first wave of the century break, as German philology reached New England. The arts and letters had been diluted and overthrown by that impact : weakness and translation were almost the only results. The sweetness of gardens had reached a chaos. We had our gardens, too. The Adamses their roses, the Gibbses their iris; but not in imitation. We were chaos, and it was sweetness and melody those early artists hunted, lonely for order and tranquillity, even though they seemed restless—even though they seemed true poets. It was the most untouched who could survive; or the ones who, touched, could absorb and resist. Poe, the angriest and most divided, came to be the American who spoke above all the rest to France; Emerson, deeply refined in German thought, made his claims in "The American Scholar"; Thoreau and Melville, at two poles, declared our scene. But their words had all been spoken. The Civil War was a trough between two waves.

The change of values that arrived with the aftermath took the form, beyond all the appearances of great wealth and the blackest industrial hell, of an "aggressive humanism," in Gabriel's phrase, a new religion of humanity. The young liberals rising after 1865, the sense of mastery that blew up among the pioneers and with the newly centralized government, turned the young generation into the hopeful of science. In a search for instruments of mastery, these humanists saw scientific knowledge, combined with the hard-headed values of faith, as their tool. In its complexity—a complexity of creation—they found their hope and their guarantee. Among the graves and the new tracks, the arrangements of society adjusted and gave way. Idealism rose, as did the Grange and the early labor unions, among the dread of the poor. Europe fed the country immigrants, supplied markets, and, beyond these, issued a wealth of scientific production, the least national of riches.

As Willard Gibbs and his sisters sailed, the progress of scientific thought was filling the laboratories and lecture-halls of European universities with material for a new period in physical science. The practical men of both continents were measuring the actions of forces, with a new fund of experimental data ready in every field. But the mathematical advance kept pace.

It was towards these possibilities that he set himself now, as the steamer lurched in the Atlantic. The ocean was waste and wild; but the shores were approaching. Last summer the cable, after all its failures, had held; it bore proofs, both in its own existence and in the news it brought. William Thomson, sailing in his fourth cable-laying trip on the *Great Eastern*, had ended six years of attempt. And, after the days of hesitation, one of the first pieces of news the cable offered was confirmation of Hubert Newton's predictions. The observations made in England checked his computations, ending the skepticism that Jefferson had voiced sixty years before, when he said that people would rather believe that a couple of Yankee professors were lying than that stones could fall from the sky.

These were years of confirmation and prediction.

Great meanings had arrived on many ships. Darwin's controversy was at its height, and Lyell was being savagely attacked for his beliefs. The period was one of generalization, and the greatest of all exact generalizations was the concept of energy.

"The day will come, it is certain," Robert Mayer wrote, "when these truths will become the common property of science." He had returned from the Indies with his shattering discovery, and he had sent to the obvious publication, Poggendorff's *Annals of Physics and Chemistry*, at Leipzig, a manuscript which Gumpert calls "an index of eternity." It was a proof of peculiar immortality, containing these lines : "Motion, heat, and electricity and phenomena which can be converted into *one* force, can measure each other, and can be changed into one another under definite laws. . . . The fundamental principle that given forces, like matter, are quantitatively unchangeable, assures us conceivably of the permanence of differences and therefore of the permanence of the material world."

The manuscript was found thirty-six years later. Unruffled, unread, unanswered. It was lying among the papers Poggendorff left when he died. Mayer had written to him and to his publisher, but had never heard a word. He belonged to no institution, he made no academic claims. He was a little doctor in a country town, outside of the councils and the universities; he brought a work of explosive genius to the experts, and they met him with their silence. Resentment and silence met his proofs; he had demonstrated the law of the conservation of energy, and the scientists were not listening, and the rest of the world judged him insane. There is no need to list his wounds : Joule's announcement of the same exact equivalence appeared, and in the year of his two children's death, he opened his fight with Joule for priority. His most important book appeared as the foremost physicists of Germany banded together, and Helmholtz, one of that group, mentioned it five years later. Of his attacks, of his disparagements, of his attempt at suicide that broke both his legs with his jump from a third-story window, his frightful days in the madhouse, grilled by doctors who shouted at him, "You have tried to square the circle!"—of the times he was declared dead; it was of these that his life was built. And he lived to assert immortality and purpose; meeting Helmholtz on the platform during an 1869 conference, Mayer freed his greatness with a word, and said, in that meeting of physicists : "We step now out of the domain of inanimate nature into the living world. While there necessity rules, and the clockwork of law, we come now into a realm of purpose and beauty. . . . Figures are the boundary marks. In physics, numbers are everything; in physiology, they are little; in metaphysics they are nothing."

Numbers had built up the foundation for the law he claimed. Count Rumford, the tory American, had adventured in Europe until, in 1798, while boring brass cannon against the threatened invasion of Munich by the Austrian and French armies, he noticed how hot the metal shavings were, and began to find how much heat could be developed by friction. Humphrey Davy, melting his ice by rubbing, at Penzance, when he was a boy, had shown that heat could not be a fluid, and the earlier caloric theory was meeting fatal disproof. But the mathematical reinforcement must be traced from the statics of Galileo, and the virtual work of Newton and the Bernouillis, through the principle of least action of Maupertuis, until in the hands of Lavoisier, Lagrange, and Rankine, a calculus of variations and a separate branch of physics called Energetics are developed. Now any material system is first seen as a system of connected particles, whose energy depends on configuration alone. Now energy-function becomes the clue, and the system becomes the unit; similarities of behavior may be charted, and systems may serve as models or diagrams of each other. Sadi Carnot made this vivid, for the four-cycle engine was, indeed, a diagram of his cycle; equivalents in nature were recognized, and equivalents of the imagination created to prove this recognition.

The background for the science was all of physics and chemistry, and a line of mathematical development that Clausius summed up. In the fifties, these fundamental questions were meeting with their first response. Regnault wrote of his efforts to solve the relation of heat to mechanical effect in 1847, and Helmholtz published a celebrated memoir in the same year, *Über die Erhaltung der Kraft*. In 1849, Joule determined the mechanical equivalent of heat with his apparatus of paddles revolving in water, with strings around their axle and a pulley and finally attached to weights. Gibbs wrote in his paper on Clausius :

In 1848 and 1849, Sir William Thomson was engaged in developing the consequences of Carnot's theory of the motive power of heat, while Professor James Thomson in demonstrating the effect of pressure on the freezing point of water by a Carnot's cycle, showed the flexibility and the fruitfulness of a mode of demonstration which was to become canonical in thermodynamics. Meantime Rankine was attacking the problem in his own way, with one of those marvellous creations of the imagination of which it is so difficult to estimate the precise value.

Such was the state of the question when Clausius published his first memoir on thermodynamics. . . . This memoir marks an epoch in the history of physics. If we say, in the words used by Maxwell some years ago, that thermodynamics is "a science with secure foundations, clear definitions, and distinct boundaries," and ask when those foundations were laid, those definitions fixed, and those boundaries traced, there can be but one answer. Certainly not before the publication of that memoir. The materials indeed existed for such a science, as Clausius showed by constructing it from such materials, substantially, as had for years been the common property of physicists. But truth and error were in a confusing state of mixture. Neither in France, nor in Germany, nor in Great Britain, can we find the answer to the question quoted from Regnault. The case was worse than this, for wrong answers were confidently urged by the highest authorities.

That question was completely answered, on its theoretical side, in the memoir of Clausius, and the science of thermodynamics came into existence. . . .

The constructive power thus exhibited, this ability to bring order out of confusion, this breadth of view which could apprehend one truth without losing sight of another, this nice discrimination to separate truth from error—these are qualities which place the possessor in the first rank of scientific men.

It was for these qualities that Willard Gibbs looked to Europe. He could not even mention the United States in his geography of truth and error. The United States did not on that map exist.

In 1854, Clausius introduced a definite quantity into the concept of efficiency. The mechanical efficiencies of cyclic processes are the same, however they operate, whatever materials are involved. The efficiency is a function of heat alone—of the temperatures at which the system takes in and gives out heat. Two other properties beside temperature, volume, and pressure are to be used in specifying the thermodynamic condition of a system. They were not understood when heat-properties were studied in the early nineteenth century, but they have come to be understood as physical realities. They are energy itself, and entropy, the consistent tendency of heat to flow from hot to cold bodies, the tendency of the material universe toward uniformity.

The true days of these years abroad are in three marbled notebooks, the broken, obscure record of Willard Gibbs's growth. Paris was brilliant, with the dazzle and music and display of the Exposition. The Sorbonne had its offerings, the courses of Liouville in Theory of Number, Serret on Elliptical Functions and Celestial Mechanics, Chasles (to whom Gibbs, remembering Hubert Newton's stories, hurried) on Conic Sections, Duhamel on Infinitely Small Series, Darboux on Mechanical Theory of Heat, Briot on the Calculus of Probabilities and the Mathematical Theory of Light, Delaunay on Physical and Experimental Mechanics and Machines, Bertin on Electricity. Gibbs bought a dark blue notebook, eagerly numbered the pages and headed them, and began his schedule : Duhamel, Monday and Wednesday at eight-thirty; Liouville, Monday and Saturday at ten; Serret, Tuesday and Friday at ten-thirty; Chasles, Wednesday and Friday at twelve-thirty—until the grey rain of the Paris winter weakened his threatened chest, and drove him South.

The South of France gave him a summer of color and renewal. It must have brought him greater warmth, more freedom, than any season he had known. There is not a word on record of this time. Some mathematician, carrying his credentials like a golden bough, may find in the caverns of the family's life some letters, some scrap of diary, that suddenly may throw the sunlight of this Mediterranean summer over the three notebooks that are left.

On July 25, 1867, Addison Van Name sailed for Germany. He arrived early in August to marry Julia. Willard and Anna Gibbs must have felt protective, almost parental, toward this younger, gayer sister who came along with them during her engagement. It was obviously the only possibility if Willard was going abroad and Anna was with him; but as clearly, Julia wished to be home and married, and Van Name came to enter the family. He must have felt that this was indeed an entrance : it was settled that they were all to live in the High Street house, which, under the terms of their father's legacy, they jointly owned. The marriage took place in Berlin on August 19, 1867, and in October the Van Names returned to New Haven, to the Library and the familiar streets.

Anna stayed on with Willard. This was the first and longest of the trips they would make together, but their closeness during these years of initiation, when he was still a student, was undoubtedly the most real part of their emotional life—the frame and language, the dependable factor.

The second notebook is full, a brown and white marbled book, with "J. W. Gibbs—Link Str. 44, Berlin Oct. 1867" written in pencil on the flyleaf. It had been bought on the Rive Gauche with the others, to be used there; and now it carried the list of University professors on its first page : Dove, Du Bois-Reymond, Erman, Kronecker, Kummer, Kundt, Magnus, Paalzow, Quincke, Weierstrass, and Förster—a faculty that included some of the most distinguished of living mathematicians.

Berlin's university was, after its museum, the city's chief pride. In these years of war, just after Sadowa, just after the creation of the Reichstag, with Maximilian dead in Mexico, and Prussia proving itself the center of European interest, the idea of war was becoming familiar to France and Germany; 1870 was preparing, and student life reflected the coming event, as Yale had reflected the coming Civil War. The student societies were fiercely secret. The drinking and duelling were heavy and bitter careers; art and letters were at a dreary standstill; but the sciences were reaching an accumulation of hope and excitement. Europe was at a turning-point; Bismarck had shouted his oath of abstinence "from every shameful union with democracy"; but the universities were thriving. The crop of Americans abroad found the new stimulus of working closely with their professors in small discussion groups and seminars, of meeting in their professors' libraries and being allowed to enter their lives. To Willard Gibbs, as to William James, who was also in Berlin that winter, there was nothing new in free association with their teachers. William James had just come home from the expedition to the Amazon with Agassiz, who took a group of Harvard students. He remembered the jungle, the feeling of mistake he had had so much of the time, the smallpox that had confined him, the frustration of not being able to get into Peru, whose revolution made Agassiz's letters of introduction useless. But he had learned; Agassiz would lock a student up in a "room full of turtle shells, or lobster shells, or oyster shells, without a book or word to help him, and not let him out until he had discovered the truths which the object contained." No one could escape the enthusiasm of the man. When the expedition left, Oliver Wendell Holmes wrote "A Farewell to Agassiz," and his doggerel chuckles :

> And glaciers crawl the faster
> To the feet of their old master—
> Heaven keep him well and hearty,
> Both him and all his party!

James had plunged from the trip, remembering the swinging hammock as the engine throbbed on a dark reach of the upper Amazon, and Agassiz calling softly, "James, are you awake?— I cannot sleep; I am too happy; I keep thinking of these glorious plans."

Berlin made one forget the Amazon, the South of France. Berlin, for all the intellectual meat, was a city whose big somber rooms were furnished with skulls and strong-lined lithographs, whose rain and low sky were a weight on the heart, whose Linden consisted of two rows of "small, scrubby, abortive horse-chestnuts, beeches, limes, and others," planted for all the world like Commonwealth Avenue. It was not much of an experience for an American to come to this city, whose unfinished look—irregular, flat, and unsettled—was like his own country. William James spent a suicidal winter. His spiritual crisis lasted until January, through all the lectures in physics, seeing from a distance all the inaccessible labs. They were inaccessible because of his lack of training. He wrote home:

If I had been *drilled* further in mathematics, physics, chemistry, logic and the history of metaphysics, and had established, even if only in my memory, a firm and thoroughly familiar *basis* of knowledge in all these sciences (like the basis of human anatomy one gets in studying medicine) to which I should involuntarily refer all subsequently acquired facts and thoughts. . . . I might be steadily advancing.—But enough! Excuse the damned whine of this letter; I had no idea whatever of writing it when I sat down, but I am in a mood of indigestion and blueness.

To William James, depressed, feeling his history, internal and external, completely uneventful, home was haunting : he thought of "the advantage of having a youthful-hearted though bald-headed father who looks at the Kosmos as if it had some life in it," and of Alice and "serene Harry dealing his snubs around." "Serene Harry" had been writing his early stories. His father had fought with editors for his sake, and "The Story of a Year," with its Civil War hero lying "not unlike an old wounded Greek," had appeared in the *Atlantic Monthly*. William was sending his reviews home; they were appearing, unsigned, in the *Nation*. He was miserable in this city of white light, raw wind, equestrian statues. He read the new French fiction, saw Bancroft and Grimm, but loved what he could in this bleak and unfriendly city, "in the way Emerson speaks of, i.e. like those people we meet on staircases, etc., and who always ignore our feelings toward them." All that was peculiar to Germany was mental, he felt, and *that* Germany could be brought to America.

The semester did not begin on time—"lazy professors have put it off to the last of the month"—but, when the lectures began, both Gibbs and James were enrolled. Gibbs's Paris notebook had ended with the scrawled phrase : "*unité dans la variété rendue sensible par la périodicité.*" The Berlin notebooks begin, as Gibbs sits in Seat 7 of Professor Kronecker's classroom, listening to the excited little man give his first deceptive lecture. The strong lines of his face—skeptical and benevolent—reflected his obstinacy, the precision that had made him a specialized master. Bell tells how his clear first lectures deluded students into believing that his course would be easy. After three sessions, only a few would be left.

Kronecker rejoiced. A curtain could now be drawn across the room behind the first few rows of chairs, he joked, to bring lecturer and auditors into cosier intimacy. The few disciples he retained followed him devotedly, walking home with him to continue the discussions. . . . His house was always open to his pupils, for Kronecker really liked people, and his generous hospitality was one of the greatest satisfactions of his life. Several of his students became eminent mathematicians. . . .

Professor Kronecker stood before his class, and said, "Analysis may give us results in the sphere of the Theory of Numbers." Gibbs was taking notes that go on :

Ex. from the Bino. Theorem we see that $\dfrac{n\,(n-1)\,(n-2)}{1\quad 2\quad 3}$ is always a whole number.—given no. found from odd nos. alone—So far all results found in this way may also be found by pure arith. considerations.

Important Theorem

If

$$\sum^{n} \frac{a_n}{n^s} = \sum \frac{a'_n}{n^s}$$

$$a_n = a'_n$$

Haupt Aufgabe

To derive all the theory of numbers in the uniform analytical method of which Dirichlet has given us the idea—see Trans. Acad. Berlin 1837 Dirichlet

[154]

Law of Reciprocity

will give all the analytical demonstrations Eisenstein's simplest & schönest. $\left(\dfrac{n}{p}\right)$ defined arith by Legendre-Jacobi

To simplify this & other formulas let us develop in a product (by means of exponentials & the roots of unity)

$$\frac{\sin n v}{\sin v} = (-4)^{\frac{n-1}{2}} \prod_{h=1}^{h=\frac{n-1}{2}} \sin\left(v \pm \frac{2\pi h s}{n}\right)$$

$$\frac{\sin n v}{\sin v} = \prod\left(\cos 2v - \cos \frac{4 h s \pi}{n}\right)$$

$$\frac{\sin n v}{\sin v} = 2^{n-1}\left(-\sin^2 v + \sin^2 \frac{2\pi s h}{n}\right)$$

when n is an odd prime and s any number prime to it. . . .
The following formula Jacobi has called the most wonderful transformation of analysis. It contains the foundation of the Zahlentheorie & of the Ellip. Functions.

$$\text{Let } J'(\rho, \sigma) = \sqrt{\rho} \sum_{\mu=-\infty}^{\mu=+\infty} e^{-\pi(\rho\mu + \sigma)^2 + \frac{\pi}{2}\sigma^2}$$

$$J'(\rho, \sigma) = J'\left(\frac{1}{\rho}, i\sigma\right).$$

σ is any quant. real or imag.

$\rho^\sigma, \rho, + \sqrt{\rho} \qquad$ must each be positive in its real part.

There are twelve pages of notes on Kronecker, and three more pages farther on in the notebook. The jotting on machines mentions double cylinders, gas machines, the use of flame instead of electricity. Professor Quincke's course on Light begins with a résumé of recommended literature, including Fresnel, the first volume of whose collected works had just appeared, "Fresnel has also written a popular work forming part of a treatise on Physik (?)–F. W. Hershel excellent combination of theory &

practice—To be found in Encyc. Met.—Forms a thick 8vo—Airy, Best math. treatise—Beer not recommended—Billet 2 v. 1858 a good compilation for Fr authorities." This is the first personal mention. Quincke undoubtedly had a word to say about drinking to all of his first classes, many of whom would go on to Weierstrass, who, among champion beer-drinkers—and Germany was populated with champions—still was famous. Gibbs goes on to list the four hypotheses, which "will suffice for all that is known of light: 1, An Aether which is also contained in the (pores of) all bodies. 2. The impulse of this in the retina is the sensation of L. 3. Color is from dif. rapidity of these impulses 452 Brill : 785 Brill. 4. Intensity from vis viva of imp.—Different colors have the same velocity of propagation." He notes that Quincke believes Thomas Young superior to Fresnel. Gibbs is here learning of Young for the first time. His note, "In his 2 qu vols of lectures very many original ideas which only much later came to knowledge of others," is followed by the misheard "Rider—Hieroglyphik reader." Newton's work on Newton's rings is held up as a pattern of physical investigation; in this fine observation, 20,000 rings are seen with common salt, and 1/182000 of an English inch makes the first ring. Vizot and Fresnel are listed as references in the study of Frauenhofer lines, along with articles in the Annals. A table of ratios of equivalence and proper thickness for greatest sensibility, of quartz, gypsum, and glimmer (mica) is noted, and there is a note on metallic reflection. "On reflexion of homogenen Korper with reference to phasen unterschied see Quincke, Pogg. 128," Gibbs notes in his student jargon, and checks as a very important experiment the one illustrated by the axis and prisms :

The jargon of the notebooks is revealing. Far from being at home in German, young Willard Gibbs was not even making the effort one would imagine him likely to make—the extra effort necessary to take down lectures in the language in which they are given. It is an extra strain, and a useless one—but with his father, and his background, it is notable that he did not volunteer to suffer it. He was undoubtedly spending most of his time with Anna, speaking English.

He did go to the homes of his professors. At one point, a particularly shortsighted professor asked him about the Connecticut Academy, one of the few scientific associations that had been founded before the war years in the United States. Gibbs told him enough about it to surprise the professor with the intimacy of his knowledge, and he finally asked whether the twenty-nine-year-old student could possibly be a member. Gibbs said yes, he was. And the German turned on him and said, bluntly: "The memberships appear to be pretty freely bestowed."

His courses kept him busy; he had a full list. Quincke lectured in Electricity and Capillarity; no notes of these are preserved except a reading list for the second course. In Professor Kundt's course on Acoustics, Helmholtz' new and brilliant book on the Sensation of Tone was recommended first, and other of Helmholtz' works followed, until any reading list of that period in science is likely to include almost the complete works of Helmholtz. Weierstrass was recommended by Kronecker, his good friend and scientific enemy—he in turn recommended Helmholtz. Kummer had been Kronecker's teacher; both of them had been led by their study of the manuscripts which Galois had left when he died at the age of twenty-one, a greater martyr to imagination than Chatterton or Keats. Kummer was teaching, as was Kronecker, the freed algebra of Grassmann and Gauss, Paalzow was using Helmholtz and Gauss; Förster recommended Gauss's *Theoria Motus;* Weierstrass compared his own article on complex magnitudes with Gauss. The interrelation of mathematics and physics, as they were taught at this period, was one of the most exciting steps in the correlation of knowledge that has ever been made. To an eager student, starved not for the material but for the relation of one branch to another that is withheld so often in this country, Berlin must have been a continual stimulus. The reading list at the end of this notebook is full of hints. Gibbs's interest widened; he picked up the ends of information he had missed at New Haven. Here is a mention of the use of locomotives to stop railroad trains that caught the eye of the young inventor who held a patent for an airbrake. Here is Lorentz' new theory of light, just published; Steiner's method of images; treatises on the essential nature of force, on the steam injector, on new electric theories, on the equilibrium of heat and electricity compared, on indexes of refraction (Mascart had just won the French Academy award), the last works of Hamilton, which would lead him back to Möbius, Gauss, and Grassmann, and into his own work.

It would be in the young sciences, the newly named : energetics, mathematical physics.

This was a season for the young sciences. As Gibbs made these notes, William James, a few blocks away, was writing home to his family, "It seems to me that perhaps the time has come for psychology to begin to be a science . . ."

And, as Gibbs begins to make his next step, William James echoes it in a fantastic parallel, writing : "I am going on to study what is already known, and perhaps may be able to do some work at it. Helmholtz and a man named Wundt at Heidelberg are working at it, and I hope I live through this winter to go to them in the summer."

The German universities were one great university. Harvard and Yale and Princeton had their snobbishness, their accents, their systems of credits and markings; but Berlin and Tübingen and Heidelberg, for example, were interchangeable. A student might take one year at one, the next at another, and his degree at a third. There were solid days of work, sometimes starting at six in the morning and not ending until ten at night. The only requirements for a foreigner were that he be the proper age and bring testimonials to his character signed by natives of his country. It cost three dollars to matriculate : one for the certificate, one for the library, one for the dean of faculty's fund. The chief prohibitions were from duelling—and many cheeks carried jagger scars—and from secret societies, which met weekly to discuss Thucydides, say, and drink gallons of Happold's Bavarian beer. The foreign students governed themselves. And there were many foreign students. Gibbs, in departing, became (according to Langer) "one of a brilliant troop of young intellectuals who were destined to play a decisive role in the cultural development of America." The breadth of learning, the freedom of research, the insistence upon productive scholarship, and above all the accessibility of strong and provocative minds, sent back to this country a group of young intellectuals with a surer perspective and a firm idealism. They were the institutors of graduate work in this country, the carriers of a personal and civilized educational method which has not penetrated into the schools and colleges, where it would mean a living education for the young. Henry Adams, instituting his seminar at Harvard, brought back the Darwinian faith and the seminar method, and was an Adams in insisting that truth be new and amusing, although his father protested that that was moral weakness. But Henry Adams had returned from Europe; his political apprenticeship in London was over while Gibbs and William James were working still with Helmholtz in Heidelberg. Adams says, in the *Education* :

> To him [Henry Adams], the current of the time was to be his current, lead where it might. He put psychology under lock and key; he insisted on maintaining his absolute standards; on aiming at ultimate Unity. The mania for handling all the sides of every question, looking into every window, and opening every door, was, as Bluebeard judiciously pointed out to his wives, fatal to their practical usefulness in society. One could not stop to chase doubts as though they were rabbits. One had no time to paint and putty the surface of Law, even though it were cracked and rotten. For the young men whose lives were cast in the generation between 1867 and 1900, Law should be Evolution from lower to higher, aggregation of the atom in the mass, concentration of multiplicity in unity, compulsion of anarchy in order; and he would force himself to follow wherever it led, though he should sacrifice five thousand millions more in money, and a million more lives.

> He was in the center : at one side, Willard Gibbs was finding himself and his future, without a thought for psychology, not even the negative thought of putting it under lock and key; on the other, William James was beginning to understand that his series of failure and despair and failure led him inevitably to this one science. But the three, in their late twenties, would have agreed : they would not paint and putty the face of Law.

In Heidelberg, Helmholtz was, as goal, as the great sun. He was the type of the creative scientist, active and unrelenting in his productive life, and the rest of his life rather bare of incident. His biographers recognize the recoil with which he would have met any purely personal treatment. His father was a philologist, and the boy, weakly to the age of seven, stayed at home, played with wooden blocks, learned much poetry, and turned to languages. His rambles around the gardens of Potsdam were what he loved, and he loved his telescope, made under the table during his Virgil class. He was early a friend of Du Bois-Reymond and Brucke, although they did not recognize the course of his life. For he was active, a surgeon in the Prussian army when his thesis appeared with its discovery of nerve cells in the ganglia. An attack of typhus the year he was twenty released him from the service; since his hospitalization was free, he was able to save his allowance and buy his first microscope. His paper "On the Conservation of Force" was presented before the Physical Society which he had helped to found, with Clausius, Kirchhoff, Quincke, and Werner von Siemens; it was this paper, which established mathematically the views which Robert Mayer had suffered to express, that Clerk Maxwell called an "irresistible driving power" to those to whom we owe the greatest discoveries in modern physics. This paper, too, was denied publication in Poggendorff's *Annals*. Slowly, as the work accumulated, Helmholtz reached his place as one of the foremost men of the nineteenth century. Work on optics, on the conservation of energy, on hydro-dynamics, on electricity and abstract dynamics was accomplished as he met long teaching schedules. He had been at Heidelberg since 1859.

Kirchhoff was there, Bunsen, Kopp, and Horstmann, in physics and chemistry; Kummer, Cantor, Hesse, Du Bois-Reymond, Eisenlohr, Weber, and Luroth, in mathematics. And Willard Gibbs was prepared for this climax of his education. Receptive as he must have been to the town in its wooded valley, with its promenades, its statues, the early unrestored charm of its castle and bridge and towers, the songs at night, the community of students and tourists—he was more deeply prepared to be receptive to Kirchhoff and Helmholtz. There is no notebook for this period. Its record is buried in the life and work of Gibbs.

William James did not stay in Heidelberg. After a week he was writing to his parents from Berlin :

You will doubtless after my last letter be astonished to read the above address. The fact is I have been to Heidelberg and fled again under the influence of a blue despair which seized me for a week. Now that I am cheerful again I do not think I did unwisely. I should not have been able to stand the monotony of Heidelberg. It is a mere village shut between two precipitous hills, the scaling of which constitutes the *only* recreation of the place. As I am inadequate to that, all that remains is to take a turn down a sunny village street and then back to my room. . . . I have learned now by experience that, my old resource of walking off tedium and trouble being taken away from me, I require to be somewhere in reach of conversation, music, French and English newspapers, or at least the sight of rushing affairs that a large city gives, to keep of sound mind.

And, a few days later, he sent a picture of Helmholtz, "begging you to notice how mean is the lower part of his immortal face. He is probably the greatest scientific genius extant notwithstanding. . . ."

Wundt was not lecturing at Heidelberg, but others were. Gibbs was not the only one that year to find what he needed. A nineteen-year-old Russian girl was studying at Heidelberg that year, working in elliptic functions with Königsberger, and in physics with Kirchhoff and Helmholtz. She was a startlingly attractive woman, with marvellous and eloquent eyes, and Weierstrass, in spite of being warned about her by more nervous scientists, was to suffer all sorts of loss at her hands. This year, however, she was working courageously, and had determined that all of her plans would succeed as well as her plan to study had. There was no chance for an unmarried girl to work at a university; and Sonia Kowalewski had got around the restrictions in the only way possible—she had married at eighteen, left the husband of this nominal marriage in Moscow, and gone to Germany. That she told nobody of her marriage—that, above all, she did not tell Weierstrass that she was married—and that she fell in love with the husband of her contractual marriage—all these followed. In the meantime, she was in the hilly town, laying the groundwork for her discussion of Cauchy's problem of 1842, the finding of a general solution of a partial differential equation of the second order. Many boundary problems in mathematical physics were leading to a re-statement of classical physics, and to new formulations. In Berlin and in Heidelberg during these years one might find the soil of an outgrowth which stretches through today's work. Willard Gibbs found a country of the mind that could provide him, and give him enough to work on quietly and alone.

He could laugh, also, about the problems he dealt with : they were everywhere. When they stopped at an inn one night, the flow of heat was brought home to him and his sister in a way they loved to remember. They took their rooms and went in to the hot, close air of a typical German house. And at once they did what hundreds of "crazy American" tourists have done in hundreds of foreign inns—they flung the windows open, and leaned out into the cool night, only to hear the landlady's shouted complaint from the door : "What! Do you think I want to heat the whole street?"

After Heidelberg, there was France, and Paris again—Paris which was a university, and a sweet drug also, that made a writer set this down, that spring, as preface to his book about the city :

> On dit : Strychnine, Quinine,
> Aniline, Nicotine,
> Je dis : Parisine.

In the café, an art student was hooted down for singing the air from "La Dame Blanche," which begins, *"Ah, quel plaisir d'être soldat."* Nobody wanted to hear of soldiers, although Sadowa was quickly preparing a way for Sedan. The growling chorus of art-students answered the solo militarist with Musset's *"Nous l'avons vu, votre Rhin Allemand."* They did not dream that next summer would hear the *"Marchons! Marchons!"* of the "Marseillaise" on these boulevards, where, in July, Henry Adams said, "the war was brought out like an opera of Meyerbeer."

What is there to invent and falsify in a man's voyages? This was a chance and a preparation. Europe, and America too, were making a stray out of Henry Adams; these years gave sadness and maturity to William James; but to Gibbs, whose choices were easier, because they did not involve people—because, indeed, they were already made—the future must have seemed directed, and Europe could be synthesized, kept a philosophic reality. He knew it as the place he looked for, from which he could learn, his reservoir. It was the country that he could expect, like home, to know the speech that was native to him. Europe made no claim on him; he had only one home, when it came to that. Even in the last spring, on the Riviera, home was with him. For Anna was with him. He had never really left home, he felt. Very well; he would go back.

He was to speak of passive resistance to changes in equilibrium. He knew that resistance, for he contained it, in another sense. He recognized his own balance; and he and Anna sailed home in June 1869. He was thirty years old, and the choice was made.

CHAPTER NINE

Return to America

Nothing can relieve the shiver of homecoming. Mystery sails into your life with a finality that no one misses, when at last the smell of land rises from the harbor, and the motion of the ship is forgotten at the first touch of the steadiness of land, and you see in a broad gaze how this place—the most familiar place of the unreliable world, the one sure home—has changed to betray your own memory and the past.

Willard Gibbs and Anna, returning in June, after three years of Europe, could see the changes that passed imperceptibly as a gradual change of light over those who lived among them. The town itself had changed : the harbor was still full of ships, some of them battered by the heavy winter weather, flung by storms against the wharves and timber, but there was a new Horse Rail Road, which met the New York night steamer and went through town for six cents; and the Railroad Depot was crowded with passengers waiting around its sunken tracks, so deep that the town was making a joke of it and calling it the "Subterranean." The tower with its goodbell stood over it, an old landmark by now, but the big illuminated clock was newer, and people talked about what a convenience it was. Hacks crowded the depot, too, calling their fares : "Fifty cents a passenger, anywhere in town!"; "Thirty-five cents for two, anywhere in town!"

The Green still looked the same from a distance, with its liberty pole and flag, and the fountain with its pump in the corner; and over there the Yale fence and the College buildings still looked the same, although Addison and Julia were full of tales of change. There *was* change; looking more closely at the Green, you could see the brick wall crossing it, and at one side, where the horsecars and the riders passed, there was a new concrete sidewalk. Addison laughed. The laws about horses and cows pasturing in the streets had been passed easily enough; but when it came to paving the sidewalk, the innovation had been too much. There had been strong opposition; one prominent citizen still walked in the street, making a show of his preference, getting in the way of the riders, and saying, with the bravado of the extreme reactionary, that God's soil was still good enough for him.

There was a bustle in the streets : the sound of more people than before, it seemed to Gibbs. And there were new stores everywhere. Hoad's, the favorite College saloon, opposite the grounds, still had food, confectioneries, and books, but the notice about Base Ball furniture seemed much more important, and most prominent of all was a notice that Mr. Hoadley was largely interested in the modern velocipede. There were new lines of stores, clothing stores, new places with German names looking almost like Berlin or Bonn, and fancy stores.

The houses had changed. Nobody was building in the old classic style; and the Egyptian influence felt on Hillhouse Avenue, as well as in the cemetery gate, was a taste that had not lasted. Here were the verandas and cupolas, the cast-iron statues and jig-saw decoration, of a new period. The houses were not close to the College, but farther east and wide around the town; however, in these towns that grow around a core, as in a tree, it is the outside ring of growth that tells the tale. And the outermost ring of New Haven declared that a new era had arrived : a period of energy and decoration, of complete lack of taste and the most furious growth the world had ever seen.

Henry Adams, just come home from ten years abroad, had seen it sharply, saying that there was no way of knowing how much the character of America was changing, but that it was clear that the force had shifted, with the superiority of mechanical energies—coal, iron, steam—over the industrial elements of agriculture, handwork, and learning.

In most towns this change meant a corresponding change in the structure of the organism. There were new towns rising, mill and factory towns, in which the plant itself was the center, the slums stood all around in rows of housefronts, dehumanized if you considered their uniformity of door and stoop and identical rooftop, but a swarming horror if in that glance you could guess at the number of lives they would be helping to dehumanize—and then, farther out in the grassland, the homes of the foremen and managers, and if the town was lucky, even the president or owner. And there were pioneer towns charting the roads West, little frame towns with their wide roads that would change into a storm of dust as the Express came galloping through, lonely, terrible towns on the prairie where a poet was writing

How lone the cracked and parchéd world, save when the trains
    go by!

And there were the great Eastern cities that could shift their centers, swallow up the outlying towns, and go on expanding, like New York or Boston or Philadelphia; and the Southern cities, growing in a trance of convalescence, still deathly ill with the aftermath of war. But New Haven, which had already been split between the College and the town, grew so that the split was emphasized. On the one side, here was a school still run the way it had been run long before the war; controlled by the Congregationalist Church as it had always been, with six members of its Corporation taken from the state government. And on the other, the industrial city grew, with new plants and an immigrant population.

As Gibbs came home, he found himself in a changing house, a changing town, and a college at whose changes the letters he had received in France had only hinted.

It was clear that the household would have to be re-established on new lines. Addison and Julia were settled and busy. Addison Van Name was a solid figure, whose activity weirdly resembled Josiah Gibbs's. He was Librarian of Yale, a college which never forgot that it was built on a gift of books, and whose Librarian has always been an important foundation of the entire institution; he was Librarian of the Connecticut Academy of Arts and Sciences, and of the American Oriental Society. His work in Oriental languages was a continuation of Josiah Gibbs's philology; and the science had found one center at New Haven, with President Woolsey and Professors Hadley and Whitney to give it eminence.

There must have been, for Willard and Anna, a curious sensation of coming home to a family not gone ahead in time so much as gone back to the time when their parents were alive. Willard and his elder sister had been the couple in authority, before Julia's marriage; now there was a new balance. The house was owned jointly by the three, and there was a little money—enough to live on, since their wants were very few, but not enough to separate the family. Addison had his position at the College, and it was an honorable and paying post; but Willard, deep in his work, was rather in the position of the repatriated artist. Hubert Newton still lived next door, and his children were growing fast; the garden looked about as it did. The house was secure, it had not changed; his room, looking over the flowers, was unchanged, and he would come back to it, as Anna would come back to hers. They had a living room of their own here, too. Addison was a busy man, full of affairs and of the difficulties of the College; he took precedence because of his business. He had a full schedule that must be obeyed. And this strange scholar, who had come back from Europe, thirty-one years old, with a vague sense that he would belong to Yale forever, and a sharp sense of new countries opening before his imagination, was willing to give the settled man precedence. It was nothing he wanted. He had what he needed : quiet, books, the countryside he knew to walk in, his sisters' devotion.

There were many changes, he noticed, as he walked through the town, and into Sachem's Wood and Highland Park beyond. Summer was over the town, and the elms were dark and shady. There was Ralph Ingersoll, old now, measuring the ground with his eye as he walked, but still erect after his long career of politician and minister to Russia; there the girls went into the ice-cream parlor, to eat strawberries and "cream" at Ferry's, whose owner was advertising that he was now making ice cream by steam; there the New Haven House took in a new group of guests. The Tontine House still stood elm-shadowed, at the Green, but the New Haven House was the first hotel in town, now that it had Mr. Mosely, of the Brevoort House in New York, in charge, and the Tontine had lost its celebrity.

Now he nodded to somebody who waved from a carriage—the Farnams, he thought, although he had not been paying attention. It was certainly nobody from the College. Yale people drove buggies, or canopy tops; it was only the richer townspeople, like the Trowbridges, or the Englishes, or the Salisburys, or the Hotchkisses, who could afford to drive in style. Other people used their buggies; or, indeed, took the horsecars, which were now running on schedule—every half-hour to Lake Whitney.

Some of the neighbors' children were very aware of the Gibbses' buggy. The Whitneys were cousins through the Baldwins of Willard Gibbs, and Margaret and Marion remember that the Gibbses and the Van Names had a horse and buggy and a cutter in winter. It was a special treat, when Willard Gibbs came to call for them, to take the children driving all by themselves with him. He was charming to them, and lifted them into the buggy, and on cool days tucked them in. The little girl sitting next to him looked up at him as they rolled along. He drove as though he liked to, and he smiled down in his reassuring way. He was a very good friend to these children.

"My best memory," says Margaret Whitney, "is driving with him in the winter in a cutter." She remembers her childhood in all its detail, as she stood in the snow beside the big sleigh, looming fine and promising above the little girl. The snow was all around, fallen and still in the crisp air, and the sleighbells rang soft and loud and soft again as they passed, while the little girl waited to be lifted in. And then they were ringing down the roads, "all the world in swift motion."

The snow and the elms could be counted on, in New Haven. They made the calendar, and they never changed. The first flurry of snow always came in the second week of November, the first real snowstorm the week after; and then the white New England winter arrived, of which young Henry James said the elms spoke, as they rose from the grass in files before the white-painted houses and open dooryards.

"See with how little we do it; count over the elements and judge how few they are : in other words come back in winter, in the months of the naked glare, when the white paint looks dead and dingy against the snow, the poor dear old white paint—immemorial, ubiquitous, save as venturing into brown or yellow—which is really all we have to build on!" Some such sense as that you may catch from the murmur of the amiable elms.

And, after all the white, the last wet snow of the first of April, and then, not a month later, the apricot trees with a shower of blossom; followed, on the first of May, by the blossoming peach trees, and on the next day, the plums, and on the next, the cherries; and then the pear and apple trees, before the middle of May, blooming with scarcely a variation from their calendar for a hundred New Haven years. And then full summer, sun-checkered under the elms, until New England stands flaming in the weeks after mid-September, with its own wildness at last owned and sanctioned. Until "the mere *fusion* of earth and air and water, of light and shade and color, the almost shameless tolerance of nature for the poor human experiment, are so happily effective that you lose all reckoning of the items of the sun. . . ."

These few elements were enough for Willard Gibbs. There were other elements; they rejected him, or tolerated him, according to their nature.

The Pacific Railroad and the Suez Canal were changing the currents of the world. Last May, at Promontory Point, Leland Stanford and Durant had met, with the band blaring and the Irish and Chinese and Negro workmen cheering and the Indians watching desperately, as the blows hammered home the golden spike and rang the bell of City Hall in San Francisco. When the Suez Canal was opened after ten years of dredging, the days of the Capes ended for a while. The British Empire and the United States were trying to belt the world. England was packed, and could well send people out to colonize; it was a different problem in America. Colonizing in the West had to be done on a grand scale, and with the axe. It was a matter of cutting down trees, and Indians as if they were trees; of putting through the railroads, building cities, and running their newspapers, their new commerce, in a flash. New England was the mother country for most of this effort. The drain on New England was not letting up for a moment; her strongest men were going West, and the optimistic said that there was no other country in the world that had the good fortune to be able to plant distant

colonies without losing its strength and energy at the center.
The center was New England; the wave of immigration that had
reached a new crest in '48 and had shown no signs of a trough
was flooding New England with farmers and factory workers,
but the English culture was deeply established, and the strongest
representatives of that culture, with its vigor, its tendency
toward exploitation, and its obverse of pallor, were heading
West.

The scholars, the frail, and most of the women remained. The
farmers went to plow the richer West and leave the rocky
Eastern pastures; the poets and the press talked about little but
the delights of the country, but the farmer went on, either turning pioneer or moving into town. The industrialization of the
towns was proving all that the theories the Brahmins and conservatives most feared; in Europe, war was gathering and Marx
was working hard, and here, labor was organizing. And in the
middle of all of this, New England was decaying. The shadow
of Barnum was hanging over Connecticut, and the river gods
were abandoned; but while Fisk and Lane were watering railroad stock in New York, said the *Nation*, why complain about
the evils of New England? Why complain, in spite of the
"scandalous stories" that rumored that "the descendants of the
Pilgrim band are taking measures calculated to still further reduce the birth rate."

The equilibrium was shifting so quickly that it was in full
consciousness. A year before the first big National Labor
Congress, it was clear that the industrial revolution was not a
climax, but a beginning.

It is safe to say that we have entered on a transition period, of
which the "disturbance," as it is called, in the relations of labor and
capital which we witness all over the world only marks the opening,
and which will hardly end without producing profound social and
political convulsions. . . .

If workingmen are going to govern the world, either they, or their
children, or members chosen from their ranks, must have access to
higher instruction in vastly greater numbers. . . . The "poor scholar"
must have again opened to him the course which he was free to
follow in the Middle Ages, and which the modern world denies him.

The fact of being denied had effected its own changes in the
scholar. The New England scholar was the best example of the

type, and actually it was in New England alone of all the sections that there were enough of the type to allow judgment. The Southern writers, like Lanier, and the Southern scientists, like Matthew Fontaine Maury, were of another calibre; but, in New England, colleges had from the beginning been schools for making ministers, and the result was that, even now, no matter how good theological training was, secular scholarship had turned into a sickly plant, an exotic that had little relation to anything but the past. The vigor was there. Everything that the country was, everything that it seemed to want, had to do with vigor that gripped its desire with a death-grip and turned a look of death on whatever it hated. The great split in our democracy had opened wide. Everything fatal in John Quincy Adams had emerged in scholarship; everything fatal in Jackson had emerged in action. The antagonism had been against the best interests of the nation, and the antagonism itself had won the victory over both contestants, who had enough good between them to create a nation. Neither of them had enough by himself. The interdependence between forces here might have been the opening of a great reinforced democracy, if it could have been recognized and expressed; but it was not.

And now there were Tweed and Jay Gould, Jim Fisk, Dan'l Drew, and all of Grant's cabinet, with the most overweening individualism and a set of precedents to back it. Or they would make their own precedents, with piracy and the Law of Wealth to go on. And on the other hand, there were the traditions of Concord and scholarship. Concord had become that shabbiest of meccas, a parents' shrine. It belonged to the generation that was passing, and the time had not yet come for a revaluation. The reading public was bored to death with the town's name, sick of "the noise about Concord things kept up by the second and third-rate luminaries of that place, and by some of the more intelligible among the many scatter-brained pilgrims to that shrine—by the excessive Concordism of those flowers which are not the rose but which have lived near it, and which smell of it as hard as they can." There was also the "Ripe Scholar"—the New England man of letters, who was (according to a contemporary article) a "recluse, ignorant of the world, bleached by a close room and an iron stove, never breathing the outer air when he could help it." Sometimes he was reputed to be a scholar simply because he was nothing else. He was a pallid product, a feeble animal thrown up on the bank beside a swirl of waters. His scholarship was not fruitful. It had no influence, no vital force in this drift toward material interest, and it came to be regarded as superfluous. Edward Everett had been the type of this scholar, more finished, of course, with many graceful additions. There was nothing creative here.

"That he should be provincial was, for a long time, inevitable, but that he was emasculate was chiefly his own fault."

No combination could have been worse for women. When they went into the forest with their pioneer husbands, they had the drudgery and ghastly loneliness of setting up a self-sufficient economy at home, while the men had the back-breaking work but the comparative charm of logging, hunting, and fishing. When they went into the cities, where the men had the liberty of the streets and saloons, they found Tartarus, in one form or another : the factory, the sweatshop, or the store. In freedom, daily life in any of these places could have been tolerable and productive—but freedom here would mean something concrete : the chance for the people who were living those lives to determine under what conditions they would do the given work. That there was no such freedom is obvious. If every city and factory were bombed to rubble, the proof of the life of women in the nineteenth century would still be before us, in the personalities of our parents and ourselves.

The "American style" of the period is visible in its houses and its chromos—and it is not a style at all. If there were a true expression, we would have a form impelled from the center, determined by meaning. But there is no form, there is only decoration, meaningless and sexless. The cupola is added to the house, the scrollwork like an excretion, the veranda. This has nothing to do with the house; this ornament comes when there is nothing to say, and no love left.

Whose passion was turned away from labor and avarice?

The Greeks turned their thoughtful love away from women, but they were spared the added stress of a business culture so flamboyant.

When most respect is taken away from the life of woman,

when she is contorted and misrepresented, you will always find the female principle inordinately large in the great men. Look at Whitman; or Lincoln.

And when there are men brought to any high level of consciousness—whether there are schools or not—there will be unusual women who, seeing them, learn to follow the least clue. And *then* you will have your Desdemonas smothered for mistaken motives, then you will have the fiercest, most tragic frustrations.

Gossip will wind in with guilty conscience, rumor of intellect with snickering dirty rumor, until the outburst comes.

In the eruption, there will be a few women cast into sharp illumination : articulate and bitterly disappointed spirits, crying "Too late!" like the victims of a fatal epidemic. And they will be called bluestockings and intellectuals, as Margaret Fuller and Frances Wright were looked on as monstrosities, until Wendell could call that intense woman of unrest, Margaret Fuller, an "unsexed Socrates." These caricatured rebels were not only intellectuals; they were speaking for that foundation-group of society, the inarticulate—women, children, the underprivileged (as did Elizabeth Phelps, Rebecca Harding, Mary Freeman) and the slaves (as did Harriet Stowe).

Beyond them, there is another group of women, who may or may not be inarticulate. They seem more finely tempered than the last group, although that may be because they lack the final courage to take their words into the open. At any rate, where the former lack control, these latter attain it. But they remain private, in a kind of suicide. The inner life need not be further hidden, it is buried already farther than any threat or lover reaches. To remove it farther is illness, or self-destruction, a little-known disease.

Women who lived in college towns, close to men of unusual gifts, were likely to be defeated. The men whom they could respect—the men who in any way could capture their imagination—would have to have power of a notable kind. The coming men : Jim Fisk, whom Parrington quotes as prince of vulgarians, shouting, "I worship in the Synagogue of the Libertines," or announcing at the failure of his Erie coup, "Nothing is lost save honor!"—Jim Fisk lived in another empire, and Rockefeller, just establishing the Standard Oil Company, and young Tom Edison, newsboy, unemployed, completely unheard of—that was another country, and communications had not been set up. As for intellectual power, there was the intramental life of the New England scholar.

And for the women who were devoted to that power? For Emily Dickinson, Alice James, Anna Gibbs?

They stand for silence and a special generosity, but the age was violent. The rapes behind the Divinity School, recorded in the New Haven papers, were nothing. The papers were full of seductions, shootings by women, shootings by avenging brothers. There was a notorious case every little while, with heavy editorial pronouncements as the verdicts were pronounced. "Women must be taught to take care of their own honor, and to bear unsupported the loss of it. The present division of the responsibility of its protection is a disgrace to our civilization." And, later, the pathetic complaint, with an aside that the fate of seduced women is hard enough, that "there is so much shooting by women."

The fight for the vote entered into much of this, as one more protest; with Margaret Fuller's *Woman in the Nineteenth Century* well remembered, the books appeared : Bushnell's *Women's Suffrage : The Reform Against Nature* was most handsomely received, and it was an attack on property changes and on the Declaration of Independence for the "transcendentalism" of its "born free and equal."

Many of the attacks on new rights were on the grounds that women could not bear various strains, including physical burdens and mental activity. In the meantime, 15 per cent of the women in the United States were employed in gainful activity, several women's colleges were in session, and the first few universities to set up co-educational experiments were valiantly facing their problems.

And Emily Dickinson was writing her poems and letters. Just this year she was writing one of the key phrases, that might horrify schoolteachers with their tart and crabbed turns, but would certainly have found agreement among the daughters of the James and Gibbs families, if they had known : "Home is the definition of God." She was cut off; but she had made an image of that amputation.

The father, Henry James, published his book, *The Secret of*

Swedenborg, a year before that line was written. The book
appeared amid a howl of controversy, and the worst contenders
were, of course, the Swedenborgians. James talked about their
"rigor and frigor" and they howled, and wrote letters, and
appeared wild-eyed in editors' offices until they had finally to
be informed that no further letters would be printed. In the
meantime, the book had tried to rescue Swedenborg from his
followers, to hold out for a living society, and to hammer the
point home that there is no infinite that is unrepresented by a
finite. But the finite is only representative.

Emily Dickinson shared that belief. In her house, looking out
at the young trees with their lifted branches, and the tall trees
downswung, the sun flat on the grass, and the little path "wide
enough for two who love," she kept an image of the world like
an infusion in a glass. In her few trips to Boston, and the one
portentous trip to Washington and Philadelphia, she knew
voyage and shipwreck; in her escapes, she found a few friends
and her sister-in-law Susan, "You from whom I never run
away"; and in Colonel Higginson, whom she could ask whether
her verse was alive, she found an adviser to whom she could
retort : "You think my gait 'spasmodic.' I am in danger, sir."
The clipped and polite cadence of a caller's speech is in all her
writing, letters and poems alike; and the eager loneliness, the
invitation to death and burial, the king-killing of much tradition,
that all combine to make her close to Gibbs. She is a close expression of American self-destruction with all its powers of
communication heightened, and with a change. She could speak
her own death, and leave the reader with a clear joy, a gift in the
hand that seemed nothing more bodied than broken light, as if
one were to hold an invisible prism.

There was always this wish, marred by coyness as in another
nature it might be marred by excessive restraint, to be her own
absolute,

> . . . independent as the sun,
> Associates and glows alone,
> Fulfilling absolute decree
> In casual simplicity.

Science could not overtake that, she felt. She had reached her
only equilibrium; and that was the only law.

There was only one poet who was writing of women with

the generosity they wished; that was Whitman. He may have withheld generosity from all women in his life; but he was contemporary, and his life was not known. New England, however, had cut him off, and Emily Dickinson was obedient. She wrote to Colonel Higginson : "You speak of Mr. Whitman. I never read his book, but was told that it was disgraceful." Obedience was another quality that removed these women from the others. They were not open rebels, like Margaret Fuller; but their obedience could not cover their steel strength. It showed as silence, and people wondered.

Anna Gibbs was known as silent. It was said that she and Willard could be silent together better than anyone else. There seems to have been complete understanding between them. Most people deserved her silence, but living persons still remember long days spent in wonderful conversation with Gibbs and his sister—on trains, or in the country.

If Willard Gibbs's life is shadowy, Anna's life is spent in his shade. There is no mention of her in any paper about her brother; indeed, in the fullest account of all, she is swallowed up completely, identified with Julia, so that Gibbs is made to have only one sister. The wish for burial is here answered completely. But it must have been a wish to be completely devoted; there is no reason to doubt that Gibbs received all the sustenance and love he wished; the change in his face is too great to leave any doubt as to his reaching the full thrust of his imaginative powers; and he seems to have done that with a reliance on the security of his home, which meant Anna, the Van Names, and the house itself. From the apparently discontented young man of the early pictures, he developed into a burning-eyed, strong-willed man. The short beard, sparse on the lower lip but with a full and heavy moustache, does not cover the petulance of his mouth as it was a few years before; this mouth shows humor and calm, and the very beautiful head has been earned.

Gibbs's mental life was lived completely alone; but his daily life was lived very close to his sister. She must be given part of the credit for signs of calmness and maturity in him. She was part of his education.

Henry Adams, who felt he could always go to women when he needed help with his education—his life—was rushing to Italy. A telegram from his brother-in-law, Charles Kuhn, had reached him soon after he arrived in London in the summer of 1870. His sister had been badly injured as she was thrown from her cab, and Henry was to come at once. He was in Bagni di Lucca two days later.

Louisa, the oldest child in the Adams household, stood to Henry in the same family relationship that Anna held to Willard Gibbs. But she was turned outward, and Henry said of her that she was the most sparkling creature he ever met. On his first trip to Italy, Henry had joined Louisa in Thun, and gone on to Italy with this sister who, "like all good Americans and English," was "hotly Italian." He had given her the reins on this trip—she wanted to go to Milan, still full of war a moment after the armistice.

She was the first young woman he was ever intimate with—quick, sensitive, wilful, or full of will, energetic, sympathetic and intelligent enough to supply a score of men with ideas. . . . It was his first experiment in giving the reins to a woman, and he was so much pleased with the results that he never wanted to take them back. In after life he made a general law of experience—no woman had ever driven him wrong; no man had ever driven him right.

And now it was this woman whom he found, stiffening with tetanus in consequence of a bruised foot. She was as gay as she had been on the earlier trip, this brilliant woman who was dying so rapidly in the Italian mid-summer.

The last lesson—the sum and term of education—began then. He had passed through thirty years of rather varied experience without having once felt the shell of custom broken. He had never seen Nature—only her surface—the sugar-coating that she shows to youth : Flung suddenly in his face, with the harsh brutality of chance, the terror of the blow stayed by him thenceforth for life, until repetition made it more than the will could struggle with; more than he could call on himself to bear. . . . Hour by hour the muscles grew rigid, while the mind remained bright, until after ten days of fiendish torture she died in convulsions. . . .

Society being immortal, could put on immortality at will. Adams being mortal, felt only the mortality. Death took features altogether new to him, in these rich and sensuous surroundings. . . . The sick-room itself glowed with the Italian joy of life; friends filled it; no harsh northern lights pierced the soft shadows; even the dying woman shared the sense of the Italian summer, the soft, velvet air, the humor, the courage, the sensual fulness of Nature and man. She faced death, as women mostly do, bravely and even gaily, racked slowly to unconsciousness, but yielding only to violence, as a soldier sabred in battle.

It is not Henry Adams' sister, but his wife, who shares Anna Gibbs's silence. A summer after Louisa's death, Henry was in the Sierras with Clarence King; and a year after that, he married Marian Hooper, whose life with him is lost in the gap in his *Education* between the chapters "Failure" and "Twenty Years After."

In this summer, he felt only the incongruity between the sensual pleasure of the Tuscan hills and the death-room where he stood. Italy had been the goal for many Americans—many New Englanders, in particular; for the weather and the legends carried the answer of richness into hearts that had been given for too long the starvation wages of a Puritan heritage. It was Rome that wrung the cry of bitterness from Margaret Fuller, caricatured and misunderstood for a bluestocking at home : "Had I only come ten years earlier! Now my life must be a failure, so much strength has been wasted on abstractions, which only came because I grew not in the right soil."

Alice James also went abroad, but not until much later. Now she was at home in Cambridge with her father, her mother, and William, writing to Henry in Europe. When Henry returned, the great part of the family was together for a while; and it was in this year of 1870 that William James went through the crisis of his life in which he touched bottom, and rose again, after a long ebbing of the will that had driven him down. The insight given him by choice, the clue to which was his reading of Renouvier, never left him. It was an insight he shared with his sister, rather than with his brother Henry.

The year, an important one for both brothers, marked the end of ease for the family, which was still supporting three grown children. Black Friday of '69 was the storm-signal, and the industrial hurricane that followed swept many family resources away forever. It swept away Garth James's plantation in Sevenola, Florida, and sent Wilky and Bob James to the Northwest and finally to Milwaukee, where they settled in business. These years were proving, above all, that no disaster was local. All calamities were general, was the word that the Chicago fire brought to the East. The roar of flames along those hollow wooden streets—"the best arrangement for extending a fire that could be made at the cost"—was an appalling voice of disaster in the East as well, as it was brought home to many New England manufacturing firms that they were living on the Middle West.

The news from Europe proved further connections. The fate of the railroads was tied somehow, people felt, to what happened to Bismarck; the French elections and the part that the worn-out conservative Thiers was taking seemed far enough away, and everyone said that the signs in Prussia were pacific. But suddenly the Franco-Prussian War, the siege of Paris, and the Paris Commune, brought home the word of blood and war to a transition time. To any observer looking for signs, the overthrow of the Commune could not be seen as an end, although international business sighed with relief. The *Nation* spoke of the ideas on which the Commune rested. "These, we may be sure, will live and grow. They have grown greatly since 1848, and they are spreading all over Europe; and they will, in our opinion, not cease to spread until they have made one great attempt for the conquest of modern society, and have in that attempt shaken our present civilization to its foundation."

Ideas were moving fast, coming in faster than the newest ships and trains. They were shaking all the institutions; even the colleges felt them. Dana had complained in his geology text-book, with over-educated impatience, that "the earth dragged slowly through its early stages!" Nobody could accuse it of that now. A swarm of inventors were sending in for patents; Westinghouse patented his airbrake, Sholes had filed his typewriter, and young Edison was working on improvements. The United States led the world in patents, and Connecticut led the United States. The excitement, and the lengths to which it was carried by whittling New Englanders, was laughed about; things had moved from the time of Yankee notions to the year of "Darius Green and his Flying Machine," a poem which proved what fools inventors would make of themselves, and what fools writers would make of themselves in mockery.

New Haven alone bragged of six inventors: C. O. Crosby, working on fishhooks and needles, O. F. Winchester and his repeating fire-arms, Sargent and Bristol, Andrews, John O'Neill. Changes were rocking the town. The fight for the site of the state capitol was raging between New Haven and Hartford, and the bribes were being paid, until the scandal broke, and everybody hooted in derision at Connecticut editors and legislators. The $20,000 spent in bribes, as New Haven lost its old pride, the capitol, when it was divided up among the members of the Legislature, was poor pay. It was easy to see that these victims knew nothing of prices.

In the meantime, the Governor had changed the course of Yale.

The "new education" had arrived; the liberalizing of schools was indicated in a thousand ways; finally Harvard and Yale must feel these movements, and when Eliot was appointed president of Harvard, and arrived with his sweeping statements on education and the open mind, Yale felt her constrictions. The Harvard stories were printed everywhere, among the ads for astral oil, Jay Cooke, billiard tables, and the *Phrenological Journal*. The Harvard-Oxford boat race was the popular item; but there were also the appeals for endowment, saying that Harvard professors were receiving three-fifths the salary of a justice of the Massachusetts Supreme Court, and everyone knew that a justice had just resigned because the pay was insufficient. Between the stories of the Carlist revolt, the French convulsion, and "The Byron Horror" (Mrs. Stowe was publishing her version of Byron's incestuous love for Augusta, and the public was taking sides for and against Lady Byron's stand in the affair) —in a press crowded by news of the West, coming from the railroads, the Indian fighters, and the men sent out on expeditions, like Powell who first canoed through the Grand Canyon, and the Yale group with Othniel Marsh—the stories of the reorganization of Harvard and Yale were one more expression of the same unrest.

The "new school" had won the fight at Harvard with the appointment of Eliot. In a letter to Henry, written on May 22, 1869, William James speaks of Charles Peirce's articles—"very acute and original psychological-metaphysical"—and adds :

C. W. Eliot was confirmed President yesterday. His great personal defects, tactlessness, meddlesomeness, and disposition to cherish petty grudge seem pretty universally acknowledged; but his ideas seem good and his economic powers first-rate,—so in the absence of any other possible candidate, he went in. It seems queer that such a place should go begging for candidates.

At Yale, the friends of the new education felt that they had on their side the spirit of the age. There was a desire for change of all sorts and in all directions. It was time to sweep out the six members of the Corporation who were in the state government; time to bring in the new winds of liberal thought, and prepare a new program. President Woolsey was about to resign after twenty-five years. Addison Van Name met with Hubert Newton, Whitney, Dana, Leonard Bacon, and the other members of a committee to draw up a set of Needs of the University; for Yale was not merely a college, its force was outside of its beginnings, and it required organization to match its power.

The English universities, after which both Harvard and Yale are modelled, were making their own changes. The declaration at Cambridge required every student "to conform to the liturgy of the Church of England." Nobody who was asked was quite sure what that meant; but it was recognized as a useful force in keeping dissenters and Jews out. A Jewish student had just taken highest honors at Cambridge, and found that it was impossible to get his emolument. There were no fellowships for dissenters of any kind. The old rules of the Church were a dead hand on education. There was only one way in which the endless haggling of the authorities could be stopped, and that way was taken. Parliament interfered, passed its law, and made a new structure possible. With such laws, there was a movement for the extension of teaching. In science, the reflection of this change was a report in 1869 at Cambridge calling for a professorship of physics, and a university laboratory, which had never existed. In 1871 William Cavendish, seventh Duke of Devonshire and the chancellor of the University, saw that there was no other money for such a laboratory, and offered the £6,300. The University could go ahead and appoint a professor. William Thomson, Hopkinson, and Helmholtz were approached in turn; finally James Clerk Maxwell, the greatest of these, was persuaded to accept the chair.

Addison Van Name came home to the house in High Street, with its dark, beautiful furniture and its Chinese silk-paintings. He had the draft of the "Needs" in his hand. Noah Porter, coming in as president, was no champion of the new education, but there was no other man. Governor Jewell of Connecticut had cut through the red tape of Yale as Parliament had cut through that of Cambridge. The Corporation was reorganized, with alumni in its seats; Yale was to be a university, and there were new professors needed. If Yale had not changed its character; if it was, as the *Nation* said, more like a school for boys than a university for men, there was no president available who could bring ideas which were still stoutly resisted. President Woolsey retired, and he spoke to the College about the new scientific doctrines "knocking at the door of truth." President Porter came in, speaking of the past, of "eminent and wakeful learning," and objecting to elective studies for undergraduates. They were unfit to choose, he said; besides, it "contracted the college term." The nineteenth century was having to make new adjustments very fast; orthodoxy resented it, and would keep its men and women children, train them to live as children, everywhere it could.

But when Addison Van Name came home with the "Needs" in his hand, two things were clear. The statement opened with a re-assertion of the importance of his position. But there was also a place in the new University for a professor of physics; and Willard Gibbs, who had not yet published a paper, who spent his time working over his desk, or on horseback up the river, or walking past the town into the countryside, had the confidence of the committee. Even in the old days before he went abroad, there had been questions about his fitness as a tutor; there had even been a movement to dismiss him. But there were people at Yale who believed in him completely. In 1871, as the College changed under the pressure of the time, he was appointed first Professor of Mathematical Physics, and the next winter, as he organized his classes on the material he had confirmed in Europe, he began the duties that anchored his life to Yale.

CHAPTER TEN

The First Papers

SUMMER WAS A RELEASE. The bells tingled in the steeples, shining through green air; Anna and he packed up, rolled through the forests and past the edge of lake where the little craft sailed, blinding white, and at last got out of the stage at Keene Flats, in the dense hot scent of pine.

A few miles west of Lake Champlain, beyond Westport and Elizabethtown, Keene lies in a wilderness of hills. The highest mountains in the state stand over the shadowed valley. New Haven's elms gave the city a name, but this little town, a thousand feet high, had the largest elm in the Adirondacks—one of many that reared and rippled over the white immaculate houses. The trail to Saddleback begins here, and to the Gothics; the summits lead away in series, through the Great Range to blue Marcy, the highest of all the succession. Nobody had yet recorded a climb to the top of the Great Range. Indeed, these places were not yet printed on any map. They were still being named in the early seventies. The landscape painters found this magnificence, the balsam paradox, when the scent lay heavy on the summer and the air itself was the lighter for it; this wilderness marked only by the scored mountains, written over with slides and timberline and snowline; screen beyond screen of receding misty ranges, tempting the eye with mountain smoke to continue the ascent at will; and the curative breath of high mountains. If Emerson and Lowell and Agassiz had had their Follinsbee and Ampersand, John Fitch had painted these lakes, perceived between falling hills and the climbing trees. Shurtleff

[*183*]

followed him here in 1868; he knew that he would come back here forever.

And soon the others came. Horace Bushnell, the Hartford theologician, spent his summers here. He had "evolved a fresh point of view," says Van Wyck Brooks, "by denying that language and logic could state religious truths exactly. An intuitive, imaginative mind, he clung to the ancient mysteries, while softening their Calvinistic rigor." There are signs of his presence in these woods today; Bushnell Falls, here, is named after him. And Noah Porter came to spend his summers here, with his sister, Miss Porter, who founded the Farmington School. Porter Mountain is named after him. The countryside began to be aware of its group of "climbing clerics," as they came to be known. Many others arrived, drawn by the place. Thomas Davidson, the fine hearty founder of the Fellowship of the New Life—the father organization of the Fabian Society—found Keene Valley the splendid and primitive place he wanted. And Alice Gibbens loved the place before she ever met William James and married him. It was James who said of Keene Valley, "I love it like a peasant; and if Calais was engraved on the heart of Mary Tudor, surely Keene Valley will be engraved on mine when I die."

The second year of his professorship was a year of intense work for Willard Gibbs. The subjects which he was teaching his graduate students are not listed in the Yale catalogue according to courses given in any one semester, but with an inclusive list of subjects: least squares, wave theory of light and sound, capillarity, potential theory with applications to electricity and magnetism. He was working hard at his classes. He was finding his limitations as a teacher. His voice, first of all, was not really good for lecturing. His classes were small; but even among these very few, there seemed not to be any students who were properly prepared. He thought with a flood of nostalgia back across the sea to the German lecture-rooms, with their unwieldy classes and the great men on the platform—Kronecker, whose heckling of Weierstrass was familiar. Everybody knew that Kronecker was making Weierstrass' old age miserable with his snapping criticism and his jokes—this algorist, this artist. And Weierstrass himself, with his rigor, teaching the new analysis he was working on with continually more unity, and more simplicity—sharing the forefront of the new combined science with Cauchy and Riemann. And the others! A West opened up before mathematical physics, a whole unexplored forest ready to be known. There was the classroom, and it was the most natural thing in the world to be teaching, and at last to be teaching his own background, material he cared about and had brought back with him, loot of the Continent. But there was also his own work.

The first paper was printed in the *Transactions of the Connecticut Academy* in the spring of 1873. It was written on the dark table in Sloane; it had been hard to write at home since the first baby's birth. There were not many people with whom he could go over the paper, and again he thought of Germany; President Porter believed in him, but then so did Professor Brush, so did Professor Whitney. This was not a question of belief, but of understanding. Inventions were one thing; anyone could praise a brake. Westinghouse's airbrake was really beginning to be used, now, and the value of anything to do with a railroad was instantly clear. Working out the formula for the lenses was simple, as far as acknowledgment went; the people he passed on High Street, the shopkeepers themselves, had heard about that, and their praise confused him when they offered it, jovially. That was not really what he had meant, at all. This is what he had been heading toward, in all his reading, in the long years of graduate study and the voyage, as he pulled farther and farther away from all the people he saw. His work pulled him away—and, he supposed, the closeness of the family. But there it was. This *was* what he meant. Addison would not be able to read it, nor Julia, nor even Anna, although they all would be pleased that he had finished a paper, he knew; he could go over it with Hubert Newton and with Loomis, and meet excitement there. And if that was about all he could hope for in New Haven, why, publication would change all of that. The *Transactions* were known wherever people read scientific papers. Even in Berlin, he had been asked about the Academy. And of course he was a member of the Connecticut Academy! And his father before him!

He wondered, as he turned the paper in to be printed, what his father—who had written so many books—would feel if he knew that his son's first work was really done, really going to be published. He was thirty-four. That would be late for a first work. But it was not late for this. One part of his work, the part that could lead only to applications for patents, was behind him, and forgotten. This was the foundation of another work. A life. He recognized the step. He could see, dimly, what it led to.

Many of the recent people had been using mechanical models in demonstration of these laws—the basic laws of thermodynamics. They did not serve Willard Gibbs well. The engine which he used to demonstrate the Carnot cycle always gave him trouble, even though it drew a perfect diagram. Other devices were not perfect; often they were not even close to the material. They did not represent adequately what they set out to illustrate. Geometrical illustrations could be used, and they were in complete correspondence with the phenomena, as he was working them out. He wanted, above all, rigor and logic, a cleanness of reasoning that no device could match; adequacy was perfection itself, there was nothing short of it, and no compromise was possible.

The only diagram which had been used extensively up to 1873 was the volume-pressure diagram—a graph in which two rectilinear co-ordinates are used, as the name says. This diagram was developed early, with the beginnings of the science of thermodynamics. Anybody considering steam notes these two factors—pressure and volume—first. Gibbs was going ahead from there, to survey the known diagrams, and to offer new ones.

On the 15th of January, 1873, Gibbs presented his paper on "Graphical Methods in the Thermodynamics of Fluids." It was referred to the Publishing Committee, and appeared in the next number of the *Transactions*. It begins:

Although geometrical representations of propositions in the thermodynamics of fluids are in general use, and have done good service in disseminating clear notions in this science, yet they have by no means received the extension in respect to variety and generality of which they are capable. So far as regards a general graphical method, which can exhibit at once all the thermodynamic properties

The First Papers

of a fluid concerned in reversible processes, and serve alike for the demonstration of general theorems and the numerical solution of particular problems, it is the general if not the universal practice to use diagrams in which the rectilinear co-ordinates represent volume and pressure. The object of this article is to call attention to certain diagrams of different construction, which afford graphical methods co-extensive in their applications with that in ordinary use, and preferable to it in many cases in respect of distinctness or of convenience.

The quantities under consideration are volume, pressure, temperature, energy, and entropy; the work done, and the heat received by the body given, in passing from one state to another.

Pressure, volume, and temperature had already been considered in researches as practical as this one. The needs of every industrialist, every worker, as well as every inventor involved with steam engines, were behind the activity that had been gathering ever since James Watt used his indicator, in 1790. Crowther speaks of Watt's difficulty in measuring the horse-power of the engines he was just beginning to manufacture. The indicator was a pressure-gauge whose motion corresponded with the steam-pressure inside the cylinder. It was very likely his assistant, Southern, who six years later gave Watt the simple and potent idea of making his steam-engine do even more than its heavy labor. If a pencil were attached to the gauge, he pointed out, the steam-engine would draw the graph of its own changes, outlining an area on a piece of paper. The area was a representation of work done, and the representation followed the work itself. The steam-engine and the actual flight of heavier-than-air machines are both realities before theory; the investigation followed the fact. "In a large degree," Crowther says, "indicator diagrams were invented and drawn by the *steam-engine*, and presented to scientists for their consideration afterwards."

Soon it was seen that diagrams including three factors were needed. The curve of pressure and volume was not enough. Temperature findings were combined with the first two properties in a diagram proposed and used in 1871 by James Thomson.

These three factors were considered sufficient when the thermodynamics of fluids were first investigated. But, at the outset of his first paper, Gibbs introduced two other properties, energy and entropy—properties of whose existence Watt had not been aware.

The framework for the new science was there, naked against its intellectual dawn; but nothing was ready, the details had not been imagined.

Gibbs uses, in these diagrams, equations "derived from simple mechanical considerations." He notes that he is using the term *entropy* in accordance with Clausius' suggestions—it had been called *Thermodynamic function* by Rankine—and not in the sense in which Tait and his followers had been using it. The points on the planes are associated with the thermodynamic states of the body in such a way as to form lines of equal pressure, equal temperature, equal energy, and equal entropy, according to the continuous states of the body. As the body changes state, the line of change is formed. This is called the path of the body, and the ideas of direction, work, and heat are involved.

The path encloses an area which represents the work done. This area is positive or negative according to the direction of its bounding lines. If it is divided into parts, "the work done in the circuit bounding the whole area is equal to the sum of the work done in all the circuits bounding the partial areas," and the sum of the heat received in all the partial areas is equal to the heat of the circuit.

The different diagrams of these relations, Gibbs points out, may be obtained from one another "by a process of *deformation*," since the relations between the networks of lines are not altered by alteration of the surface on which they are drawn. If a face is drawn on a rubber balloon, the nose will remain between the eyes, no matter how you blow the balloon up or collapse it. If we think of mass as belonging to surface, he says, we understand that the mass included within given lines will not be changed by any deformation.

The choice of the method of representation is of course to be determined by considerations of simplicity and convenience, especially in regard to the drawing of the lines of equal volume, pressure, temperature, energy, and entropy, and the estimation of work and heat. There is an obvious advantage in the use of diagrams of constant scale, in which the work and heat are represented simply by areas.

There is an infinity of methods which may produce these diagrams. But among these ways of using plane figures, there are two that are especially important—the volume-pressure diagram, which is the ordinary method, and the *entropy-temperature* diagram. In explaining the advantage of his diagram, the second, over the ordinary one, Gibbs reasons that, in thermodynamic problems, heat received at one temperature is quite different from heat received at another—1,000,000 calories at 150° is a different thing from 1,000,000 calories at 100°. "But no such distinction exists in regard to work. This is a result of the general law, that heat can only pass from a hotter to a colder body, while work can be transferred by mechanical means from one fluid to another, whatever may be the pressures." It becomes much easier to deal with the total amount of work than to use various heat-areas.

Gibbs takes up two forms of perfect thermodynamic engines, which are to be compared with real thermodynamic engines in these studies. The simplest form can be represented in his entropy-temperature diagram by a rectangle, whose sides are parallel to the axes of the diagram. Comparisons are much easier, of course, if the perfect engine can be represented so simply.

He is quite aware of the seeming obscurity of his method, which he proposes for "the popularizing" of his science. He wants simplicity and ease in his methods. There is always the requirement of an adequate audience, but he was thinking of the ease with which the mind could accept what he proposed. He states his position in a clear and fine paragraph :

The method in which the co-ordinates represent volume and pressure has a certain advantage in the simple and elementary character of the notions upon which it is based, and its analogy with Watt's indicator has doubtless contributed to render it popular. On the other hand, a method involving the notion of *entropy*, the very existence of which depends upon the second law of thermodynamics, will doubtless seem to many far-fetched, and may repel beginners as obscure and difficult of comprehension. This inconvenience is perhaps more than counterbalanced by the advantages of a method which makes the second law of thermodynamics so prominent, and gives it so clear and elementary an expression. The fact, that the different states of a fluid can be represented by the positions of a point in a plane . . . this fact, clumsy as its expression in words may be, is one which presents a clear image to the eye, and which the mind can readily grasp and retain.

It is nothing more than a picture of the second law; you may derive the law from this expression of it at once.

If, then, it is more important for purposes of instruction and the like to familiarize the learner with the second law, than to defer its statement as long as possible, the use of the entropy-temperature diagram may serve a useful purpose in the popularizing of this science.

As Crowther explains, the lines in the old pressure-volume diagram are "curves difficult to draw. New curves must be drawn for each particular problem, and the axes are the only permanent lines in the diagram." The idea of this diagram had been chalked in by T. Belpaire in the same year that this paper was presumably written, 1872; four years later, the principle was also found, as so many of Gibbs's principles have been, independently discovered by the chief engineer of the British Royal Navy, McFarlane Gray, who was interested in its application to the engineering problems of the performance of steam-engines. The diagram came to be known by the name he gave it, the theta-phi diagram, and in several forms it is used widely by engineers. It gives information at once about the efficiency of the engine and the loss of efficiency due to incomplete expansion; it can be read for the energy of the steam, as well as for wet steam and superheated steam, since it applies not only to uniform fluids, but in one general gesture, which Gibbs was to use as a pattern for all of his work, to mixtures of fluids as well.

The paper goes on with the analysis of several cases : the case of a perfect gas, defined as a gas whose *vp* varies directly with the absolute temperature, and whose energy also varies directly with the absolute temperature—the case of bodies which pass from liquid to gas. Then he deals with diagrams in which variable *scales* may be used, in order to get straight lines of equal volume, pressure, entropy, etc.

The volume-entropy diagram, which most of the rest of the paper estimates, has substantial advantages over any other method. It is particularly convenient for dealing with bodies made of a mixture of parts in different states. Lines may separate the states themselves of, say, ice, water, and vapor.

The first paper ends with diagrams that radiate out from points; and with a significant note, pointing ahead to his next work. Gibbs has based his diagrams very closely on the properties of his material. The states of the bodies he has considered are each capable of two and only two variations, *like the position of a point in a plane.* He concludes : "It is, perhaps, worthy of notice, that when the diagram is only used to demonstrate or illustrate general theorems, it is not necessary, although it may be convenient, to assume any particular method of forming the diagram; it is enough to suppose the different states of the body to be represented continuously by points upon a sheet."

In Keene Valley that summer, he rode and climbed, and was happy. The mountains hung over him : Basin Mountain, with its face slashed and marked by slides, the splendid Gothics, and Noonmark's rocky cone. The Gothics had been named only a few years ago, and named with the obvious suggestion of their cathedral shapes. Country to worship in, the names observe : Chapel Pond is here, too. And there was worship in these birch groves.

Whatever frailty he accepted at home seemed to drop away here. He had been trained to consider himself frail; but perhaps it was not true, after all, he felt, as he climbed, as he went ahead with his work, as he rode. He was a splendid intuitive horseman. One little girl saw him on his way back to his boarding-house, in Keene Flats (it was not re-named until much later). The horse was rearing and plunging in a frenzy, and Willard Gibbs, as he charged by, kept a good seat and seemed firm and fine. Little Lillie Kingsley recognized what a good piece of horsemanship she was watching, and the danger scarcely seemed to matter, as the horse braced itself to throw its rider. He resisted, and his control began to take effect; the horse reared and tossed once more, and gradually quieted. He went on. But, as everybody who knew Willard Gibbs at all knew, that was like him. He would master anything he undertook.

He climbed with the others and alone. Lying on the high ledges, he could see the shadows cross the mountains, throwing new contours into shape every new minute. Lines of these shadows fell across his view, shifting, proceeding, seeming to create the surfaces on which they lay. The country had its marvellous distinction; there had been nothing in Germany like this. The

Yosemite, Keene Valley, and Franconia Notch have been proposed as the three unlike glories of American mountains; and Keene, surrounded by lower heights than the others, was called by William James "one of the most beautiful things in this beautiful world."

James was finding his own release this summer, reading Renouvier on freewill, and gradually working free of the jacketing panic, the ice of weakness, in which he had been for so long confined. He was in Cambridge, seeing Emerson, who was losing his memory "so fast he can hardly write a letter"; among the laurels and surf, the wash of light, at Magnolia, and at the Isles of Shoals, among alternating fits of depression and misery, and exhilaration so high they made him "feel like living entirely on poetry for the rest of my days." He felt cut off from the men with whom he could talk for hours on end about generalities : Wendell Holmes, Putnam, Charles Peirce, Bowditch, and his brother Henry. Many of his friends had married. Among them—among the "high-toned friends" he complains have been "married in secret" is Clover Adams—Marian Hooper, who married Henry Adams the summer before and was still abroad. We have some of the pictures the Adamses took on that trip that ranged from England to Egypt, and always back again to Wenlock Abbey, the home of Charles Milnes Gaskell, where Henry might wander on the Edge and find his parentage. One snapshot Marian Adams took, of Henry in the cabin of their Nile-boat, the *Isis*, is fresh and vivid —Adams with his dark half-head of hair and beard looking down at something in his hand as he sits at the round table, covered with figured cloth—the palm-branches on the wall, the bright Egyptian sun throwing all white objects into dazzling overexposure, the intimate reality of the half-open door. And another posed group makes them both clear among the ruined arches of Wenlock Abbey, on a moist, lovely, underexposed English day, and we have the ivy, the group of seven friends disposed on the stone and grass, Marian Adams looking away from the camera across the ruined thirteenth-century enclosure, Henry, one leg advanced in a posed step toward her, looking at his wife.

There is a clear image of Willard Gibbs's summer, not in any preserved snapshot, but in a description. Newell Martin was a sophomore at Yale that year—the son of W. A. P. Martin, who has been described in Pearl Buck's *The Exile*, as the gentle old man on ship-board during a typhoon in the China seas entrusted with a woman's little baby, as she watches over her dying child—and has written, for Margaret Whitney, an account of the season.

On an evening in this July, Martin drove up to Dibble's barn-like boarding-house. It was late, as the ramshackle mail wagon slowed to a stop, and Martin was on his way to that other hotel—Smith Beede's white-painted, primitive place, with the fields of the farm that is now the Ausable Club's golf course. William James, Bowditch, and the Putnams had bought Smith Beede's original farm-house, next to Giant Brook. There was a proviso in the deed that forbade them to take boarders. They made over the house, and turned the sheds into shanties for themselves, living in the camp. But the hotel was Martin's destination; he was going to stop there and then go on to the Maine Woods.

The inhabitants of Dibble's came out to get their letters and papers; Martin was delighted to see that Gibbs was with them. He said later that it was the most honorable event of his long life that Gibbs was glad to see him.

He and I stood beside the wagon, in the dusk, and he argued with me. I am, perhaps, the only man left alive in all the world that ever argued with Gibbs. I told him that I was on my way to the Upper Works, to spend two weeks on Mt. McIntyre and in the Indian Pass; and that, at the end of the two weeks, I was to meet a man in the Maine Woods. It should be remembered by my descendants, to the ninth generation, in my honor, that Gibbs took the trouble to persuade me to change my plans. He argued that the huckleberries and porridge of Dibble's were as rich and nourishing as those of Smith Beede's mountain boarding house. Defeated in the argument, I changed my plans and dined at Dibble's, with him and his sister and a group of young women of extraordinary merit. To that group I have been devoted for 63 years. When a philosopher of the first magnitude is associated with anybody less than Lord Rayleigh or Einstein or Bertrand Russell—when he is surrounded by common people—one of the common people does not seem to him any flatter or duller or less instructive than another. Gibbs was one of those that made the summer of 1873 an astonishing delight. I did not know, then, that he was an epoch-making philosopher. But all of us younger people had sense enough to see that his mind travelled on serene heights beyond our reach. We climbed, with him, the mild peaks that surrounded us; we rode, with him, on rough farm wagons, to picnic, at all the flumes and glens of the East Fork of the Ausable;

and, most immoral of our pastimes, we went, with him, to church on Sunday. Our church was a birch grove; and he and I shared, for the singing of hymns, one hymn-book. I knew, quite well, that his calm and contemplative mind did not regard the statements, as to cosmogony and history, or the theories as to the future, set forth in those hymns, as either accurate or important. But I never ventured to hint that I suspected him of any lack of orthodoxy.

Other Yale teachers used to attend those birch-grove services. Noah Porter and his sister were there. Newell Martin continues :

In those days, although college students were less numerous than they are now, there was a little more distance between students and professors than there is now. For instance, some of my class-mates wished to choose one of our number to ask Noah Porter whether he believed in the existence of "a personal devil." We never got up the courage to put the question. Nor did I ever in all the walks and talks that I had with the great Gibbs have any talk with him that was any more intelligent than the talk I had with other educated men. We, younger people, took pleasure in being with him; but we had no suspicion at that time that he was one of the greatest philosophers. . . . I have heard Willard Gibbs abstain from statement many times. Often have I heard him refrain from disquisitions in philosophy. Few men, of those now living, have held so many opportunities as I have had to hear Gibbs indulge in judicious silences.

There was little enough judicious silence. Black Friday of '69 had been merely a forerunner of industrial depression. During the summer of 1873, with the hoarding of solid values and the rise of interest rates, the way was laid for the August corner in gold. But on September 19th, the panic fell. The New York banking-houses were suspending almost daily, and on the 18th, Jay Cooke & Co., led by the pious Sandusky clerk, the heaviest investor in the Northern Pacific Railway, the critic of Lincoln because of his "laxity on the Sunday question," suspended. The brokers began their stampede.

Friday was rainy, and the darkness over the crowds that filled Wall, Broad, and Nassau Streets mirrored the dark-packed, murmuring people. The bewildered faces, with their foreboding, and the grim brokers' clerks pushing through the crowd, were full of the same gloomy excitement. The men in their offices talked about the weather in a show of poise. The crowd on the street, the crowd on the balustrade of the Sub-Treasury under their umbrellas, rustled with the short phrases and nervous, little gestures of an intent audience just before the curtain rises The howl broke loose at half-past ten that morning, when the failure of Fiske & Hatch, known as a highly conservative firm, was announced in the Stock Exchange. The tickers were running in a stream of business disaster; money-lenders were being swamped at the corner of Broad and Exchange.

The Stock Exchange, with its gas-lit, brilliant Renaissance dome, was the chief stage. On the floor, the tide of screaming, roaring men—all brokers and brokers' clerks—surged among twenty groups, hammering down the prices of stocks including New York Central, Western Union, Wabash, Erie, Northwestern. In the center of the floor was one small table, with a great basket of flowers making an incongruous stillness of color among all that milling black. The blackboards on the walls held the figures for a moment or two, before they changed again. The president, at his desk, shouted in a strong tenor above the babel; and the spectators' gallery would have been a fatal hazard, if the police had not straight-armed the crowd away. A thousand indicators in the city were flashing quotations of this fearful bear Friday. The names of eighteen more failures reached the street, and the crowd pushed at the windows of these fallen offices, trying for one glimpse of the despair inside. The rain slowed toward evening, and the clouds lifted over Wall Street and Trinity spire. As the crowd thinned out and the shining pavements showed, the little Broadway coupés drew up to the curb and rattled off, growing fainter in the clearing night, and the newsboys stopped shrieking.

On Saturday the Exchange was closed for the first time. The next day, President Grant and Richardson, the Secretary of the Treasury, arrived to consult with Vanderbilt and Clews, among others. Andrews' account of this week suggests that the vacillation of Richardson was responsible for the uncertainty of the public. The public had reason for alarm. No policy was announced; most of the $13,500,000 set loose was hoarded or used to buy other bonds; Jay Gould, who had been so fierce a villain of the first Black Friday, saved half of Wall Street this time by buying up railroad stock, particularly Vanderbilt stock; but on the 25th, the Treasury stopped buying, and in spite of the clearing-house device which the New York banks began and many others followed, the run on the banks began. The panic was on in full force; manufactured goods stood still, agricultural prices fell farther and farther, and the factories began to close throughout the country. The longest and slowest depression the country had yet seen was beginning.

Edison had made $40,000 out of the first Black Friday. He had vowed, after his first patent—the electric vote-recorder—had been neglected, never to make anything that people didn't want. The telegraph was what they did want, and they wanted it improved and elaborated. He invested his $40,000 in machinery, acting as foreman on both the day and the night shift in his Newark plant. During the six years beginning in 1870, Edison patented inventions at the average of an invention a month. Working on the aspects of telegraphy, he had gone ahead after the invention of the diplex telegraph, which can send two messages in the same direction on one wire, to new combinations. He was applying for the diplex patent this year—the year of his marriage to Mary Stillwell, his assistant in work on paraffin paper, and the year of his unsuccessful trip to England to demonstrate his system of automatic telegraphy. As soon as he returned, in apparent defeat, he went to work on the development of multiple transmission. He was combining the diplex with the duplex telegraph, which sent messages in opposite directions on the same wire.

His concentration was so great that one day, notified that he would be fined if he did not pay his taxes immediately, he went over to the Newark City Hall, well before the nine-o'clock deadline. When he appeared before the window and was asked his name, he could not answer. He had forgotten his name; and by the time he remembered it and re-appeared in line, he was too late to escape the additional 12½ per cent.

This winter, with the quadruplex still in a crude and unsatisfactory state, eight operators worked with Edison in the New York offices of the Western Union. At last all the improvements began to fall in line. Edison looked up at his assistants and said : "Boys, she is a go. The principle is all right, and the sharps upstairs can get the bugs out of it. We cannot do it down here, for the troubles with telegraphic appliances can only be gotten out

in the same way the Irish pilot found the rocks in the harbor—
with the bottom of his ship."

He was completely engrossed in this invention, and worked
the way he always worked, not outward from completely understood scientific principles, but inward from an idea of apparatus.
He knew apparatus thoroughly; he was drawing abstractions
from what he knew was wanted.

Edison said of the invention of the multiple system that "it required a peculiar effort of the mind, such as the imagining of
eight different things moving simultaneously on a mental plane,
without anything to demonstrate their efficiency."

Gibbs was working in the other direction. Edison, with the
world before him, was making his inventions, beating a track to
the Patent Office. But Gibbs answered the lines of Percival's :

> The whole machine of worlds before his eye
> Unfolded as a map, he glances through
> Systems in moments, sees the comet fly
> In its clear orbit through the fields of blue,
> And every instant gives him something new. . . .

The world was not a machine; that was becoming more clear
with every imaginative turn of research, every discovery. But the
map, to Gibbs, indicated certain realities.

On October 22, 1873, Professor Newton presented the second
paper to the Academy. He spoke of the paper briefly, read its
title—"A Method of Geometrical Representation of the Thermodynamic Properties of Substances by Means of Surfaces"—and
moved at once that it be referred to the Publishing Committee.
It begins:

The leading thermodynamic properties of a fluid are determined
by the relations which exist between the volume, pressure, temperature, energy, and entropy of a given mass of the fluid in a state of
thermodynamic equilibrium. The same is true of a solid. . . .

Now the relation between the volume, entropy, and energy may
be represented by a surface . . .

He was taking his volume-entropy diagram and extending it
another dimension, making a statue of a diagram. The "points
upon a sheet" had become a surface, the face of a solid object.

The paper is twenty-one pages long, and explains the surface, the nature of that part of it which represents mixtures, and properties of the surface which indicate whether the body's equilibrium is stable, unstable, or neutral. It also deals with the character of the *primitive surface* (which represents the homogeneous states of the substance) and the derived surface (representing all other states). The surface of absolute stability, the section representing a compound of three states, and the parts which represent compounds of two states, form a continuous upward-curving sheet, called the *surface of dissipated energy*. The problems of work related to this surface are discussed, and this paper ends, as does the first, with a paragraph which opens up a wide field of discussion, the clue to Gibbs's plans. In this instance, with that squirrel instinct for tucking away valuables, he dismisses it in a footnote to the last paragraph :

The body under discussion has been supposed throughout this paper to be homogeneous in substance. But if we imagine any material system whatever, and suppose the position of a point to be determined for every possible state of the system . . . the points thus determined will evidently form a solid figure bounded in certain directions by the surface representing the states of dissipated energy. In these states, the temperature is necessarily uniform throughout the system; the pressure may vary (e.g., in the case of a very large mass like a planet), but it will always be possible to maintain the equilibrium of the system (in a state of dissipated energy) by a uniform normal pressure applied to its surface. . . . And in regard to such problems as have been discussed, . . . the surface will possess, relatively to the system which it represents, properties entirely similar to those of the surface of dissipated energy of a homogeneous body.

The behavior of bodies in mixed states is understood from the surface. The nature of change is seen from it; it treats the continuity of change in such a way as to show that parts of a body may suddenly enter other states. Under some circumstances, the introduction of a particle of a substance in equilibrium is enough to break the equilibrium and transfigure the killed state to a new equilibrium. The surface indicates the determining factors for stable and unstable equilibrium, the tendency of separate parts in a substance to pass from one state to another.

In this paper, Gibbs was dealing with energy, used as *"includ-*

ing the vis viva of sensible motions," and entropy, defined according to Clausius' equation

$$dS = \frac{dQ}{T}$$

where S denotes entropy, T temperature, and dQ the element of heat imparted to a body. Gibbs explains that if the right side of the equation had had a negative sign, what he calls capacity for entropy would be *available entropy*, "a term more convenient on account of its analogy with the term *available energy*." Tait, he points out, uses the second value. And Clerk Maxwell uses the word as "synonymous with available energy, with the erroneous statement that Clausius uses the word to denote the part of the energy which is not available." (*Theory of Heat*, pp. 186 and 188.)

It was Clerk Maxwell who saw the value of this paper.

Two years before, James Thomson had proposed and used a model which dealt with the *v, p,* and *t* of bodies. But this model bore the same relation to Thomson's that the earlier plane diagrams bore to the indicator diagram of James Watt. It gave a far more complete knowledge of the relations of the body; and, in these matters, completeness is the only simplicity, even though the language be more complicated. It is complicated in order to represent complexity in the most direct way.

Percival wrote, in another part of "Prometheus":

> ... Mind can raise
> From its unseen conceptions, where they lie
> Bright in their mine, forms, hues, that look Eternity;
> That send through the long waste of ages, pure
> From the corruption of a grosser time
> These models of perfection, which endure. ...

This surface, so accurately delicate, as beautiful as a piece of fine abstract sculpture, shares with the sculpture of stone, the sculpture of mountains, the nuances of a perfectly created object. The play of light and shadow on the surface is like the shadow-play on the mountains Gibbs knew well. But the line of shadow signifies directly, it is a history; every wavering of line gives information.

Willard Gibbs

As the volume-entropy diagram has come to be used as a foundation-picture in thermodynamics, particularly in the study of steam, the source of power of the nineteenth century, the thermodynamic surface has played a great part in the development of a science of low temperatures. Crowther notes that the liquefaction of helium, with its tremendous implications to everything from radio-activity to aircraft and absolute zero, is based on this. Kammerlingh Onnes, who achieved the liquefaction of helium at Leyden in 1908, was one of the chemists who most advanced the work of Gibbs.

Refrigeration depends to a large extent upon these findings. The knowledge of the efficient expansion and contraction of substances and mixtures stems from such researches. Ammonia and sulphur dioxide have been explored for properties Gibbs's surface builds into contours. "Even the quick service of ice cream and chilled champagne," says Crowther, "the importation into Europe of beef and apples from Australia, and the functioning of the refrigerator in the domestic kitchen, owe something to Gibbs."

When Marlowe's Faustus is granted impossible wishes, one of the most remote is "Grapes in January!" Gibbs's surface, to that wish, stands as a talisman which holds the mystery of the impossible.

"Fertile of results," says Bumstead of it; and Donnan sums up :

In the first two papers published by Gibbs, he made great advances in the application of geometrical methods to the study of the thermodynamic properties of substances. We may say, indeed, that already in these first two papers, he created the *general* subject of graphical thermodynamics. The new geometrical methods developed by Gibbs have been of the utmost importance to the scientific engineer, who was thus provided with a tool comparable in power and scope with his graphical statics derived from the science of mechanics.

It is possible to explain supersaturation, explosive boiling, explosive freezing when ice is introduced into supercooled water, explosive crystallization in salt, and explosive effervescence in supersaturated gas, by means of such surfaces.

The first two papers, logical precursors to Gibbs's great work, have been fertile and useful in many direct ways, says Bumstead, although E. B. Wilson asserts that Gibbs left out detail, and that there is no indication that these two papers are in themselves significant for future science. Donnan says that the discussion of the volume-energy-entropy surface opened up a new, powerful, and fertile field in physico-chemical science. Bumstead goes on: "The exceptional importance and beauty of this work by a hitherto unknown writer was immediately recognized by Maxwell."

Clerk Maxwell, busy, active, and many-minded at the new Cavendish Laboratory, recognized Gibbs at once. He wrote into the next edition of his *Theory of Heat* a new chapter. It may have been through Gibbs's correction of Maxwell that the two papers were brought to his attention. Whatever began the notice, one of its results is this chapter on "Prof. Gibbs' Thermodynamic Model," in which Maxwell says, "Prof. J. Willard Gibbs, of Yale College, U.S., to whom we are indebted for a careful examination of the different methods of representing thermodynamic relations by plane diagrams, has introduced an exceedingly valuable method of studying the properties of a substance by means of a surface."

In the article on Diagrams, he wrote for the Encyclopaedia Britannica, "The use of diagrams in thermodynamics has been very completely illustrated by Prof. J. Willard Gibbs. . . ."

Maxwell spoke to the Chemical Society of London, and the lecture was later printed in *Nature*. It is a striking first instance of the attention of chemists being called to Gibbs, as Maxwell says: "I must not omit to mention a most important American contribution to this remarkably simple and thoroughly satisfactory method of representing the relations of the different states of matter by means of a model. By means of this model, problems which had long resisted the efforts of myself and others may be solved at once."

Maxwell's genius could recognize Gibbs's genius; his persuasive grace in teaching could help him to explain, by elementary statement, what Gibbs had done. It was the only kind of recognition that Gibbs could accept; recognition from a master in his work, a happy welcome from a great imaginative man. And Maxwell was bringing his work to the right people; he had already seen the application to chemistry of Gibbs's description. Gibbs had not written in chemical terms, and hardly ever did. For years, it was impossible for chemists to read his work, and they were kept from a reservoir of possibilities. They did not follow Maxwell's suggestion; but he had made it and emphasized it.

Maxwell went even farther. The surface had been described, but again Willard Gibbs had stopped at the bare idea and left undone that step which might have bridged the gap between himself and his audience. Maxwell added the last personal expression, which must have touched and delighted Gibbs more than any other gift. They were both scientists using the most contemporary methods of making models and discarding them in time, instead of submitting to them, as did Lord Kelvin, for example.

Gibbs had not made a model. He had fallen short. Maxwell did that, sending a plaster statue to Gibbs in New Haven, and keeping two others for the Cavendish Laboratory.

The package arrived, and Gibbs took his model to class, although he did not include this material in any of his lectures. Somehow the story of Maxwell's gift got around the classroom, and one boy, more daring than the others (Leonard Bacon says it was his father), finally approached Gibbs, and asked him, after admiring it, where the model came from.

He might have been asking him about "a personal devil" instead.

"A friend sent it to me," said Gibbs with his own punishing modesty.

"Who is the friend?" the boy asked, knowing very well who it was.

But all that Gibbs would say was : "A friend in England."

YOUNG WILLARD GIBBS

Courtesy of J. McKeen Cattell, Scientific
Monthly.

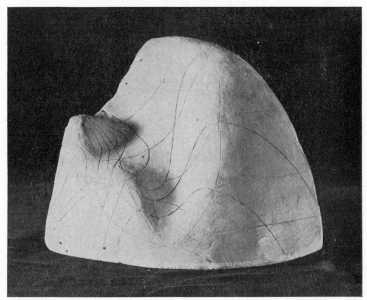

Photo by James Pickands, II.

THE SURFACE

Clerk Maxwell, in Cambridge, made this "statue of water"
according to Gibbs's paper and sent it to Gibbs, in
New Haven.

CHAPTER ELEVEN

A Chair in Mathematical Physics

THE SURFACE which Clerk Maxwell sent to Willard Gibbs was a statue of water.

This model is a concrete image of sympathy between two great and subtle minds. Besides being a delight to Gibbs, "the compliment to a young man on his first two papers," says Crowther, "from the man whom many regard as the greatest physicist of the nineteenth century, was marvelous."

Gibbs had shown, in these papers, that he could use illustrations without being bound by them. He need not be trapped, as so many people of his period were trapped, by mechanistic ideas. A graph would be drawn, or a piece of apparatus used, and then, as if the thing itself had will, it would lead them by the nose into the nonsense of which so many of the most prominent were capable. An analogy has a life of its own, and the seductive glitter of analogy has destroyed many scientists, many historians, many human beings who have caught the resemblance between seemingly unrelated forms without keeping their awareness of the difference. Lord Kelvin, for example, was trapped by his engines and jellies and springs. At the end of his life, feeling frustration and failure, he doubted everything that science was disclosing. He was aware of the trap.

Clerk Maxwell and Gibbs, Crowther goes on—

used geometrical and mechanical models when these had an analogy to some *part* of their problems, but they did not try to force the whole of their theories into forms of analogy to simple machines. Maxwell discovered his electro-magnetic theory of light with assistance from a model . . . but he dispensed with the model when he had got what he wanted out of it. . . . The attitude of Maxwell and Gibbs, of using mechanical and geometrical illustrations, without following them slavishly, is consonant with that of contemporary physicists.

The study of the behavior of atoms has been accompanied by the use of models which explain *partially;* we have abandoned any attempt to construct a complete model. These new researches have clearer and clearer relations to the scientific needs of the rulers of our civilization. They are reflected in science itself, in war, in industry, in education, and in the imaginative lives of our most creative men and women.

The pressures behind imagination have not come into clearly seen relationships. But, as we gain distance on a period, we may see what relevance certain unique creative acts have had to the prime wishes of their age; Watt as he walked down the green at Glasgow and first conceived the engine; Kekulé on the bus, seeing the constitution of the benzene ring as a ring of monkeys, holding each other's tails—all the choices of invention, clarified in that last moment of elimination, until one image surpasses all the rest, and is seen as new—those choices may later be seen to have the pressure of whole cultures behind them. The work of Willard Gibbs is in itself a representation of that pressure, and the resistance to it which also lies within a civilization. There is, also, a model for those forces—a *partial* model, to be discarded after use. It is the history of education of his time : a history with certain corresponding points.

In 1871, Willard Gibbs's chair at Yale, in mathematical physics, was founded. In 1871, the chair at Cambridge, in mathematical physics, was founded, and Clerk Maxwell occupied it. In the same year, Henry Adams and William James at Harvard entered parallel positions.

A hundred years before, at Yale, the second professorship, in mathematics, natural philosophy, and astronomy, was founded. That trio of sciences formed the base of the mercantile civilization of the century, and that year found an awakening to the future in several forms. A startling piece of evidence was reprinted in a New Haven paper. It is a letter of prophecy, written on April 27, 1771, from Naples by the Abbé Galiani to Madame d'Epinay, and it foretells, for the Europe of 1871, two distinct religions, one for the "higher and lettered classes" and one for the people. The letter speaks of the population of Europe as growing more like the Chinese; it sees England united with America, and says that the chief sovereign of Europe will be the monarch of the Tartars, the ruler who has under his sway the region south of the Baltic. It speaks of a despotism that will be everywhere, whose object will be to get at the wealth of individuals. Our millionaires will be our mandarins, it says; the military will be only for parade, and our manufacturers will flourish everywhere, as they do now in India.

That letter was written as the mercantile society founded on shipping was gathering together for an immense increase. Navigation, and the sciences serving navigation, were the bases of that civilization. Astronomy, as Crowther points out, was the science with the greatest prestige, and every business man could recognize its value. Elihu Yale himself, as governor of the Madras settlement of the East India Company, was in the background; and Newton, whose discoveries in mathematical astronomy "were a product of the urge of the ruling mercantile classes to discover how they could increase their knowledge of the technique of transport, and discover new sources of wealth, and increase their freights and profits."

Before 1871, there had been no official teaching in the universities of thermodynamics, which stands in the same relation to the nineteenth century, and is the formulation of the power of the steam age. The sociological meaning of the foundation of Gibbs's and Maxwell's chairs was in their relation to the needs of the ruling industrialists. "The motives for the changes in courses of education are not always clear at the time they are made. The directors of educational policy who make original changes have a sense of what developments are needed from the general atmosphere of their time, long before the reasons for the changes are clear."

But it was closer, even, than that. All the developments were along the same lines, and all of them predicted the close of a mechanistic period. They predicted, as surely as the statue of water, that the coming age would be concerned with change as the essential part of the universe. Marx, above all others, outlined the ideas of process in society, although the method of argument was the method of the German schoolroom, and went back to the Middle Ages; but the theme was process, and the basic ideas were parallel to the ideas of not only the other creators of the period, but to the ideas of change that have entered into recent science, in which we are given only three absolutes : number, action (the product of energy and time), and entropy. This last concept, a concept of passage and change contained in the second law of thermodynamics, describes, writes Dampier, "the one, all-important process of nature which corresponds with the remorseless march of time in the human mind."

The chair in mathematical physics recognized the coming importance of the science, long before the scientists themselves could be recognized.

Gibbs's appointment did not mean recognition. His field was far from understood; it was hardly named.

In 1869, a stir of protest began to move at Yale. Harvard had recognized the "new school" in education; it had won its battle with the appointment of President Eliot, as everybody repeated to the Yale corporation. In this struggle, which was now an open battle for liberal thought, Harvard and Yale were the great prizes. Harvard was now ripe, and the event was only a question of time; Yale was a harder place to besiege, and the assailants, according to the magazines, "are, as might be expected, encountering a much more vigorous resistance."

Yale was stagnating, for all its School of Fine Arts and the Western expeditions. The new people understood that clergymen and college professors were the only groups in the United States who lived their lives for their own sakes, without an eye to "the main chance." But college, they insisted, was a place whose *influence* was of greater value than the knowledge brought away, which was comically small. It was the argument for a tone of mind, an attitude, a receptivity—and besides, Harvard, everybody knew, could beat the Yale crew whenever it wished. A partisan of the existing order answered the complaint : of 52 instructors, only 9 were clergymen, and 6 of these were at the Theological School itself. In the meantime, Harvard was pleading for further endowment, and news of the English university struggles were reaching New Haven. The change had actually come.

A Chair in Mathematical Physics

The pamphlet that best records the critical moment is the pamphlet which Addison Van Name and Hubert Anson Newton helped to formulate. "The Needs of the University," a statement directed by the faculty to the corporation and an audience of possible contributors, was presented on July 10, 1871. President Woolsey was about to retire, it pointed out. The schools were in imperfect unity, and this proposal contained the suggestions for a necessary expansion.

The office of the Librarian, which Addison Van Name held, was considered first. Yale was a library before it was a college; the gift of books had made it, and it had a librarian before it had either a rector or a tutor. There were general needs, which the increase in students (and more exacting students) and the rise in prices after the Civil War had sharpened. The Library itself needed an increase and an income. Only in Oriental philology and literature, owing to the gift of Professor Salisbury, was it above want. Its income was $1,800 a year; it needed $10,000 a year.

The consideration of the Faculty of Philosophy and the Arts now included Yale College and Sheffield Scientific School. Recent graduates should be included among the staffs in mathematics and ancient languages, but outside men should be made more permanent officers. A professor should be added to the departments of mathematics and Latin; here it was noted that a successful tutor might be induced to remain as assistant professor, with some increase of salary.

As the center of Yale is the ancient school for liberal education, the Academical Department, and its aim is—

liberal culture as distinguished from preparation for specific employment and pursuits. . . . A college for liberal education can never become stationary, without ceasing to answer the ends for which it exists. In the learning which it imparts, in its methods of teaching, in its means of intellectual and esthetic culture, and in the discipline by which it forms the moral characters of its pupils, it must advance with all the progress of science and of letters, and must command the highest respect and the full confidence of all who are expected to entrust it with the education of their sons. The demands, therefore, of this Department, for more teachers and for a larger apparatus and equipment are always urgent.

Willard Gibbs

The real estate of Yale was of great and indefinite value, but it brought in little income—"the College may justly be called poor," the pamphlet continues, with an appeal for two professors of rhetoric and English literature where there is now only one, for separate chairs of French and German, instead of a combined chair; and "recitations in Natural Philosophy are wholly conducted by tutors. But a field so vast as that of Physics, and one in which the onward march of science is so astonishingly rapid, demands the labors of a professor who shall be permanently and exclusively devoted to it."

The list of professors grows longer, and the list of expenditures more exact. Money needed for officers is described specifically, as the income from a fund of two hundred thousand dollars.

Willard Gibbs, in assuming his new role of Professor of Mathematical Physics, may have reminded some members of the committee of his father, whom President Woolsey had called, just after his death in 1861, "Gibbs, the honest, doubting, comprehensive scholar, as modest as he was able, and in pure philology *facile princeps* upon our side of the Atlantic," who, nevertheless, "found it hard with his modesty and want of positiveness to keep up an interest in his teachings."

Woolsey retired, with his farewell speech about the new scientific doctrines "knocking at the door of truth," and his bow to the religious conflict—"sciences built on observation of nature, and those built on the primary convictions of man, and on historical evidence, cannot be really hostile." Noah Porter came in as president. He was sixty years old, and had been a professor for twenty-five years. He was as little a hero of the new education as can be imagined. The *Nation* railed; Yale would go on being a school for boys, instead of a university for men; but there was no other candidate. There was a scarcity of educators. Dana talked about the salaries again, saying that the salary of a full professor was reckoned at $3,000—about two-thirds of what he requires if he has a family—and that of a tutor averaged $1,350. On that calculation, $785,000 was needed.

Willard Gibbs came into one of the new professorships under Noah Porter. He was completely identified with the University. It could have recognized his ability. Everyone who knew him, no matter how slightly, knew he was an original worker, not a teacher. There is ample evidence that his greatness was unknown, as the knowledge of a college community goes. The honor of his position, for example, was as hollow as the authorities could make it. For the first ten years of his professorship, Gibbs did not receive a cent of salary.

Clerk Maxwell, in 1871, was forty years old, at the climax of a career that marked the peak of classical physics. It did more than that; in the person of this Edinburgh genius of many fields, intellectual freedom reached one of its highest levels. It was the flexibility of his imagination that made various critics compare him to Shakespeare and Beethoven; that vigor that can only be called dramatic power, wherever it appears. In his early work in the polarization of light, in his first important paper On Faraday's Lines of Force, in his researches on color-vision (which corresponded to Helmholtz' work), and in all his writings on electricity, which were to be extended by himself, he was a master of physical thought, and of the application of mathematics to physics. But he had an additional power, that made it possible for him to pursue his work to its social end, and set it before its audience. In the verses he wrote, in his lectures to workingmen, as well as in the actual conception of work which assumes that it is not finished until it reaches its far audience, he proved his effectiveness. Isaac Newton had written two hundred years before : ". . . I see a man must either resolve to put out nothing new, or to become a slave to defend it." Clerk Maxwell had a special talent for that slavery, and in his lectures the defense became fresh and unencumbered. The dead weight in any kind of knowledge that must use analogy to find its theories is very often the chain of method—one method will be used for appropriate and inappropriate material. Clerk Maxwell, coming to his prime, the period of five years before his thirty-fourth year, had adjusted himself to a number of ways of expression. His Christian Socialism drew him into the simpler lectures, and his relation to the work of Faraday, whose translator he regarded himself, kept the fresh and deep principles of simple statement, ranging from religious to physical belief, before him always.

When he was appointed to the control of a new laboratory at Cambridge, he had the four papers on physical lines of force be-

Willard Gibbs

hind him, the *Treatise on Electricity and Magnetism*, *A Dynamical Theory of the Electro-magnetic Field*, and many other works; the entire electro-magnetic theory of light, the investigation of waves that placed the emphasis on the intervening medium rather than on the study of force itself had been accomplished. Of his religious love for his wife, and of his religious life itself, we know little except what has survived in scattered letters. Crowther says :

Maxwell's religious interests are of great psychological importance, but unfortunately inadequate accounts of them have survived, apparently owing to the mistaken idea of his contemporary relatives and friends, that the world was not entitled to know them. His biographer, Lewis Campbell, was a priest, and writes that he would not describe things "wherewith the stranger intermeddles not."

This destruction was, of course, the worst and most negative form of intermeddling, and has removed one source of knowledge about Maxwell. But in his attitude toward his teaching, we have a clear indication of his relation to the world about him—although the most vivid evidence is in his collected papers.

William Cavendish, seventh Duke of Devonshire, K.G., Chancellor of the University, presented the fund of £6,300 after two years of useless appeals for funds; and Maxwell's first effort was the establishing of the Cavendish Laboratory. He pledged his own equipment; went over the designs with the contractors and architects, persuaded the Chancellor to add certain sums to the first gift; and while he was delivering a famous series of lectures as Cavendish Professor of experimental physics, the laboratory rose, in Ancaster stone, with its great gateway, its heraldic motto, *Cavendo tutus*, its statue of the robed duke. Carved in the massive oak of the door, the only ornate detail of this first Cambridge laboratory, is the legend written in the warped old English letters :

Magna opera Domini exquisita in omnes voluntates ejus.

And when it rose, Clerk Maxwell's lectures set forth the relations of the university, as the Yale faculty had done, but in a spirit far removed from theirs. With the humor and shyness that may be seen in his verse and drawing, he delivered the inaugural lecture to a small group of students in a corner of the University. The great of Cambridge crowded into his lecture-room for the

A Chair in Mathematical Physics

first announced hour, to be put through the ordinary introductory speech on the difference between Centigrade and Fahrenheit, spoken by a twinkling and sly Maxwell. But his first lecture, in October, spoke of the change in language and thought that had come into science, owing to "sound dynamical ideas." He looked at the term Experimental Physics—"we may consider either the Physics or the Experiments as the leading feature," and he went on to talk about research and illustration. "There is no more powerful method for introducing knowledge into the mind," he told this first small group, "than that of presenting it in as many different ways as we can."

He told them of the link between the abstract part of their work and the rest of it—that part, indeed, which the world was ready to accept:

It is not till we attempt to bring the theoretical part of our training into contact with the practical that we begin to experience the full effect of what Faraday has called "mental inertia"—not only the difficulty of recognizing, among the concrete objects before us, the abstract relation which we have learned from books, but the distracting pain of wrenching the mind away from the symbols to the objects, and from the objects back to the symbols. This however is the price we have to pay for new ideas.

That is the process of learning. It is with that process that the teacher is concerned. And science, with its new possibilities, could be converted by laboratories like the one under construction. Maxwell talks of teamwork in research, of the Magnetic Union of Humboldt, Gauss, and the others, and describes how the scattered forces of science "were converted into a regular army and emulation and jealousy became out of place, for the results obtained by any one observer were of no value till they were combined with those of others." This was his hope for the new laboratory : that it might be a center for such experiments, one among the "great workshops of our country." While the Yale committee was calling for a professor to be exclusively devoted to physics while "the onward march of science is so astonishingly rapid," Clerk Maxwell was placing the emphasis elsewhere, asking why he should speak of what science might do for a university. "Let us rather speak of the help which the University may give to science."

He ended the lecture with a sketch of the scientist in the world. He speaks of the notion of the scientist as being cut off, and defends him as not isolated "so long as he lives in intellectual fellowship with men who have devoted their lives to the discovery of truth. . . . It is true that the history of science is very different from the science of history. We are not studying or attempting to study the working of those blind forces which, we are told, are operating on crowds of obscure people, shaking principalities and powers, and compelling reasonable men to bring events to pass in an order laid down by philosophers." The scientist will see not only masses, but men more free of passions—not only successful investigations, but failures and errors of reputation.

Maxwell saw all the sciences dealing with things without life as undergoing or preparing to undergo a fusion. He believed that the form which each finally assumes is a branch of dynamics. His ability to use analogies, like models, and discard them as no engineer could bear to, gave him a resourceful strength. He insisted on the equal value of both kinds of imagination, saying "scientific truth should be presented in different forms and should be regarded as equally scientific whether it appears in the robust form and vivid colouring of a physical illustration or in the tenuity and paleness of a symbolic expression." But it was form and process itself which captured his belief, until he said, in one of his forward-looking bursts of statement which shaped the great results of the laboratory he inaugurated : "It is only when we contemplate, not matter in itself, but the form in which it actually exists, that our mind finds something on which it can lay hold."

At Harvard, the new education found its champion in Charles William Eliot, who began to call in the young men who were beginning to combine the fields of knowledge in order to understand process. Henry Adams had his talk with President Eliot, and the few words are preserved in the *Education*. "But, Mr. President," said Henry Adams, "I know nothing about Medieval History." And Eliot blandly smiled and firmly answered, "If you will point out to me any one who knows more, Mr. Adams, I will appoint him." In September 1870 Henry Adams found himself assistant professor of history at Harvard. His salary was four hundred pounds a year, he wrote to Charles Milnes Gaskell, and he had two hundred students. His pasture was the period from 800 A.D. to 1649; he spent nine hours a week lecturing; he was conscious of being brought in to strengthen the reforming body of Harvard, and he knew that his predecessor had been turned out for being a Comtist. He had the wry satisfaction—one of the most gratifying for anyone with so bitter a tendency to self-disparagement—that Harvard College was expressing its hope for him in appointing him against his will; and a month after his appointment, he was frightfully hard at work, complaining about the damnable winter climate of Boston, the hideous country, and the loss after Washington. Society was three miles away, he complained, and then tore the irritation away with the first of his peppery attacks. He didn't believe in this system, he growled, he disliked and despised the ruling theories of education.

Almost at once, he began to bring in methods of learning which he himself needed. If he knew nothing about medieval history, he would learn with his class. He said that his ignorance did not trouble him. It was his skeleton; he built up his own personality, the body of his life, from there. He recognized his own lack, and the importance of his new role. "A parent gives life," he wrote, "but as parent, gives no more. A murderer takes life, but his deed stops there. A teacher affects eternity." He told his students that the facts were there, and the College expected them to know facts. They could get them where they pleased; as for the teacher, his business was with questions, not with facts. "The only privilege a student had that was worth his claiming, was that of talking to the professor, and the professor was bound to encourage it." Henry Adams encouraged it by working intimately with his students, and he introduced the class conversation. The seminar method was in use in Germany, but Adams had found there only the lecture system "in its deadliest form as it flourished in the thirteenth century." He would allow no touch of that dead hand in his work, but instead invited his group to dine and spend the evening at his Marlborough Square house, sent them to primary sources for their material, and founded the first true seminar in the country.

Teaching, to Adams, meant a long and deadly impersonal routine. He spent his faculty-meeting time like a bored schoolboy at classes—writing letters, while "thirty twaddlers" sat around him, discussing discipline. He complained that he had not "seen the hem of a female garment" since he arrived to be "shut up in this Botany Bay, working like a scavenger." And, in the middle of his work in new methods, he who had given due credit to women for the best of his education found ill-temper enough to rail at Gaskell about women, praising his aunt, who "with all her love for speculation shrank from this sort of pure science by a feminine instinct which I think was much to her credit. And her experience is another evidence to me, if I wanted another, that it is worse than useless for women to study philosophy. The result is to waste the best feminine material, and to make very poor philosophers. . . ." That was in spring of his first teaching year. That summer, to blow Harvard out of his head, he took the first train into the open West—to Wyoming Territory—with Emmons' Fortieth Parallel Survey, through Greeley, the Uintas and Estes Park, where Clarence King proved the bubbling, charming, many-sided friend he needed. In the Uintas, that summer, Adams decided that "education, systematic, or accidental, had done its worst." He ends the chapter called "Failure" on that note, and begins his twenty-year gap of silence.

But the following year included the establishment of the Harvard Graduate School, and more grinding work, after the trout-fishing, the hot days and icy nights of the alkali desert. It was in this year that Henry Adams found and married Marian Hooper, who belonged "to a sort of clan," as did Adams, and would have been far happier than he to have seen his father elected President that year. But he sailed for Europe that summer with his wife, left his students and the editorship of the *North American Review*, at which he had also been working, and did not return until the fall of 1874, when he began to plan for his freshman courses in American colonial history, as well as his new graduate courses with such students as Henry Cabot Lodge, Edward Channing, J. Laurence Laughlin, Ernest Young, and Henry Osborn Taylor. In the years following his return, he felt the restlessness of the search for a basis of faith in general principles, the philosophic hunt which was to take him closer and closer to Willard Gibbs.

He found it a daily struggle to make boys with no mind understand that they could be content without the education of a Newton, and at the same time make boys with mind see that education had not stopped with Newton. His crusade was "against Culture with a big C. I hope to excite the hatred of my entire community, every soul of whom adores that big C. I mean to irritate every one about me to frenzy by ridiculing all the idols of the University and declaring a university education to be a swindle."

Adams' function was to irritate. He was not yet ready for his own History. He found an answer to his divided heart about teaching in the smug faces of his classroom, which grew yearly more full, until he had uncomfortably large audiences for an Adams of his generation—one class near seventy. He wrote then, coming to the end of what he felt was a barren time, that he addressed his class with foul and abusive language, hoping to drive them away. It is the only way to treat people who ask for knowledge; they are to be discouraged to the point where you may know whether they may be discouraged. But Adams spoke gravely of himself : "I regard my university work as essentially done."

William James said of his academic beginning as Instructor in Physiology at Harvard, with three exercises a week :

The appointment to teach physiology is a perfect God-send to me just now, an external motive to work, which does not strain me—a dealing with men instead of my own mind, and a diversion from those introspective studies which had bred a sort of philosophical hypochondria in me of late and which it will certainly do me good to drop for a year. . . .

Although his eyes were not good for more than three or four hours of reading a day, James welcomed the beginning of experimental physiology at the Harvard Medical School. This beginning was to lead to evolutionary philosophy, and through that to his work in psychology. He was thirty, Adams thirty-four, Gibbs thirty-three; these three young men were instituting three of the greatest combinations in science that their time required. But this year, William James felt cut off from his associates, although he found his new work "very interesting and stimulating. It presents two problems, the intellectual one—how best to state your matter to them; and the practical one—how to govern them, stir them up, not bore them, yet make them work, etc." It was his father who really expressed the release that his teaching was to him :

. . . [William] gets on greatly with his teaching; his students—fifty-seven of them—are elated with their luck in having him, and I feel sure he will have next year a still larger number by his fame. He came in the other afternoon while I was sitting alone, and after walking the floor in an animated way for a moment, broke out: "Bless my soul, what a difference between me as I am now and as I was last spring at this time! Then so hypochondriacal"—he used that word, though perhaps less in substance than form—"and now with my mind so cleared up and restored to sanity. It's the difference between death and life."

He had a great effusion. I was afraid of interfering with it, or possibly checking it, but I ventured to ask what especially in his opinion had produced the change. He said several things : the reading of Renouvier (particularly his vindication of the freedom of the will) and of Wordsworth, whom he has been feeding on now for a good while; but more than anything else, his having given up the notion that all mental disorder requires to have a physical basis. This had become perfectly untrue to him. He saw that the mind does act irrespectively of material coercion, and could be dealt with therefore at first hand, and this was health to his bones. It was a splendid declaration, and though I had known from unerring signs of the fact of the change, I never had been more delighted than by hearing of it so unreservedly from his own lips. He has been shaking off his respect for men of mere science as such, and is even more universal and impartial in his mental judgments than I have known him before. . . .

But this release had its drawbacks, in strain and the last fatigue of depression through which he had come. The next summer, and a few months in Europe before his decision to go on in comparative anatomy, ended the period. The sciences which he was teaching were the most dramatic, or the most easily dramatized, of all developments, because of the storms raging about the concept of evolution. James acknowledged as his teachers in biology three masters : Darwin, Agassiz, and Jeffries Wyman; their attitudes toward experiment, the observation of facts, and the relevance of theory to fact, were reflected in his own attitudes. Ralph Barton Perry points out that James had no experience with quantitative methods, beyond his early studies in chemistry, and warns that one must not lay too much emphasis on the approach to philosophy through science, since Mach, James, and Bergson reached so close a philosophical agreement through their separate avenues of physics, psychology, and mathematics. James's own antipathy to mathematics and formal logic would cant his prejudices toward the empirical method. At any rate, he was at once in the hottest of disputes, and in the most important constructions of his subject. In the winter of 1874–75, or the following winter, "I forget which," James wrote, "I, myself, 'founded' the instruction in experimental psychology at Harvard . . . For a long series of years the laboratory was in two rooms of the Scientific School building, which at last became choked with apparatus, so that a change was necessary." Fifteen years later he was to raise the money for a new laboratory, fit it up, and introduce lab work as a regular part of undergraduate work. But, for the time, the two rooms were his place. These first years of teaching mark his meeting with Alice Gibbens, and his marriage; his contract for the *Psychology*, and his first contact with the term pragmatism, which he heard from Charles S. Peirce, and which he was in so many ways to make his own.

Peirce, in Paris, wrote back to William James, about Henry :

MY DEAR WILLIE,—

Your letter led me to look up your brother whose presence here is a great thing for me as I am lonely and excessively depressed.

. . . Your brother is looking pretty well, but looks a little serious. He is a fine fellow. I have always thought I should admire him if I knew him better, and now I shall find out . . .

Henry James, who had just finished *Roderick Hudson*, his first full novel, and had just decided to live his life in Europe, had an unexpected friendship with Peirce. He wrote to his brother ten days after that letter :

. . . I have seen few people—chiefly Turgenev. . . . He is a most attractive man and I took a great shine to him. . . . Also Charles Peirce, who wears beautiful clothes, etc. He is busy swinging pendulums at the Observatory, and thinks himself indifferently treated by the Paris scientists. We meet every two or three days to dine together; but though we get on very well, our sympathy is economical rather than intellectual.

William James answered with a smile :

. . . I am amused that you should have fallen into the arms of C. S. Peirce, whom I imagine you find a rather uncomfortable bedfellow, thorny and spinous, but the way to treat him is after the fabled "nettle" receipt : grasp firmly, contradict, push hard, make fun of him, and he is as pleasant as anyone; but be overawed by his sententious manner and his paradoxical and obscure statements—wait upon them, as it were, for light to dawn—and you will never get a feeling of ease with him any more than I did for years, until I changed my course and treated him more or less chaffingly. I confess I like him very much in spite of all his peculiarities, for he is a man of genius, and there's always something in that to compel one's sympathy.

Henry James wrote the following spring—March 1876—to say that Peirce had left for Berlin, and his letter contained a note of complaint at Peirce's lack of social grace, and a strained comment, mostly protest, that he could not have done more socially than he had done for Peirce, although the latter seemed not to believe that.

Perry sums up the differences between Peirce and William James, crediting the immense influence Peirce, with his boldness, his sense of connections, and his feeling for doubt and belief, had on James. But he points out that the personal differences between the two men were flagrant : the social and more easygoing James contrasted sharply with Peirce, in his touchy and difficult manner. The intellectual differences were those between a man devoted to exact science, with its sureness and accuracy and clearness, and a man who set more value on fertility, delicacy, and the sensitive and practical touches of insight. James, the second man, said that he did not understand Peirce; and Peirce agreed; Perry adds, "It seems to be generally assumed that Peirce understood James. But it is to be noted that James rarely claimed to understand anybody, whereas it was characteristic of Peirce to feel that he understood everybody—only too well." Perry says of the following letter, from Peirce in New York, that it "reveals the interior of that apparition which Henry James in Paris had contemplated from without" :

MY DEAR WILLIE,—

... I am in process of moving and was forced to come here for the night. Imagine my disgust at seeing in the *Herald* this morning that Prof. C. S. Peirce of Harvard College is sojourning at the Brevoort. Particularly as I am rather ashamed of my partiality for the Brevoort. But I have always come here for many years; I am known to every waiter etc., and find myself at home. It is frequented by a class of

A Chair in Mathematical Physics

people very *comme il faut* but not in my line. I insensibly put on a sort of swagger here which I hope I have nowhere else, and which is designed to say : "You are a very good fellow in your way; who you are I don't know and I don't care, but I, you know, am Mr. Peirce, distinguished for my varied scientific acquirement, but above all for my extreme modesty in which respect I challenge the world."

Willard Gibbs's modesty could not be covered; it could not even assume the front of a swagger at the Brevoort. In New Haven, he was known to everyone; and, at the same time, nothing pertinent to him was really known. His life had taken its direction from the time he recognized, among his graduate studies or earlier still, what he was to be. But there was this withdrawal of a personality whose strongest abilities would be seen *as abilities* but nothing more. His community would know that here was a man who was doing something, was as absorbed as a Connecticut inventor. For all of them, he might have been concerned nightly with black magic, except that this was New Haven, and the one instinct such a town will foster is the sensitivity to what is done and what is not. No, it was not black magic. He went to church of a Sunday in the new College chapel. And he went driving, around town and out the well-driven roads, and deep into the fields up the valley, and he went skating, like everybody else.

The whole family loved to skate. A good part of New England's year, even in this southern corner, is frozen winter; and the whole lifetime of the Gibbses had seen skating come up from something that boys did to a national passion. It was to that time what skiing has become, in the snow country : not a pilgrimage for tourists and aficionados, but daily simple pleasure, as commonplace as gossip. The papers carried notices in February, saying happily, "The skating mania is at its height"; the New Haven shops sold the newest models, with leather heels and a broad two-strap leather band almost covering the foot, and upcurled runners; and the newspaper verse began

> I met her on the ice
> Amid the flying skaters
> And the flashing of the steel. . . .

All the Gibbses were enthusiastic skaters, and it was a bitter disappointment to Julia that she must stop to have her children and take care of them. The first boy, Willard Gibbs Van Name, was born in April 1872; and a girl, Theodora, early in 1874.

Willard went skating with the rest, when he finished his class-work. He was doing his own work, writing, his students knew; but there was no mention of his activity in class. He taught from the texts he had worked with : Fresnel, Cauchy, the *Traité de mécanique* of Poisson, and the course included an exposition of Fresnel on diffraction and polarization, and the generalized laws of reflection. This was followed by work in waves—studies of water and light at the boundary in cases of total reflection. He knew at the outset of his teaching career that there were few students ready at the moment to go on with his work, few to understand the work itself. One of his pupils wrung a promise from him to publish a book on waves; but he felt there were difficulties. In the early '70s, physical optics was a well-defined domain; and he hesitated.

Hesitation had come to be a deep current in his life. He must have felt himself moving more and more easily in a rhythm of hesitation. And it must have seemed justified. Talk was possible inside the family, but his thought was running in ways that seemed to be set counter to what Addison, and, for that matter, his father, had meant. Communication was something very different to them; and to the people who came to the house, family friends, old graduates on reunions, callers, he seemed, like any artist, away from them. He went to the reunions, he smiled at the callers. When his class came back in '73, there was a dinner given at the Insurance Building, on the south side of the Green, and Addison furnished roses. Gibbs was there. He would always be there. But there was reason for hesitation.

Skating permitted nothing but the even sweep; in the dark afternoons, filling with the clear green glow before the trees turned black and the ringing ice held its own light; in the evenings, with the upward ripple of big fires; in the last blue moments during the days of snow.

The one line of story about him holds all the starved years, as a fragment and a laugh, a silhouette remembered by a younger boy. They tell the line :

"He once held the hand of a Mrs. Blake, while skating."

The scene rises in smooth ice and darkness, the laugh of skates cutting notes out of the air of winter; crackle of fire; and the doubt, the hesitation, all the impossibilities of his life. There were negatives in his background, and deep-drawn negatives in him; what did he have to say, that could not be said? What was he writing, that could not be received and understood? What quietness bound him and his sisters together?

"He once held the hand of a Mrs. Blake, while skating."

Retiring and preoccupied, what friends were there? Newton next door, who was busy with his lectures on astronomy. He had been working in what Gibbs called "the wilds of a *terra incognita*, which astronomers had hardly troubled themselves to claim as belonging to their domain." His map of the heavens for plotting meteor-paths had increased the value of all his observations; and in 1872, a brilliant shower of meteors could be connected with the orbit of Biela's comet, which had been seen to break up under the influence of the sun. The return of a shower of meteors in 1866 was predicted by Professor Newton, and confirmed dramatically, after many had given up hope, by a late report on the new Atlantic cable. Clerk Maxwell entered the talks that Newton and Gibbs continued for years, taking up the next day, as Newton's daughter remembers, at the same place in mathematical discussion where they had stopped, as if nothing had intervened. Gibbs told later how Newton had pointed out to him a bit of Maxwell's writing, in which he described the work that Newton was doing. In his work on the properties of shooting stars in general, Newton had been occupied with "those average values which relate to large numbers of these bodies not belonging to any particular swarm."

"This kind of investigation Maxwell had called *statistical*," said Gibbs, "and has in more than one passage signalized its difficulties." It was the method that might be used, for all its dangers, in dealing not only with meteors but in any groups in which the similarities as well as the randomness must be considered. Gibbs's own work was leading him through the halls of that method; and his own work was going on, in the house where his sisters would wish to know, but would never know, what he meant, toward what end he was tending; in those classrooms where he read Clausius to students who were unprepared, standing long over the work on potential theory, and particularly, in the spring of 1873, over the fruitful conception of entropy.

Into his work these values came, to be generalized and concentrated. He would be prolific, he felt, though he might never be seen as any more than the rather dried young man his students saw. His intense face, the compression of what he said, the passion—now that he was on the trail of certain discovery—might all go unseen.

Maxwell had seen it. He was a distant friend, the one friend who might know the meaning of what this New Englander, eight years younger than he, was doing. But Maxwell was rich and various; the easy smile and great classes, public meetings and dinners and honors, were all in keeping with his rich work. He was various, like some English poet; like Shakespeare. Boltzmann knew that language, and he wrote of it:

It is this very simplicity, the indispensableness of each word, each letter, each little dash, that among all artists raises the mathematician nearest to the World-creator: it establishes a sublimity which is equalled in no other art,—something like it exists at most in symphonic music. . . . How expressive, how nicely characterizing withal is mathematics! As the musician recognizes Mozart, Beethoven, Schubert, in the first chords, so the mathematician would distinguish his Cauchy, Gauss, Jacobi, Helmholtz in a few pages. Extreme external elegance, sometimes a weak skeleton of conclusions, characterizes the French; the English, above all Maxwell, are distinguished by the greatest dramatic bulk. Who does not know Maxwell's dynamic theory of gases? At first there is the majestic development of the vibrations of velocities, then enter from one side the equations of condition and from the other the equations of central motions— higher and higher surges the chaos of formulas—suddenly four words burst forth: "Put $n = 5$." The evil demon V disappears like the sudden ceasing of the basso parts in music, which hitherto wildly permeated the piece; what before seemed beyond control is now ordered as by magic. . . .

But this outburst had little place in New Haven. Gibbs knew better than to look about, repeating the question, "Who does not know Maxwell's dynamic theory of gases?"

Here, perhaps, was the dramatic nature that was his other spirit. Here, perhaps, in this friend, writing a chapter about Gibbs's work, peppering articles and speeches with references to him, was the ordered release of all the forces and hesitations at work within him. This man was what he needed, above all, the creative antagonist, as Jackson had been to John Quincy Adams

—only without the hatred—as, if he had guessed it, Hawthorne must have seemed to Herman Melville only a few years before at Lenox in the Berkshires—that friend in meaning with whom his own meaning could be whole, almost a Platonic half to his half.

The fraternity of feeling struck Melville with a joy of madness and relief. It seemed at first the end of a search—the hunt of which *Moby Dick* was one emblem—and Melville wrote to Hawthorne of his shock : "But, believe me, I am not mad, most noble Festus! But truth is ever incoherent, and when the big hearts strike together, the concussion is a little stunning."

Maxwell's insight must have reached Gibbs as the authentic confirmation, the rigorous positive that alone could touch him. There was no other recognition; and long after, recognition itself was to start tears at his eyes. But his own contracting diffidence again stood in his way. Clerk Maxwell wrote to Gibbs —we know that; the model he sent is preserved at Yale, but not a single letter from Maxwell has been produced. John Johnston (then professor of chemistry at Yale) wrote of Gibbs's correspondence in the February 1928 issue of *Scientific Monthly :*

Letters . . . are preserved by the Van Name family (his niece and nephews) who have kindly permitted me to examine them and to use such as are of immediate interest. A perusal of this correspondence shows that many of the letters had not been preserved by Gibbs; for, though among the writers there are a number of conspicuous names, others, equally outstanding (for instance, Clerk Maxwell) who are known to have written to Gibbs, are missing.

This burial went on in Gibbs's own spirit, we are led to believe —a burial that was to carry a penalty, for he was not only denying himself, he was denying the world. In the meantime, Maxwell was doing what he could.

If he could be answered in this way from London, it was time to publish his work—the big work which carried on the two papers. Maxwell must see more than that.

And now the stories grow, as he approaches the open offering of his work. Washington has his cherry-tree, Newton the classic apple. Gibbs's household emblem is the chicken dissolving in the soup; but these other tales are his cherry-tree stories, the incidents—however fabulous and out of character—by which this man, of whom so few stories have been told, is recognized.

One, whose origin and truth cannot be known, says that he left the first part of the paper on his sister's desk, as a spiritual gift. In the stories about Gibbs, the figures have shifted and drowned, so that the two sisters are merged into one in the tales. Although perhaps even that is appropriate to him. The story says that this gift, the most he could ever offer in the world, was passed by without a word. That seems unlikely in this home; even the story does not speak of the place of wordlessness in this family that had been so concerned with words.

He was seen driving daily. That was how most people knew him, driving with Julia. In the beginning, that seemed quite natural, as indeed it was. And then the legend grew, until in one form or another it was the one story that people knew about Willard Gibbs, whether they ever heard his name in any other connection : He was a great man, and he drove his sister. The embroidery began : one version said that he would not have any fresh air, if his family did not send him out, like a schoolboy. Another said the horse needed exercise, it was for the horse— and it was a headstrong animal, not fit for a lady to drive. And another, more sly, most malicious, which was the most absurd of all, was that of course it was up to Willard to do the family errands, since Addison was the important one, with an important post at the College, regular hours, and Willard had only a few hours' work in a little obscure professorship. Addison was Librarian. What was Mathematical Physics? And the legends grew, until people would come to say that Willard Gibbs wore livery driving his sister to market, which was not only a lie, but ridiculous to anyone who knew the circumstances of New Haven, or the family, or the gentle habits of these people. Willard could take time.

Willard did take time. Driving in the slow, sunny spring days, and among the snow and ice of winter, with the horse steaming after a brisk hour, he considered his time; and finally brought his paper, with the encouragement of Hubert Anson Newton, to the Connecticut Academy.

On the 17th of June, 1874, Willard Gibbs presented a communication to the Connecticut Academy on "The Principles of Thermodynamics as Determining Chemical Equilibrium." It was noted in the minutes of the meeting; and it was undoubtedly a draft of the third paper, on which he was working.

There was no money for publications at that time. The only funds that the Academy had were the annual dues of about a hundred members—its entire list. The interests of the country were with invention in these shouting years—Connecticut inventors had a box in the local papers, where their new patents were announced each week. Bell was working; the first experiments were made, and the words said: "Mr. Watson, please come here, I want you." The "homespun" apparatus, the whittling boys—they were likable, the whole picture was readily taken, any storekeeper could see what they were driving at. But this, with its exalted vision, its epigraph of Clausius' couplet as base, its seven hundred closely locked equations, its concept of phase which was to open up empires and industries and hold the fate of wars—this was a different matter, a very difficult thing.

A. E. Verrill tells the story. He was president of the Academy during the period, and was on the publications committee while the great paper was being sent to press. Those were hard articles to print. "They were expensive to set up, owing to the complex mathematical formulae. Our funds were small. On nearly every occasion we had to go out and raise a subscription to pay the cost, partly among college men and partly among the business and professional men of New Haven." There is a story that the shopkeepers, who knew Willard Gibbs well from his talk with them as he made the rounds of errands, helped to publish his work. He could talk freely with other social groups—like Whitman, for example, like many men who have good reason to fear misunderstanding from people who consider themselves intellectual equals or superiors, the flight is to the simple. It is not flight, but balance; it has its rewards.

Long discussions took place as to our ability to print the articles. Two able mathematical professors were on the committee—Loomis and Newton. Both protested that they did not understand Gibbs's papers at all. . . . Yet we all believed that what Gibbs wrote must be of intrinsic value in his branch of science. Therefore we raised the money and printed each paper as it came in. I remember that on one of these occasions Professor Loomis, as chairman, appointed Professor Newton as one to raise funds. Professor Newton begged off because he had done that duty many times, but Loomis would not excuse him because he was the most successful, and then, in his usual sudden or abrupt way, he adjourned the meeting and seized his cane and tall silk hat to leave the room.

Professor Newton jumped up and said, "Hold on, Professor Loomis, I have something to show you." Then he took from his pocket a subscription blank already prepared and said, "I want you to head the list with $100." We all laughed, of course. Professor Loomis looked at us with a broad smile and without a word wrote his name down on the $100 page.

The gesture had been made. The paper would at last be published.

CHAPTER TWELVE

The Great Paper

IF THE LEADING IDEA of the eighteenth century had been the idea of progress, with all that it meant for the human being and the young nations, the leading idea of the nineteenth was the concept of energy. Both of these concepts were closely tied up with causal relationships : progress was an idea that depended on a definite and optimistic connection between a series of causes and results, and energy was a statement of power in the terms of the results alone. Energy could be measured by the work that it did; and the forces of the century were obsessed by these matters.

Work, its speed and cheapness, and the results of work. These were what the great concepts had become; they were translated into the terms of profit and profit's goals. The age of Newton had pulled on America in a parallelogram of forces—four forces, actually, as the Beards point out : the triumphs of European natural science, the achievements of the English inventors who expressed the Industrial Revolution, the dynamic impulse of the idea of progress which arose in France, and the impact on political thought of the French Revolution.

Now, with the reconstruction of the country under the double pressure of the Civil War and machine technology, ends were found.

The Republic was a hundred years old. There was reason for celebration. And the hundred years came to its close in a burst of celebration, whose gifts were the inventions that showered on the country from a thousand toolshops and cellars, and the attics of electricians. They were the leaders, the inventors. We had our cable and web printing press, our reaper, typewriter, the duplex telegraph, the refrigerator car; and only a few months before, Bell had picked up the first telephone and said to his assistant, "Mr. Watson, please come here, I want you." The chilled plow and the self-binder were beginning a line of relentless changes in farming values; Edison, dissatisfied with his Newark workshop, had moved to Menlo Park, there to run his hive of a laboratory and machine plant.

All of these gifts were assembled at the Centennial. Fairmount Park, in Philadelphia, had been chosen as the site for this first exposition of the industry of all nations. Ground had been broken two years before, the Federal government backed the fair with money and exhibits, and on May 10th, President Grant opened the almost completed exposition, "accompanied by suitable ceremonies, military and civic, of music and of speech, and in the presence of numerous dignitaries, home and foreign, and of the people."

There were 250,000 people on the grounds that first day, when the President—no longer the tragic, war-demented, stained and exhausted man of the Brady photographs, but the business-hardened executive—and Dom Pedro de Alcantara, the Emperor of Brazil, started the Corliss engine which ran the equipment of Machinery Hall.

Machinery was the god of this centennial, the pride of our hundred years. Machines, the consciousless implacable, and the giants with which we surround them, in the Main Exhibition Building, "the largest building in the world. . . . Here is to be seen almost every thing that the globe, through the industry and skill of its men, produces, except what is peculiar to the other buildings." Agricultural Hall, the Fine Arts Building, Horticultural Hall, the Government Building, and the separate exhibits of the shoe and leather industry, the Singer Sewing Machine Company, the Campbell Printing Press, and the foreign buildings were all outdone by Machinery Hall, which covered thirteen acres of this park overlooking the turns of the river and the straight red brick city. The Corliss Engine, the Fair's treasure, was of 1400 horsepower and ran the several thousand machines in the 1500 sections of the building. The symbol of the building, the symbol of the age, was to be found here : a waterfall, "36 feet wide, 33 feet deep, and four inches thick, carrying 30,000 gallons per minute." Machinery, power, labor-saving devices—out of these was made the jubilee.

The Centennial followed, as such giant celebrations seem infallibly to do, on the heels of national disaster. The Civil War, Leo Huberman says, freed the capitalists; and their freedom was marked by a spectacular and dreadful series of calamities, from the crash of '73, of which Jim Fisk's failure was the trademark, through the long wild list of bank closings, panics, strikes. Around the Exposition itself, the thrifty of Philadelphia still raged against the locked Franklin Savings Fund bank; Pennsylvania's last opponent of Standard Oil but one had just fallen; the railroad owners saw their problem staring at them with a new face; and the railroad workers were gathering forces for the fight to win such improvements of their condition as full crews on all trains.

The country was expanding, breathing-in the people it needed to fill a continent. The population was to increase one hundred per cent in this last quarter of the century. Cities bloomed out like animations in a film. The wave of Irish and Germans had given way to the English and Scandinavian arrivals looking for farmland, hypnotized by the railroad and steamships agents who were drumming up Europe, promising a new heaven and a new earth.

There was a new earth. Loosely and in the most dangerous and over-simplified terms, it was the new earth released by the new energy. These continents, these forces, are not discovered; they are *released;* and steam had opened a dominion, releasing a period which might easily be mistaken at first glance for a new period in human civilization.

It was not that. But there were cultural expressions. On the one hand, there was the Centennial Exposition, with its buildings, its pairs of showy vases, its "Ox of 4,000 pound weight," its implements of precision "including topography and music," its free band concerts, its pavilions, its "many wonderful labor-saving devices . . . in which it is probable the United States takes the lead." On the other hand was Willard Gibbs, now thirty-seven, beginning the publication of his third paper on thermodynamics, that study in relationship which Crowther calls "the finest cultural expression of the age of steam." It is this great paper which devotes itself to relationships at a time when only concrete factors could seize the public mind; that sums up in itself not only the work that Gibbs had already done, that lays down not only the complete basis of a new science and a dynasty of applications, but that also foreshadows—that *releases* —an age.

His teaching was not interrupted. The subjects he was covering in these years were the same : capillarity, the wave theory of light and sound, least squares, the potential theory with its ramifying applications to electricity and magnetism. He taught in the rough, ill-lighted rooms of Sloane, and then went home to work on the dark tables, sometimes returning to his office in the evenings to burn the lamp as long as he felt his health could bear the added hours.

The practical men of his time were measuring, not the forces themselves, but their actions. However, there was a new force breaking with the light of another sun into realization. The conception of energy, developed in these years, is perhaps the greatest of all exact generalizations; it reached immediately through all levels, from the most rarefied speculation to the kitchen and the work-bench. As abstract thought, at the beginning of a immense movement, it was incapable of guiding research; actually, there was no research in this country. Edison's Menlo Park was the metaphor of all research; but Edison was your pure inventor, measuring not forces but their actions. The spirit of the times was with him, in a way apparent to anyone who read a newspaper. With Gibbs, the spirit of the times stood in another relation, as now with Einstein; so that the crude spectator might well deny that there was a real connection, deny that his work had its ancestors in the world, although as even the man in the street grew old, he might trace its descendants.

But New Haven held many of the keys to his connection with the world; and in 1876 Gibbs took the sheets to the Academy meetings, knowing that even there, among colleagues and neighbors, he could not hope for understanding. He could, however, hope for sympathy and publication. The Academy had no funds from Yale, no publication subsidy. All that it had was the dues of its hundred members.

Of all these members, not one would have claimed to understand the paper. Professor Loomis and Professor Newton, able mathematicians and friends of Gibbs, were on the committee, and they both protested that they did not understand the work at all.

His loneliness must have been even deeper now. Loomis did not know, Hubert Newton did not know. But these people—a few members of the faculty and his sisters—brought to this first glimpse of his paper the sympathy that looks for the mind's equivalents. His sisters' faces tell their discipline, and we may always guess at the closeness of this family; Julia's children insist that she accepted her brother's work to the full extent of her capacities. And to the loving mind, there are equivalents; at certain points, when great achievement is set before the imagination, there arrive flashes of insight which prove that the imagination works on many levels with the same design. There is a subtle way by which the links of Gibbs's imagination is made known, by translation—a far translation into another logic. There is a way by which we can come to perception. This is a study of relationships that disregards many of the physical factors of the substances which such relationships bind. From a distance, and in other terms, anyone deeply aware of the importance and universality of such relationship comes to these meanings. The gestures which must be made—like the gesture made in first printing this work—are acts of faith.

The College was not part of this gesture, as the century was not. But they were involved, and deeply.

The world-wide applications of this masterpiece of Gibbs will be indicated in a later chapter. The most appropriate introduction to Gibbs's great paper is in his own words of appreciation of the award of the Rumford Medal, when he said:

One of the principal objects of theoretical research in any department of knowledge is to find the point of view from which the subject appears in its greatest simplicity. . . .

The leading idea which I followed in my paper on the Equilibrium of Heterogeneous Substances was to develop the *roles* of energy and entropy in the theory of thermodynamic equilibrium. By means of these qualities the general condition of equilibrium is easily expressed, and by applying this to various cases we are led at once to the special conditions which characterize them. We thus obtain the consequences resulting from the fundamental principles of thermodynamics (which are implied in the definitions of energy and entropy) by a process which seems more simple, and which lends itself more readily to the solution of problems, than the usual method, in which the several parts of a cyclic operation are explicitly and separately considered. Although my results were in a large measure such as had previously been demonstrated by other methods, yet, as I readily obtained those which were to me before unknown, or but vaguely known, I was confirmed in my belief in the suitableness of the method applied.

A distinguished German physicist has said,—if my memory serves me aright,—that it is the office of theoretical investigation to give the form in which the results of experiment may be expressed. . . .

The form in which these results are expressed is one of the most difficult of all languages to follow—physics and chemistry in their highly complicated reaches, set down in terms of mathematics. The paper in which they are collected has given Gibbs the highest rank in American science. Henry Adams called Gibbs the "greatest of Americans, judged by his rank in science." In this paper he created the science of chemical thermodynamics, at a time when nothing existed in this field; and with this "single stroke he has brought this knowledge to such a degree of perfection that in fifty years almost nothing has been added." Condensed, rigorous, full of the most terrifying difficulties, even for the specialist—to find an equivalent for this paper is to search the furthest wealth of imaginative effort. The contents of the work are of enormous importance at this moment, and intense work along the lines of its suggestions is in progress. The principles it sets in view have opened up a world of process and speculation to which the door itself has barely been touched.

Gibbs was one of those rare intellects which tower over art, over many kinds of conquest, as over science, from whom the human race receives its pictures of the world, and one such picture is contained in this paper. "The Equilibrium of Heterogeneous Substances" is a great, comprehensive, and generalized statement—an abstract theoretical contribution to science which, more than any other, has exerted its profound effect on basic industry. It has provided a foundation for physical chemistry as we know it today, and its accomplishment alone raises Gibbs into the rank shared by Newton, Maxwell, and Einstein—that top level of creative power which has turned toward unknown illumination the idea of the universe. Larmor says of this work, "His monumental memoir . . . made a clean sweep of the subject; and workers in the modern experimental science of physical chemistry have returned to it again and again, to find the empirical principles forecasted in the light of pure theory, and to derive fresh inspiration for new departures."

The paper, as printed in the *Collected Works*, includes three hundred pages of fundamental work, followed by a seventeen-page abstract, which Gibbs published in the *American Journal of Science*. The paper itself opens with this statement of Clausius', iterated with final simplicity, used as epigraph, as statement of theme, and as an indication of method :

> "*Die Energie der Welt ist constant.*
> "*Die Entropie der Welt strebt einem Maximum zu.*"

Gibbs was cutting down his equipment, indeed killing his kings, and these two lines—"The energy of the world is constant. The entropy of the world tends toward a maximum"—are his weapons, the cornerstones of the new church. This compressed and ringing summary of the first two laws of thermodynamics stands at the head of his paper. And then, after the two lines of commandments, it begins:

> The comprehension of the laws which govern any material system is greatly facilitated by considering the energy and entropy of the system in the various states of which it is capable. As the difference of the values of the energy for any two states represents the combined amount of work and heat received or yielded by the system when it is brought from one state to the other, and the difference of entropy is the limit of all possible values of the integral $\int \frac{dQ}{t}$, (dQ denoting the element of the heat received from external sources, and t the temperature of the part of the system receiving it,) the varying values of the energy and entropy characterize in all that is essential the effects producible by the system in passing from one state to

another. For by mechanical and thermodynamic contrivances, supposed theoretically perfect, any supply of work and heat may be transformed into any other which does not differ from it, either in the amount of work and heat taken together or in the value of the integral $\int \frac{dQ}{t}$. But is is not only in respect to the external relations of a system that its energy and entropy are of predominant importance. As in the case of simply mechanical systems, (such as are discussed in theoretical mechanics,) which are capable of only one kind of action upon external systems, viz., the performance of mechanical work, the function which expresses the capability of the system for this kind of action also plays the leading part in the theory of equilibrium, the condition of equilibrium being that the variation of this function shall vanish, so in a thermodynamic system, (such as all material systems actually are,) which is capable of two different kinds of action upon external systems, the two functions which express the twofold capabilities of the system afford an almost equally simple criterion of equilibrium.

The concern of the science of thermodynamics is in these two forms of the same thing : energy and entropy. It is concerned with these, regardless of the system under discussion, and the power of this paper is partly in its independence of the nature of any system. Gibbs is here defining his own terms. He is absorbed in the problem of equilibrium between two or many components. He is dealing with the behavior of the components, whatever they may be, and the system, whatever it become. Crowther points out that all of these—Carnot, Mayer, Joule, Helmholtz, Clausius, Kelvin, and Rankine—inspired by the behavior of steam inside an engine cylinder, were fascinated by the work they could get out of that steam. They were fascinated by its *public life*. Gibbs, moving ahead, was concerned with internal relations, in "the private lives of systems." He goes on to set forth his terms, the criteria of equilibrium and stability of a closed system. Such a system can be considered stable if in all possible variations of its state which do not alter its energy, its entropy's variation shall vanish or be negative; and in all variations which do not alter its entropy, its energy's variation shall vanish or be negative.

The discussion of mixtures whose contact is not influenced by any of the ordinary forces—of gravity, electricity, distortion of the solid masses, or capillary tension—follows, with a leap into the world of the ideal, the "supposed theoretically perfect" world. Now the system is closed in a "rigid and fixed envelop." We are now in the world of pointer-readings, the world not involving consciousness, the non-reversible physical world; and we are there "in order to arrive as directly as possible at the most characteristic and essential laws." Gibbs reminds us that this supposition does not involve any real loss of generality. If any mass is in equilibrium, it would also be in equilibrium if part or all of it were enclosed—out of the world.

System, as used here, refers to any portion of the universe which we choose to separate in thought, in order to consider it.

The variables of any system include all the factors of the system and its behavior. To the other concept, Gibbs added thermodynamic potential and chemical potential, the "free energies" which have since taken his name. Massieu had used the ideas and symbols for these thermodynamic quantities, but Gibbs employed them with a largeness never before achieved, and introduced to the list of variables *mass* itself. This last use made the study possible.

Early in the paper, in equations 15–21, are stated those equations of condition from which so much that follows is derived. The groundwork for the Phase Rule is here laid. All is deduced from the two lines of Clausius, rigorously and without mathematical digressions, or the examples which would appeal to physicists or chemists. He moves at his own convenience, choosing examples for their simplicity, independent of any theory. In considering one kind of equilibrium—water, free hydrogen, free oxygen—he calls attention to the components; and in discussing sulphuric acid and the vapor which it yields, he points out that the acid and the water are the only two components. These passages are studded with expressions of simplicity : ". . . for brevity's sake," ". . . limit the generality of the problem" . . . and the choices are all made ideal—"The time must be chosen so that the change does not take place in it infinitely slowly, which is always easy, as the change which we suppose to take place cannot be infinitely slow except at particular moments."

The variations already discussed do not consider *new* formations. The next section explores infinitesimal masses entirely different in state and composition from any initially existing.

These are bodies capable of existing in mixtures—ice in water and vapor, crystals in clear solutions. This explains, in equations 35–57, the stability of a fluid, if every possible new formation requires an increase in energy, while the entropy and mass remain constant. But some liquids, stable to certain changes, are unstable to others; and when a new body is introduced, terrific changes occur. There are, too, *practically* unstable equilibria, such as supersaturated solutions, superheated waters, etc., in which a very small change in the initial state, a change which entirely escapes our powers of perception, is sufficient to destroy the equilibrium. Gibbs marks the end of this discussion with a signpost; he says that it will be understood in the ways he has indicated "(or in others which will suggest themselves to the reader)." This parenthesis is a mark of greatness; it also carries its own penalty. It is an assumption of equality which the world has never tolerated, even in those regions where the notion of equality has been most freely entertained.

The paper's next three sections discuss the effect of solidity of any given part of the mass, of additional equations of condition, and of a diaphragm. This last is a study of the equilibrium of osmotic forces—a mass is given, enclosed as before, and "divided into two parts, each of which is homogeneous and fluid, by a diaphragm which is capable of supporting an excess of pressure on either side, and is permeable to some of the components and impermeable to others. . . ." E. A. Guggenheim, in the *Commentary on the Scientific Writings of J. Willard Gibbs*, says that nowhere are the power and elegance of Gibbs's methods better illustrated. The three conditions of temperature, pressure, and chemical potential are explored. The unit of quantity is denoted, without a specific unit's being used; but the same unit of mass is used throughout, and this, coming before the complete establishment of the molecular theory, makes his theory generally applicable. Guggenheim also refers to the extreme care —a care of avoidance—of certain terms, and it is this *avoidance* that gives to much of Gibbs's style its aesthetic quality, as well as the safety of its general application. Much of the current attitude towards electric potential is in accordance with this set of Gibbs's views; and the equations of activity leading to the modern theory of electrolytes may be obtained from this passage.

The discovery of the chemical potential has been called

The Great Paper

Gibbs's greatest discovery. It was left to Maxwell to provide the clearest verbal definition, in an abstract of a speech he made this same year, at an occasion that is bound dramatically with both the Philadelphia Exposition and the printing of the paper. Maxwell writes :

By differentiating the energy with respect to the volume, we obtain the pressure of the fluid with the sign reversed; by differentiating with respect to the entropy, we obtain the temperature on the thermodynamic scale; and by differentiating with respect to the mass of any one of the component substances, we obtain what Professor Gibbs calls the (chemical) potential of that substance in the mass considered.

MacInnes, quoting this definition, feels the significance of having to go to Maxwell for explanation; in Gibbs's work, everything must be deduced, there is no willingness; and at the same time, by the same token, there is no condescension. His own attitude towards his work is reiterated with every gesture : his choice of the Academy as his place of publication, the way in which he handled his classes, the sparseness of his developing equations.

The discovery of the chemical potential was the Northwest Passage of this science; it was the link between classical thermodynamics and contemporary physical chemistry and electrochemistry. With Clausius' two sentences, and the chemical potential, Gibbs deduces the Phase Rule, one of the most important instruments of science, one of the world's great tools.

The Phase Rule occurs incidentally in a four-page section, "On Coexistent Phases of Matter." The word "phase" is here introduced as being any part of a system which is homogeneous throughout. It is conceived as having its own surface, and being mechanically separate from the other parts of the system. This is Gibbs's definition :

In considering the different homogeneous bodies which can be formed out of any set of component substances, it will be convenient to have a term which shall refer solely to the composition and thermodynamic state of any such body without regard to its quantity or form. We may call such bodies as differ in composition or state different *phases* of the matter considered, regarding all bodies which differ only in quantity and form as different examples of the same phase. Phases which can exist together, the dividing surfaces being plane, in an equilibrium which does not depend upon passive resistances to change, we shall call *coexistent*.

The most familiar example of a system containing several phases is ice water, which includes ice, water, and vapor—each with its bounding surface, and contained in a glass. The condition of true equilibrium, on which Gibbs insists, is not likely to be satisfied here, for we often drink the mixture at a temperature far above zero, its temperature at equilibrium. The rule that follows gives no indication of anything except the conditions once equilibrium has been reached. It does not speak of the processes by which equilibrium is created, but of the state itself, and the relationships within it. It is an instrument whose parts are relationships. They are the components, n, so that the phase of the body is capable of $n+1$ variations. The number of variables needed to define a system is called the degree of freedom of that system; and if there are r coexistent phases in the system, each with the same n variable components—the number of degrees of freedom of the system in equilibrium is defined as

$$n + 2 - r$$

This is the Phase Rule, one of the most celebrated and beautiful laws of theoretical physics. Let us see how it works. In the glass of ice water, considering it for a moment as simply water and ice, we have a substance in two phases, so that $n = 1$ and $r = 2$. According to the equation, the system has one degree of freedom; that is, if we change either the temperature *or* the pressure, say, the mixture will lose its equilibrium. If we add water vapor to our mixture, adding another component, we can change neither the pressure nor the temperature. There is but one specific pressure and one specific temperature at which this mixture can rest in equilibrium.

If a system has four phases, the result is -1, a meaningless number in this instance; so that we may assume that one of the phases will pass into the other three, which can remain in equilibrium.

If a system has four phases in two different substances, that is, if $r = n + 2$, no variation is possible. Gibbs says, "It does not seem probable that r can ever exceed $n + 2$." He gives as an example any substance of invariable composition; and says that in the case of sulphur and some other simple substances, it is "not improbable" that there is more than one triad, but that it is improbable that there are four coexistent phases. An example of $n = 2$ and $r = 4$ is a solution of a salt in water, vapor of water, and two different kinds of salt crystals.

One of the immediate applications of these conditions of equilibrium, the state of maximum entropy, can be seen if we suppose that salt is sprinkled on ice. Some of the salt dissolves, and some remains; some of the water evaporates, and some remains. We now have water and salt, our two components, in four phases—salt, salt water, water vapor, and ice. The Phase Rule gives us zero for number of degrees of freedom. That is, equilibrium is assumed, and held. It is that which we count on when we use this mixture for a freezing mixture. We know from experiment that the temperature of this combination will automatically go to —22 degrees centigrade, and stay there.

The Phase Rule has become a guide, by which innumerable experimental details can be classified, by which facts can be explained and gathered in from their scattered outlying districts. By this application of the principle of energy, Gibbs—in a stroke —advanced the expression of an age to its high point.

Revolutions had already been brought about by the idea of energy—definitions, criticisms, recastings had been under way. New departures had been made in philosophy. These had found reflections in mechanics, in physics, chemistry, and physiology. The underlying unities of every gesture of the universe had been detected. Since every act depends on the exchange and transformation of energy, which is measurable in one of two ways—as motion, or as heat—the language for this transformation had to be developed. It was Willard Gibbs's function to find a language for an underlying process. He did this without introducing any hypothetical quantity, such as the atom; by concentrating on a purely mechanical assumption, the idea of degree of freedom which adds direction to the three dimensions of space. His theory correlates all forms of energy in the same way that the general theory of relativity later correlated other factors.

The prodigious advance in physics, transforming daily life

with the new uses of heat, light, and electricity, has changed our century through its greatest generalization—the law of the conversion of energy, which is the foundation of modern chemistry as well as physics. But a combining science was needed; it was impossible for the chemists to reach this law—for the law to reach the chemists, if you will—since the chemists were confined to reason from observation, without the notation they might have used. The physicist, according to Slosson, "starting from a few well-established fundamental principles makes use, in drawing deductions from them, of the most powerful intellectual tool in the hands of men. . . . Physics and chemistry have not been on speaking terms, for they talked different languages. It was largely due to Willard Gibbs and others working along the line he indicated that they are being brought together."

The paper—this "triumph of creative intellect"—laid the foundation for the new science. It laid down laws for problems yet unproposed, and contained that foreboding that is essential to great work. It was possible to go on from here in great leaps. It was a theory capable, in Gibbs's own words, of "giving shape to research."

After a discussion of internal stability, the paper turns to geometrical illustrations, surfaces and curves to represent the constant and variable composition of bodies. In the earlier papers, Gibbs had described thermodynamic surfaces for substances of invariable composition. Now he was representing the equilibria of phases graphically, in triangle diagrams in which sheets of lines resting on each other stand for three-phase equilibria, and each additional phase requires another rank of lines in the figures. The surface which represented the properties of homogeneous bodies was called the *primitive surface;* the *derived surface* represented the properties of bodies in equilibrium but not homogeneous. This method has been applied to the determination of the composition, not only of liquid and vapor phases at given temperatures, but to the structure of alloys. These heavy-walled triangles were more "models of perfection," in Percival's phrase. Some of the primitive surfaces are radiating furrows, and others the complicated figures that many-phase systems offer to representation. In the *Commentary*, Schreinemakers says that a full account of this method would require an exposition of the whole subject of generalized graphical thermodynamics. In thirty pages, he analyzes only the representation by means of the free energy function, which is one of many factors.

The passage on *critical phases* defines the term as one at which the distinction between coexistent phases vanishes, as a critical state is one at which distinctions of state vanish. The relation of critical phases, and the phases in their vicinity, to stability are given. A critical phase is capable of $n - 1$ independent variations, and there are only two independent equations of this phase. Gibbs refers to an abstract by M. Duclaux which came to his attention after this passage was already set up.

He deals with ideal gas-mixtures in a re-phrasing of Dalton's law, and with the *phases of dissipated energy* of ideal gas-mixtures, that is, those phases which cannot be affected by any catalytic agent. From gas-mixtures with convertible components, he goes on to a study of equilibrium of stressed solids. But there was a gap of a year between the printing of the two parts.

The first half of the great paper appeared in the *Transactions of the Connecticut Academy*, III, pp. 108–248, Oct. 1875–May 1876. The second part included pp. 343–524, May 1877–July 1878.

One climax in particular strikes at the universal. Suddenly, in the midst of the discussion of conditions relating to the increase of entropy due to the mixture of gases by diffusion, the clue to the seemingly hopeless universe is expressed, in a sentence which speaks for the greatest possible optimism set down with all the cautiousness and all the finality which were at once native to Willard Gibbs.

Clerk Maxwell had imagined a quantity of gas, of the same pressure and temperature throughout, divided into two portions (A and B) by a partition full of little trap doors over each of which sat a demon—in this instance, a selective demon. These conscious and efficient beings sorted the travelling molecules, as they hurtled across the chambers, according to their velocity. The slow ones were sent through the trap doors to chamber A, the fast ones were ushered in the other direction to chamber B; so that, as they were sorted out, the temperature of B was raised, and that of A lowered, without any loss of energy, and without the performance of any work. The double-chambered apparatus now could be attached to a heat engine, which would function until an equilibrium of temperature was established between A and B. And then the demons would get to work again.

This notion of Maxwellian demons seemed the only one possible for the reconcentration of diffused energy. According to what was known of the nature of the physical world in the nineteenth century, the degradation of energy, the running-down of the universe continued until entropy was general, until there was nothing but a futureless and mechanical conception of the heat-death, a grey wilderness of infinite monotony, without change and without meaning.

But to accept the idea of entropy, we must necessarily accept the concepts of infinity and eternity, which contain in themselves infinite and eternal possibility. Gibbs begins, on p. 167 of his work, to refer to the possible re-separation of a homogeneous gas into the two parts into which it has once been divided, and he makes the statement, for him, of final concession :

"In other words, the impossibility of an uncompensated decrease of entropy seems to be reduced to improbability."

What was his life during this time? What was the life of his work?

Of his own life, we do not know.

The town was changing. Inventions were doing that. It was not only that the Winchester Co. had a new plant and workmen were coming in. In January 1878, the first telephone exchange appeared in New Haven, set up with twelve wires linking the fifty subscribers whose names were published in a card list. It was a new era. The town was quiet; it boasted that there was a steady demand for the labor of independent, conservative workmen; there were no absentee owners; everyone worked hard; there were no "serious labor disturbances and strikes."

But this did not touch him. The country changed wildly : these were the years of Custer's last stand, of the appearance of *Tom Sawyer*, *Anna Karénina*, *Daisy Miller*. Gibbs was not a novel-reader, although these books would all reach Yale, to be catalogued by Addison Van Name's staff. But if he passed over these years lightly, the years had glanced obliquely at Willard Gibbs. There was a moment of deep recognition—recognition of the highest kind, again by Clerk Maxwell, again unnoticed and unabsorbed.

In the same year as the Philadelphia Exposition, the first international loan exhibition of scientific apparatus ever held was opened in London, at South Kensington. Crowther's account of the fortnight, begun with a formal opening over which Queen Victoria and the Empress of Germany presided, gives full attention to the drawbacks of British relations with the United States. England could not forget that the Philadelphia fair was in celebration of 1776, and although England had sent an exhibit to Fairmount Park, there was a poor showing of American interests at South Kensington. All the apparatus was at the Exposition. Helmholtz and many other leading European scientists attended, but when Clerk Maxwell made a speech—at one of the many lecture-meetings—"On the Equilibrium of Heterogeneous Bodies," no notice was given his speech beyond mention of its title. The abstract of what Crowther calls "virtually the same lecture" is in Maxwell's Collected Papers; this abstract was printed in 1876, after only the first half of Gibbs's memoir had appeared, in the *Proceedings of the Cambridge Philosophical Society*. Maxwell illustrates his abstract with two experiments, Guthrie's on sodium chloride, according to Gibbs's theory, and "Mr. Main's experiments on coexistent phases of mixtures of chloroform, alcohol and water."

The second half of Gibbs's paper "On the Equilibrium of Heterogeneous Substances" contains clues as rich as those in the first half, which have led to explorations in geology, metallurgy, the study of the blood, political economy, historical theory, exchanges of goods, theories of currency, refrigeration, the interpretation of the properties of steel, the airplane industry, the work in high explosives and the study of salt deposits that in some measure account for the roles of England and Germany in the World War of 1914–18, and the explanation of the activity of certain volcanoes.

In this second half are the foundations for the thermodynamical theory of surface tension and capillarity, of colloid chemistry, work on the galvanic cell which has given Gibbs his tremendous influence on electrochemistry, and the work on films and crystals on which some of the researches of Einstein and Pierre Curie, to name only two, have rested.

He begins with a discussion of the effect of gravity on the conditions of equilibrium, a problem in which a long line of physicists and chemists, including Galileo, Laplace, and Boltzmann, have been engaged, according to the *Commentary :* "It is Gibbs' characteristic role to have shown how these special relations of gravity and fluid equilibrium fit into the general scheme of thermodynamics in a way that permits of the widest sort of application." Gibbs here shows that the barometric formula, offering pressure as a variable depending on height, "takes its part in the thermodynamic scheme," thus following up the work of Galileo, Périer, and Laplace. This equation was used in relation to the concentration of solute in a solution, in its variation with the height. Colloidal solutions forwarded this research, in the work of Einstein, Perrin, and recently, The Svedberg and Tolman.

The study of fundamental equations of ideal gases is an acceptance of Clausius' concept, then the most recent step in a study in the response of gases which goes back to Boyle, Gay-Lussac, and Avogadro. Gibbs's re-statement of Dalton's law has added his name to it, and it is now called the Gibbs-Dalton law. The treatment and representations here always indicate the role of entropy constants, and lead up to Nernst's work. Again, here the possibility of generalization sets the work marvellously high in unpredicted uses, even as far as separating helium from natural gas in Texas.

It is always true to say that nobody is aware of the future; that no discoverer, no scientist, knows what he is opening. The cry, "Christopher Columbus, Christopher Columbus, what did you do when you discovered America?" is just as futile as the praise many have given to the great dead fathers of our scene. But Gibbs was aware of the future. He may not have been aware of it concretely; we are not sure how much concreteness he bestowed upon his present. But when he considers the inferences, which have led to "a large portion of the principles and doctrine which have found application in physical chemistry in the last half-century," Gibbs himself must be referred to by the *Commentary*. And Gibbs says here, "This seems to indicate that the law expressed by these equations has a very general application." This cryptic and incidental hint is part of his method; it is the furthest concession he would make to general communication, and he suffered the full penalty of his reticence in preparing an audience. But the work is here; it is buried for the future; and the penalty is that of not only his method, but his language, his character, and his background.

His background enters more and more clearly into the work. In the study of conditions of equilibrium for solids in contact with fluids, with regard to all possible states of strain of the solids, Faraday's experiments in 1861 on Regulation are invoked, and James Thomson, in commenting on the experiments, had said : "There seems to me to be yet a field open for much additional theoretical and experimental investigation in this respect. . . ." The steam-engine always haunts these researches; the envelopes which contain systems are likely to be cylinders. But Gibbs's studies in strain proceed to discussions which apply so completely to metallurgy and crystallography as to advance entire new sciences. The change of state in solids, the elastic solid theory, is treated with profound and mathematical brevity. Long, complicated analyses must be undergone before the section is intelligible, according to the *Commentary;* it remarks wryly :

The very first page of the section is a case in point. Moreover, this analysis usually forms part of one of the more specialized courses in the physics or mathematics department of a university, and even students of physics, not aiming at a highly specialized degree in that subject, might well find their knowledge of stress and strain too rudimentary to follow Gibbs at this point.

The next large section deals with surfaces of discontinuity between fluid masses—a surface of discontinuity being a very thin non-homogeneous film, actually an abstract *idea* of such a dividing surface, a geometrical fiction with which to express a surface existing in the physical world in three dimensions. After formulating the conditions of equilibrium in a surface phase between fluids, Gibbs derives the adsorption law, which has become famous under this name, which he actually never gave it. This entire section is a clue to the working of Gibbs's imagination, another picture of the world in which it worked; a world of form, which had its counterpart, detail by detail, in the physical world, but was always more simple, more rigorous, and indeed more rewarding as a laboratory. His attitude toward the world can be seen in these steps of imagination. It is an attitude that has its costs, in personality as well as in the effect of his work; and Gibbs faced penalties. But whoever ventures here, without stopping to make the public gestures continually that will explain his course, runs these risks. Gibbs could be followed, by those whom he hoped to reach directly, only, say, as the *Amistad* was followed by those who could not understand the many motives which plotted that course up the Atlantic. The ship could be seen from time to time. The necessary zigzag is the wrenching of the mind from the symbols to the objects and back again, which Maxwell knew as the price we have to pay for new ideas.

The adsorption theory is the result of investigated forces at the surfaces of liquids in which substances have been dissolved which change the tension at the surface of the liquid—that skin which alters with the altered content. Gibbs, in working out a thermodynamical theory for the changes, founded the work in colloid chemistry which Graham had defined. His study of interfaces and membrane equilibrium has had immense value for the study, not only of colloids, but of related organic equilibria, in the blood and in such isolated substances as organic proteins. The stability of surfaces of discontinuity is also dealt with here, and the conditions relative to the formation of new phases and new surfaces of discontinuity.

Liquid films are also treated here. When a fluid exists between other fluids in the form of a surface that in itself is a very thin film, its properties are defined as they change, and as these changes satisfy the conditions of equilibrium. Gibbs gives here, too, an exact theory of the black spots which break out on the surface of soap bubbles. The soap bubble is used throughout these discussions as an example—for surfaces, tension of surfaces, interfaces, and liquid films.

The last section of the paper deals with the modification of the conditions of equilibrium by electromotive force, and proposes a theory of a perfect electrochemical apparatus. Gibbs has had a tremendous effect on the science of electrochemistry; and the last four pages of this paper contain the first clear statement of the operation of that powerful tool of research and application, the galvanic cell. If this section had been digested by later workers in the field, says MacInnes, "a vast amount of error and misapplied energy would have been avoided." Gibbs makes here the connection between the electromotive force of the cell and the energy of the process taking place, showing that the force is determined by what we now call the Gibbs Free Energy of the process. This relation was discovered independently by Helmholtz four years later, as so much of "The Equilibrium of Heterogeneous Substances" was to be re-discovered before the paper itself was read.

Other discussions in these pages are of the effect of gravity and centrifugal force on the galvanic cell, and of the effect of pressure on the potential of the cell. Gibbs here leads up to the modern theory of electrolytes.

The paper, according to Crowther, "established the principles by which the materials of life and industry, which are mixtures, could be managed more efficiently." It is one of the immense landmarks of imagination which could immediately be applied in almost every branch of science and, obliquely, to the humanities which scientific thought can reach. Clerk Maxwell, in South Kensington, tried to bring it before the part of the world he touched. But the Americans were not represented here; American independence was still, a hundred years after, a touchy subject in England; and this paper, an axiom-breaking declaration of another kind of independence, swung between celebration and celebration, lost to the world for the time being, except as the Maxwellian demon of this instance, the Connecticut Academy, permitted it to rush through the trap door of print into the consciousness of the nineteenth century.

CHAPTER THIRTEEN

"Mathematics Is a Language"

Lord RAYLEIGH, complaining in 1875 that the second law had not received full recognition—"And yet the question under what circumstances it is possible to obtain work from heat is of the first importance"—did not know his year. Horstmann, Maxwell, and Gibbs (most fundamentally) were doing their work in that mine. But it takes a genius to recognize a genius, they say; it certainly takes an equal to make the first gesture. Maxwell was the only one to speak. But his influence was felt, and he was doing what he could. The following year this letter reached New Haven:

Darroch, Falkirk, 15/Dec/76

Professor W. Gibbs
DEAR SIR :
   Some months ago I had a letter from Professor Clerk Maxwell, of Cambridge, in which he calls my attention to some expositions of yours on the thermal equilibrium of bodies in different states. Since then I have "moved heaven and earth" in the shape of printers, publishers, booksellers, agents, etc. to get me a copy of your work but unfortunately all without effect. As a last resource I have ventured to come to you, to ask you to send me such information as will enable me to send for a copy of your work, or if it is not trespassing too much on your time to ask you to have the kindness to order a copy to be sent to me.
   I have sent you by this post a copy of a paper of mine on a similar subject. From it you will see that the nature of the vessel in which water is boiled has no influence on the boiling point. Water may be

[*248*]

raised far above its boiling point in vessels made of metal as well as in glass vessels.

Trusting you will forgive this trespass on your kindness,

I have the honor to remain,

Yours truly,

JOHN AITKEN

Maxwell felt that Gibbs's methods, more than any others, were likely to enable us to comprehend relations between states of bodies. But he was not able to make the paper be read. If its value had been understood, the *Transactions of the Connecticut Academy* would have been placed high among the valuable scientific journals; as it was, some of the blame has been placed on Gibbs for publishing in an obscure and inaccessible place. Not one out of fifty thousand in the United States has read this paper, whose influence on research has never been exceeded.

Merz has pointed out how little, at the *beginning* of scientific movement, purely abstract statements are capable of guiding research. It takes a Maxwell, at first, to be able to respond; and he, with his molecular demon, his flight of brickbats about Saturn, his verses—

We honor our fathers and mothers, grandfathers and grandmothers too;
But how shall we honor the vista of ancestors now in our view?
First, then, let us honor the atom, so lively, so wise, and so small;
The atomists next let us praise, Epicurus, Lucretius, and all . . .

and the parody of Shelley—

My soul is an entangled knot
Upon a liquid vortex wrought . . .

This open-hearted and many-minded man, seizing with brilliance on the discoveries made and published in journals which could not be obtained by moving heaven and earth—not in Scotland, at any rate—was the perfect champion for Gibbs. Dramatic, subtle, convincing because he was recognized widely, he held political beliefs which, perhaps more than any other reason, made him recognize that he had a direct responsibility. Crowther asks : "Is it possible that Maxwell's intelligibility was

[*249*]

a reward for social conscience, and that Gibbs' unintelligibility was a penalty for the belief that he had no duty to ensure that his discoveries were understood and used?"

That question is justified. But it assumes the slavery that Isaac Newton could not bear for himself—slavery to a new idea, that sentences its maker to a life term of continual repetition and propaganda. It also presupposes an easy relationship between the creator and society. It implies that there is a penalty for contempt of the people as people, at their most human. That is the sin against democracy, and it carries a heavy penalty. But the belief alone will not bridge the gap.

The fact is that the audience itself was not ready. New Haven proves that point as well as any other example. Here is a college, founded in John Davenport's time for the benefit of the community, growing away from its town as quickly as it rose to wealth and academic power. Its history is that of the stiffening of the form. The College itself had not fulfilled its obligation to the people. It did not matter that the Connecticut Academy, for example, began to send out its *Transactions* to three hundred other societies in 1866, when it resumed publication, and then deposited these exchange journals—more than a third of them foreign—in the Yale Library.

It has been taken for granted that Gibbs was not aware of the significance of his work, that he was not only ignorant of his audience, but ignorant of his own gifts and his own superiority. Even his friends and students have sometimes drawn the picture of a shrinking, over-modest man, who could not see the implications of what he did or what he shrank from doing. But he understood what he was doing in relation to society; we have his own words for that. And, if it would be foolhardy to say that he anticipated the inventions which would use his work, it would be stupid to over-simplify either his problem or his capacities. C. S. Peirce finally blew up at the idea that Gibbs *did not know*; that would come too near, he wrote in a review, "to making him a gifted idiot, rooting up his mathematical truffles like a Périgord pig, and as oblivious of being deprived of them."

Gibbs was not a Périgord pig; but neither was he a Maxwell. Together they play a great drama of passionate and fertile ideas; they are in their way the Adams and Jackson of a great idea, illuminating it from opposite sides. Gibbs could give Maxwell what he most loved : strong, finely focussed principles, capable of being developed in a thousand ways. And Maxwell had already begun to give Gibbs what he needed : a bridge to his audience, who would not listen.

One of the most tragic wrongs of waste in the history of science was the breaking off of their contact.

Maxwell had been having dyspeptic symptoms; when he finally called the doctors in, they told him how ill he was. He had nursed his wife through severe sickness, and there was one period of three weeks when he lectured and went to his lab, although he had not once been to sleep in a bed during that time. Now, when she was a confirmed invalid, he knew that he would die before his wife. He did not complain during this last painful illness, except on her account. He died on November 5, 1879.

A member of the Connecticut Academy said, in meeting, "Only one man ever lived who could understand Gibbs' papers. That was Maxwell, and now he is dead."

Maxwell, who wrote with such sparkling clarity, was attacked as harshly as Gibbs for the way he taught. When P. G. Tait was elected to the chair of natural philosophy at Edinburgh, a chair that Maxwell had also applied for, the newspapers supposed that it was because the University needed someone who could speak with the "supposition of imperfect knowledge or even total ignorance" on the part of the audience. Maxwell was criticized as having too much *learning and originality!*

This was the man of "abundant genius," as Planck says, whose supreme contribution, the theory of the electric field, plays such an enormous part—this man who was ready to alter, as Einstein insists we must always be ready to alter, "the axiomatic basis of physics, in order to take account of the facts of perception with the greatest possible logical completeness." With his lapses in mathematics, with his toys—the zoetrope, the diavolo game—that led to such fertile thoughts, with his flight of brickbats that solved the rings of Saturn and drew him towards the statistical method; and with his speculations, which he used as subtle tools to make known the physical world—he is, says Sir Joseph Larmor, to be considered in relation to the giants who guided the evolution of an abstract universal science of energy :

Willard Gibbs

Carnot, Joule; Mayer, Waterston, W. Thomson, Clausius, Helmholtz, Boltzmann, Willard Gibbs.

"The most important service that a university can do to the world," writes Edwin Slosson of the one big chance that was offered to Willard Gibbs to uproot himself, "is the early recognition and encouragement of men of exceptional ability who are willing to devote their lives to the extension of human knowledge, yet this is the service most likely to be neglected. Yale has no name upon her roll of honor that stands for more originality or profundity than that of Gibbs, but it is a mere chance that it was not lost to her."

When Johns Hopkins University was founded, in 1876, its first president, D. C. Gilman, was alive to the resources of the country. There was poverty, as far as mathematics was concerned; he was informed, and wrote to Gibbs. One side of the correspondence has been preserved, at Johns Hopkins. The first letter in it is an answer:

New Haven
May 17, 1876

Pres. D. C. Gilman
MY DEAR SIR

Your very kind letter was rec^d two or three days ago. In reply I need only say that I feel favorably inclined toward spending some time—perhaps rather shorter than what you mentioned—in Baltimore next winter, to see the work that is going on & to take such part in it as I may be able.

I regret that I cannot conveniently arrange to come on to see you & your colleagues this summer.

I may add, that as my knowledge of your present courses is quite accidental & fragmentary, if you have any schedules, or can otherwise inform me of the courses w^h are already provided for in the departments of mathematics & physics, I should be very glad to receive such information.

I remain

Very sincerely yours,
J. W. GIBBS

Early the next month, as the plans went along, he answered a definite suggestion:

"Mathematics *Is* a Language"

New Haven
June 5, 1879

Pres. D. C. Gilman,
MY DEAR SIR

I take pleasure in acceding to your very cordial invitation. I can come early in January to stay a couple of months and give lectures—at least as many as Prof. Rowland mentioned (15 or 20)—on Theoretical Mechanics. There will be some points of detail in respect to the topics to be treated on which I may ask the advice of Prof. Rowland.

Yours very truly
J. W. GIBBS

Henry A. Rowland was nine years younger than Gibbs; he had spent one year at the Sheffield Scientific School, but he had two stronger connections with Gibbs. Rowland's work, going ahead with the early experiments of Rumford, was in the field of heat, and his first work was an accurate measurement of the mechanical equivalent of heat. Then, too, his recognition by Maxwell was in even more violent contrast with the treatment he had received at home. Rowland's first paper, on the magnetic circuit, was rejected here; but Maxwell, to whom he sent it, recognized its quality at once, and had it published immediately in the *Philosophical Magazine*. It had been held up long enough, Maxwell felt, and he read the proofs himself, so that it might be rushed through.

When the description of Gibbs's lectures arrived, its schedule was set at four or five times a week during January and February; its plan was to take the principle of *virtual velocities* as a point of departure, and using the outline of the *Mécanique analytique* of Lagrange, to go ahead with other methods of developing the subject. The notations of direction and magnitude were emphasized. Gibbs, in 1879, was already occupied with these notations, leading up to his vector analysis, which he did not introduce to his own class at Yale until two years later. "The object of this course," he concludes in his description, "will be to develop the general principles of Mechanics in their mutual connections, and to explain their most important methods."

Rowland, at the time of Gibbs's first connection with Johns Hopkins, wrote a statement about the visiting professor. The

[253]

fate of the Gibbs papers—that extraordinary fate, in which the pattern of loss, destruction, forgetfulness, is repeated until it seems impossible that there is no conspiracy against this man— is at work here. That there should be no record of Gibbs's childhood is understandable, and one may realize why families burn old packets of correspondence; but the break in this document is a fair symbol of the break in the material about Gibbs, wherever it turns up, the confusion of names that mistakes him for Wolcott Gibbs, the Harvard chemist, so many times, that gives his father's dates for his in the best-edited references, that sets him down as William Gibbs, Joseph Gibbs, and once even as Dr. Sibbs, in beautifully printed indexes. This is the broken fragment of Rowland's statement :

. . . I may mention Cayley & Sylvester on the mathematical side, and Helmholtz, Thomson & Maxwell on the mathematical-physical side, and in the latter class should also be included Newton, who was indeed the beau ideal of this class of minds. Prof. Willard Gibbs belongs preeminently to the latter class; to men who not only grasp the subject from a mathematical standpoint but who see the subject in *all* its bearings, and to whom the problems of nature are something more than targets on which to practice with their mathematics.

As to his eminence there can be no doubt. Maxwell, in his small work on the "Theory of Heat" has introduced no less than thirteen pages from the papers of Prof. Gibbs, and he told me personally that the new method of Prof. Gibbs allowed problems to be solved which he . . ."

The single page ends there.

Late in the summer, Gibbs visited Johns Hopkins; and on his return, sent the following courteous refusal of funds to cover his expenses :

New Haven
Oct 4 79

MY DEAR SIR

My visit to Balt. was not only very pleasant but also advantageous for me, as enabling me to see how to shape my lectures. I certainly do not wish any other return for the expense, w^h was moreover quite trifling.

Yours very sincerely
J. W. GIBBS

Pres. D. C. Gilman

"Mathematics *Is* a Language"

And a few weeks later, he sent the description of his lectures, with a reading list that includes Sturm's *Cours de mécanique*, or Todhunter's *Analytical Statics*, with Tait's and Steele's *Dynamics of a Particle*, and recommends as additional readings the treatises of Delaunay, Duhamel, Laurent, and Resal.

New Haven
Oct. 23, 1879

My DEAR SIR

In accordance with your suggestion, I send a programme or announcement of my course—It is rather long, but may be more satisfactory on that account.

I have not forgotten the very cordial reception w^h I met at Baltimore, both at your house & with different members of the University.

Please remember me most kindly to Mrs. Gilman. I remain

Yours very sincerely
J. W. GIBBS

To Pres^t D. C. Gilman
Baltimore

The lectures were given in January and February. That they went well, we know by their effects. The full force of their success was felt by Gibbs in March, and he answered Gilman's letter :

New Haven
Mch. 30, 1880

My DEAR SIR

I enclose a memorandum of the subjects of my lectures, w^h I remember that you once asked for, but w^h I neglected to give you while I was in Baltimore.

With regard to the subject of our last conversation, if the views of the Trustees should correspond to those w^h you expressed, I think that I should be inclined to regard the matter favorably. In any case I remain

Yours very sincerely
J. W. GIBBS

He had been asked to join the faculty of Johns Hopkins University. During all the years that he had taught at Yale, in spite of the proposals of the pamphlet "The Needs of the University," he had not been paid any salary. He was a full professor; he had very few wants, and they were satisfied; but this outside recognition was a balm.

He considered the new offer; the demand had come from the outside, and he brought all the choices of his life to it. He wrote the letter to President Gilman.

Professor Thacher came to call on Gibbs that day. He saw, standing white and stiff on the mantelpiece, a letter addressed to Johns Hopkins. Thacher had just learned about the invitation, and he had been suddenly distracted at the thought of Gibbs's leaving Yale. It seemed very unlikely, though, he thought. Gibbs was Yale through and through, and his father before him, and his household. Still half afraid, but half sure that nothing would change this quiet man, he asked what the answer in the letter was.

Gibbs looked at him, very directly, for a moment; then he told him. It was a letter of acceptance.

Thacher picked up the envelope and waved it at Willard Gibbs. He was terribly upset; everything that he refused to believe was happening.

But Gibbs only smiled and, mildly, asked for his letter.

"Just let me keep it for a little while," Thacher pleaded. "Just for a few days—two, or at the most three." He saw that he would have to give an assurance of some sort. "Nothing will happen to it," he went on, and the note in his voice changed to open begging. "It will be safe with me—but promise me you will wait. You may mail it—or I'll mail it myself—if nothing has happened within a day or two." And he hurried off.

He must have gone striding down High Street, his coat-tails lifting behind him; he must have almost run to the first faculty member he could think of, and then to another, and finally to President Porter's office, urging Gibbs's importance on them—and Newton, now abroad, could bear him out—telling them that he could be of real importance to the University. Yale knew Gibbs; he was part of their society; they took his works on faith. If he had value to the new Johns Hopkins, whatever his work might mean, he was worth more than he had been to them. He had an offer—and they were cynical enough to believe, whatever they had promised and left undone, if Johns Hopkins promised a professor's salary, they would pay—and it was time to make a counter-offer. They did the handsome thing. They promised him his salary.

This promise swung Gibbs. He was touched; after ten years

of service, they were acknowledging a cold value to his work. It was the first fee he had ever seen. The patent had fallen through; he had become a professor, but he had never been paid; his papers were being published, but he knew the struggle it had been to raise the subscription money. He was strongly moved at this response to the most important personal decision he had ever made : the decision to change his life. It was an omen; there was no change to be made. He resumed his habit, and sat down to write again.

New Haven
Apr. 29, 1880

My dear Sir

Within the last few days a very unexpected opposition to my departure has been manifested among my colleagues—an opposition so strong as to render it impossible for me to entertain longer the proposition w^h you have made. I had not previously spoken of the matter outside of my own family, except in confidence to Prof. Newton as he was leaving for Europe. I only mention this to explain why after so long a time I have arrived at a decision contrary to that to w^h I was tending.

I remember your saying that you told Prof. Sylvester that you thought it would be hard for me to break the ties w^h connect me with this place. Well, I have found it harder than I had expected. But I cannot omit to say that I am very sensible of the cordial sentiments w^h have been expressed by yourself, as well as by other members of your University. I mean especially Professors Sylvester & Rowland.

Very truly yours,
J. W. Gibbs

The first letter might have set Gibbs before the world. It was the second letter that was sent. He belonged here, after all.

If he had gone to Baltimore, he would have been entering a different world. It was not only that Johns Hopkins was a new university, starting out adventurously and devoted to science wholeheartedly, with a concentration and with opportunities for research that, if Yale had them at all, would be confined to one department; it was not only that here, in Baltimore, his students would have come to him more fully prepared, ready for the hardships and enthusiasms of a large graduate school. It was more than that. Johns Hopkins was inviting scholars from abroad, as it had invited Gibbs. President Gilman, advised to start with a nucleus that would include "the best mathematician he could afford," finally invited James Joseph Sylvester to come to Johns Hopkins, at a salary of five thousand dollars a year.

Sylvester had had one harrowing and short experience in teaching in the United States, and had rushed back to London from the University of Virginia, eager for any other form of drudgery. He had worked for insurance companies, prepared abortively in law, and even, during the early years of his work on invariants with Cayley, had been the tutor of a young woman working as conspicuously in mathematics (when women *never* did) as Sonia Kowalewski in Heidelberg. The young woman was Florence Nightingale. One of her other teachers was the Belgian, Quetelet, who in 1829 broke down the Belgian census, and provided the early basis for life insurance. It was as a disciple of Quetelet that Florence Nightingale said, "To understand God's thoughts, we must study statistics, for these are the measure of His purpose." The year that Florence Nightingale went out to the Crimea, Sylvester applied for two professorships, failed at the first, and committed the horrible mistake—the mistake of Maxwell and Gibbs—of lecturing too well for the second. However, he finally stabilized his life with a professorship, which he kept until he was retired at the age of fifty-six. That year, he published *The Laws of Verse*. He had been interested in verse and versification all his life; and when he finally came to Johns Hopkins, six years later, Sidney Lanier, poet and prosodist, wrote in his "Ode to Johns Hopkins" of the University as

Led by soaring-genius'd Sylvester.

Sylvester began a new mathematical career, and an active one, in Baltimore. He founded and edited the *American Journal of Mathematics*, which, E. T. Bell points out, "gave mathematics in the United States a tremendous urge in the right direction—research."

Gibbs spoke of Sylvester as "the distinguished foreigner whose sojourn among us has given such an impulse to mathematical study in this country." His own work was in physics inextricably mixed with mathematics, and this decade of his life included a body of work in the latter. At Yale, he founded the Mathematical Club—and said at one of its meetings, with his ready and wry humor, "A mathematician may say anything he pleases, but a physicist must be at least partially sane." The Club was, in a small and private way, Gibbs's product at Yale, as the Cavendish Laboratory was Maxwell's at Cambridge, and the *Journal* Sylvester's at Baltimore.

It was typical of the stagnation at New Haven. Baltimore was a key industrial city, and a series of industrial struggles that amounted to a new civil war was begun. New Haven felt the wave of strikes, with their violence and the terrible recriminations that followed, less than almost any other city in the United States. New Haven was surpassed in heavy industry by all the centers, but for her carriages, her repeating rifles and carbines, her locks and combination locks, cutlery, sewing machines, edge-tools, rubber goods, and her clocks, she was famous. This stability was reflected in a certain smugness and stagnation, and also in the appearance of the town. It looked rather like Philadelphia north and west of the Green, with its straight streets. It had laid out its squares earlier than Philadelphia, the chamber of commerce bragged; and New Haven was not a brick town, but a wooden town, with no two houses alike, with yards and happy gardens, and three coats of white paint each year. South of the Green, the factory district had sprung up—and out, with blocks of low-lying plants, their huge chimneys and rows of windows, and the great slaughter-houses just out of town. And on Saturday nights, Chapel and Church Streets were full of thousands of shop and factory girls, pouring out on the gas-lit streets after their crowded weeks, pouring out and filling the widest streets in town, along which the young gentlemen of Yale used to fight the firemen.

The young gentlemen could talk now, as the country was talking in its parlors and dormitories and council rooms, not of fighting firemen, but of fighting labor. Grant wished he were President again, so that he could lead a charge against the Brotherhood of Locomotive Engineers; but those were the bloodshot dreams of an old soldier. Jay Gould, the "dynamo in a tubercular body," dreamed other and more poisonous dreams; he had suggested publicly that the country would do better under a monarchy. In the summer of '77, open warfare broke. Nine strikers and spectators were killed in Baltimore when the soldiers arrived; the Columbus workers went on a travelling strike, closing plants as they moved about the city; in Chicago, battle raged all day when the police tried to beat down a meeting, and nineteen were killed; cities across the country grappled; and on the fiercest scene, Pittsburgh, the Beards write, "a regular pitched battle was fought; when the militia-men marched into the midst of the assembled strikers, they encountered a resistance which developed into a guerilla war ending in several deaths and the destruction of the railway station, roundhouses, and hundreds of freight cars, causing losses running into the millions."

At Yale, William Graham Sumner was fighting labor with all the resources he had; and, at Yale, Sumner had the big guns. He was the most important influence, to quote the Beards again, on "a whole generation of young business men at Yale," and he taught what he believed to be, not prejudice against labor or any group, but law.

The summer of strikes, with labor dogged and defiant and the conservatives panicky, seemed like a beginning. There was shock abroad, and people seemed, as they do in any wartime, to open their minds to their relation to human beings. In this sudden awakening to old relationships, they searched for new ideas.

One young graduate student at Johns Hopkins was beginning to make up his mind to accept a lifework which most of his friends were advising him to drop. He was at the point where he knew the difficulties, and felt that it was not in his nature to let go because of them; but he knew that if he did not find encouragement soon, he might very well reach discouragement. Josiah Royce decided to find the one man who might understand him; he went to William James. As he told the story, years later, it began "in the house on Quincy Street," when Royce "was permitted to pour out my soul to somebody who really seemed to believe that a young man might rightfully devote his life to philosophy if he chose. . . .

"Sometimes critical people have (said) that James has always been too fond of cranks, and that the cranks have loved him. Well, I am one of James's cranks."

The next spring Royce sent his thesis to Noah Porter, who accepted it with approval. Its title was, "Of the Inter-dependence of the Principles of Knowledge."

"Mathematics *Is* a Language"

Before Maxwell had died, he had published a short paper, "On the Equilibrium of Heterogeneous Bodies." It was a transcript of the speech made at the South Kensington exhibit; and it did not reach its audience. An abstract was published in the *American Journal of Science*, and emphasis was put on Gibbs's work. Boltzmann's paper on gas theory appeared, with its statement that the entropy of a given state of a system of molecules is proportional to the logarithm of the probability of its occurrence—that statement from which the radiation theory of Planck was deduced.

The first telephone switchboard in the country was installed in New Haven, and the exchange grew rapidly during its first few years. But neither Gibbs nor Van Name seemed to have found any use for the new convenience, and when an instrument was installed in the house, eight years later, it was listed under Van Name. This listing remained in the directory, which in the beginning was printed on one side of a small sheet of paper, until it disappeared five years later. It reappeared in the last years of Gibbs's life, but his name was never listed. The directory read :

874–12 Van Name Addison, h.........121 High

for the house which Willard Gibbs shared with his sisters and his brother-in-law.

New Haven's streets, these nights, were bright with arc-lights, and a new well with a three-handled pump was a little monument at the corner of Church and Chapel.

Henry James published *Daisy Miller*, and Emily Dickinson's lines about the "dry wine of logarithm" were written in her wide-spaced hand at Amherst.

Karl Marx, seeing the labor situation lining up according to the strategy he had foreseen, wrote of "the great labor war . . . the beginning of a revolution. . . ."

Harper's Weekly published the climax in a series of anti-Communist cartoons, with the label : "King-killing association."

It was in these summers that Gibbs, having seen the complete publication of his big paper, went on with his work in dynamics, and vapor densities, and relaxed by going walking or climbing among the red cliffs around the city. Old Milton Seward, who planned to float off the top of East Rock in a side-paddle boat, kept the land away from the city; in '69, there was a summit house and a debris road; in 1880, it was finally·bought and turned into a park; but West Rock was wild, and wonderful to climb, as young Raphael Pumpelly had known when he as a boy went up its basalt pillars. Willard Gibbs was built on a fine, slight scale, but he was strong to a degree belying his slightness. The way he handled horses proved that, and the climbing he did; the story had grown up in the family about his weak chest, and later it would be said that he never married because "of his chest." But he used to go and call on the little girls who lived near by, and one of them went with him on a Fourth of July picnic.

They went up the rough trail, all the way to the forbidding cave that faced them suddenly from a thicket, a dark crack in the rock, and a perfect hiding-place. Unfenced and unmarked as it was, it was famous all around the countryside. This was Judge's Cave, where Goffe and Whalley had hidden, while the townspeople fed them and protected them from their condemners. It was safe and deep in the forest, as seen from below; but if you stood here, you could see far down the valley to the shining Sound. The place was full of legend; and the stern revolutionary words of king-killers echoed in the ears of anyone who came here : "Resistance to tyrants is obedience to God." Its metric bit into the brain. It was strange to stand high over this white town, almost concealed by its elms, and know to what a point that grim morality had come. "Resistance to tyrants is obedience to God." It was a word for regicides; a word for truth. You felt very strong in the green silence, and a Fourth of July picnic, with its laughter and little girls, remembered the blare and bunting in the middle of town. Willard Gibbs was very gay and strong. He carried little Emily all the way down, on his back.

Whittling boys, foreboding, labor-saving, and conflict. The currents were strong, but they left the rocks untouched. There were men coming up, working in these years, who spoke more directly to people than they could bear, for a while. They were linked together, and they needed to speak; they needed to be asked to speak, however; for dignity included reticence, and more than that, what they had to say required a demand. The early life of this country, and then the burden of guilt of the war, had suppressed many of the possible audience. And as for the creators, the greatest of these had to recognize the meagerness of their knowledge and rest on possibility. This was expressed in varied ways : Whitman, with his "Resist much, obey little" was putting the king-killers' motto in quantitative terms; the inventors of Connecticut, falling back on the white secluded winter and the resourcefulness of a countryside drained of many of its men and women, were enforcing another Connecticut motto : "Wear it out! Use it up! Make it do!"

Lewis Mumford says of this time :

A genuine culture was beginning to struggle upward again in the seventies : a Peirce, a Shaler, a Marsh, a Gibbs, a Ryder, a Roebling, a Thomas Eakins, a Richardson, a Sullivan, an Adams, a LaFarge were men that any age might proudly exhibit and make use of. But the procession of American civilization divided and walked around these men.

Gibbs was gaining recognition, however. Hubert Anson Newton had given an address before the American Association for the Advancement of Science at a meeting in Detroit, a lucid and passionate argument proving the nation's need for mathematics. Sylvester, at Johns Hopkins, said in 1877 that the new algebra was almost unknown on this continent. And Gibbs was working in the new algebra.

He was doing many kinds of work. His paper on vapor densities was a study of certain anomalies in densities of mixtures. He was demonstrating earlier equations that had been worked out in the great paper—demonstrating them according to experimental tables that had been made by others. It was a detailed study of the interpretative powers that were contained in the bristling paper, whose hundreds of equations, confined in their narrow space, were to release such prolific multitudes.

Gibbs at one time wrote to Lord Rayleigh, who was working to give him the Davy Medal against a strong (and eventually victorious) opposition, and who was clearly protesting the compression of the great paper :

I thank you very much for your kind interest in my "Equilibrium of Heterogeneous Substances." I myself had come to the conclusion that the fault was that it was too *long*. I do not think that I had any sense of the value of time, of my own or others, when I wrote it.

He was working from the immense suggestions in that paper to set up what Donnan calls—

a new science in which nearly all the artificial distinctions between physics and chemistry have vanished. In the period 1878–1900, Gibbs effected a . . . fusion, by uniting physics and chemistry in a great science of equilibrium, in which the statistical equilibria of masses of matter, enormously great in comparison with molecular magnitudes, were deduced from the two laws of thermodynamics in the most complete and general manner.

This creation by Gibbs of a comprehensive physico-chemical thermodynamics was, and long will be, of enormous importance both for chemistry and physics. However much we may learn about the individual units of the physico-chemical world, we shall always be vitally concerned with certain very important aspects of the average behavior of the "crowd."

In the same year, he published "The Fundamental Formulas of Dynamics," in the *American Journal of Mathematics*. The paper starts with Lagrange's formula of motion, and works out the formulae for the variations of acceleration, according to the principle of virtual velocities. He deals with discontinuous changes of velocity, and other properties of motion, using a statement closely related to Gauss's law of least constraint. The final section offers the equations of motion of a rigid body : classical equations derived by Euler.

This year, 1879, marked—in April—the thirteenth month of Edison's experiments with filament for the incandescent lamp. He put aside platinum and went back to carbon. There were thousands of failures. He sat at his table, running one hand through his hair and tapping absently with the other. His fingers tapped another sound; he had touched the little heap of tar and lampblack which was used in transmitter experiments. He rolled the soft black paste against his thumb. After a half-hour, he stood up abruptly and called a boy. The boy ran to get the spools of cotton Edison ordered, and in a few minutes he was carbonizing the thread. On October 21, he sealed the bulb and turned the current on. The light burned bright; electricity subdivided, against the demonstrations of its impossibility.

"Be not discouraged, keep on, there are divine things envelop'd," Whitman was writing. As D'Alembert had said, long ago, to his discouraged friends, "Go ahead, faith will follow."

But Henry George was writing, in *Progress and Poverty*, just published : "The fiat has gone forth! With steam and electricity, and the new powers born of progress, forces have entered the world that will either compel us to a higher plane or overwhelm us."

Gibbs was elected to the National Academy of Sciences in 1879, and in England, Lord Kelvin and P. G. Tait were working on the law of least action in connection with entropy.

As the '80s began, New Haven was engrossed in the Mary Stannard poisoning, and at the trial there were, among the 176 witnesses, eight Yale professors, talking about arsenical octahedrons and the blood of "goats, pigs, dogs, rabbits and men." The testimony of Professor Edward S. Dana marked the highest level of the State's prosecution of the Reverend Mr. Hayden—whose case depended on the facts of blood equilibrium, as well as the structure of arsenic.

This year—the year of Swift's comet—Gibbs published nothing, and in 1881, he dug in deeper on High Street. He had always been close to his old school, which was a constant reminder to him, as the boys streamed out of the house across the corner, at High and Wall. This year, he went back to it, in that he accepted a position as trustee of Hopkins Grammar School. The school was having its difficulties of finances and attendance; its board was made up of old boys, and it was the most natural thing in the world for him to tie himself to it again; his roots were locking him down to High Street. Again, he published nothing, but circulated in his classroom sheets for a new course in vector analysis. These sheets, privately printed, looked forward to years of future work. An award he received summed up his published work. On January 12, 1881, he was awarded the Rumford Medal by the American Academy of Arts and Sciences. In the recommendation, Gibbs's work had been characterized as "severely mathematical, and incapable of being translated into common language. The formulas, however, are not barren abstractions, but have a physical meaning." Joseph Lovering, who made the recommendation, was president of the Academy by the time the medal was presented. His address began with an account of the Rumford Medal and its history, and went on :

On the mechanical theory of heat, as a foundation, has been erected the grandest generalization of physical science, the Conservation of Energy. The results of observation and calculation agree, whenever a comparison is practicable, if the calculation is made upon the assumption that the totality of energy in a system, potential as well as dynamical, is as unchangeable as the totality of matter. . . . The conversion of heat (which is supplied to an in-definite amount by the consumption of the forest and the coal-beds) into ordinary mechanical energy or work, is of the highest significance to the advancing civilization of the race; but heat cannot be transformed into work without the transformation of a larger amount of heat of high temperature into heat of low temperature. This passage of heat from hot to cold bodies, without doing work, reinforced by the conduction and radiation of heat, creates the tendency to what is now called the dissipation of heat. This is what the writer in the *London Spectator* meant when he called heat the communist of the universe, the final consummation of this dissipation being a second chaos. Sir William Thomson has computed that the sun has lost through its radiation hundreds of times as much mechanical energy as is represented by the motions of all the planets. The energy this dispensed to the solar system, and from it to remoter space, "is dissipated, always more and more widely, through endless space, and never has been, and probably never can be, restored to the sun without acts as much beyond the scope of human intelligence as a creation or annihilation of energy, or of matter itself, would be."

Listing the work to date of Gibbs—the three papers—with a word of reference to the praise of "the late Professor J. C. Maxwell (whose early death is ever a fresh grief to science)" Lovering gave the medal to the secretary, for Gibbs, adding :

I cannot but think that if Count Rumford were living, he would regard with particular pleasure this award. For the researches of Professor Gibbs are the consummate flower and fruit of seeds planted by Rumford himself, though in an unpromising soil, almost a century ago.

"Mathematics *Is* a Language"

Gibbs's letter filled some of the gaps in the presentation, in which the content of his papers was never mentioned. He wrote:

To the American Academy of Arts and Sciences :
GENTLEMEN,

Regretting that I am unable to be present at the meeting to which I have been invited by your President, I desire to express my appreciation of the very distinguished honor which you have thought fit to confer upon me. This mark of approbation of my treatment of questions in thermo-dynamics is the more gratifying, as the value of theoretical investigation is more difficult to estimate than the results obtained in other fields of labor. One of the principal objects of theoretical research in any department of knowledge is to find the point of view from which the subject appears in its greatest simplicity. The success of the investigations in this respect is a matter on which he who makes them may be least able to form a correct judgment. It is, therefore, an especial satisfaction to find one's methods approved by competent judges.

The leading idea which I followed in my paper on the Equilibrium of Heterogeneous Substances was to develop the *rôles* of energy and entropy in the theory of thermo-dynamic equilibrium. By means of these quantities the general condition of equilibrium is easily expressed, and by applying this to various cases we are led at once to the special conditions which characterize them. We thus obtain the consequences resulting from the fundamental principles of thermo-dynamics (which are implied in the definitions of energy and entropy) by a process which seems more simple, and which lends itself more readily to the solution of problems, than the usual method, in which the several parts of a cyclic operation are explicitly and separately considered. Although my results were in a large measure such as had previously been obtained by other methods, yet, as I readily obtained those which were to me before unknown, or but vaguely known, I was confirmed in my belief in the suitableness of the method adopted.

A distinguished German physicist has said,—if my memory serves me aright,—that it is the office of theoretical investigation to give the form in which the result of experiments may be expressed. In the present case we are led to certain functions which play the principal part in determining the behavior of matter in respect to chemical equilibrium. The forms of these functions, however, remain to be determined by experiment, and here we meet the greatest difficulties, and find an inexhaustible field of labor. In most cases, probably, we must content ourselves at first with finding out what we can about these functions without expecting to arrive immediately at complete expressions of them. Only in the simplest case, that of gases, have I been able to write the equation expressing such a function for a body of variable composition, and here the equation only holds with a degree of approximation corresponding to the approach of the gas to the state which we call perfect.

Gratefully acknowledging the very favorable view which you have taken of my efforts, I remain, gentlemen, very truly yours,

J. WILLARD GIBBS

New Haven, Jan. 10, 1881.

The inexhaustible field of labor which was to be the experiment for Gibbs was, in fact, the great empire of industrial chemistry as we know it today. The experiments which prove him are giant plants, one-fourth of the industry of the United States. And beside this enormous spawn of a paper which was, in its way, lost, is the metal industry, work in soils and membranes and colloids, in the electrical industry, aeronautics, cement, explosives, philosophy—there are few witnesses to human imagination that are not also witnesses to Gibbs.

At home, a joke grew up. It was at the dinner table of the High Street house, and there was a moment of debate as to who would mix the salad dressing—until Willard took over, smiling and saying, "I am the authority in this household on the equilibrium of heterogeneous substances."

It was not a year for modest statement. When President Garfield was shot and dying, he turned to his attendant to ask, "Old boy, do you think my name will have a place in history?" And Garfield was answered, "Yes, a grand one, but a grander one in human hearts."

Gibbs's work in vector analysis, worked out between 1881 and 1884, was circulated in a highly condensed version. He felt that his system of notation, which derived from his study of Grassmann and multiple algebra, perhaps owed too much to the *Ausdehnungslehre* of 1844, although he had added and changed, until, as Leigh Page points out, "the value of his work lies more in the formulation of a convenient and significant notation than in the development of a new mathematical method." Gibbs said often that multiple algebra gave him more pleasure than any other intellectual work.

"Mathematics *Is* a Language"

Vector analysis provided an expression for space relations. Simple quantities, time, temperature, density—all those ideas which can be contained in single numbers are one group, and there is an algebra which deals with them. But there is another group—such as force, velocity, acceleration. Each of these has *direction* as well as magnitude. A vector, by definition, has both direction and magnitude; taken together, these become a unit, which may be expressed by an arrow—in which the length signifies *magnitude,* and the position *direction*—and then, as Gibbs says, "nothing prevents us from using a single letter for its symbolical designation."

This notation seemed to him more useful than the system of quaternions of Sir William Rowan Hamilton. Quaternions themselves have a long history, but Hamilton's system dawned on him on October 16, 1843, as he crossed a bridge during a walk with his wife. Hamilton was the versifier, the friend of Wordsworth and Coleridge, and Wordsworth had said that these were the only two men in the world with whom he felt inferior. E. T. Bell says of Hamilton that his tragedy was neither alcohol nor marriage, "but his obstinate belief that quaternions held the key to the mathematics of the physical universe." Tait, Hamilton's disciple, was the champion of his method, and when Gibbs, who had not yet published his course, began to send communications to the scientific magazines on vectors and orbits, vectors and Grassmann, and finally pieces in defense of vectors against quaternions, a historic row with Tait followed. But that came ten years later; and his course, edited by his student, E. B. Wilson, did not appear until 1902, when Gibbs was deep in work on his Statistical Mechanics, and wrote nothing more than an eighteen-line introduction saying that, in answer to an expressed desire, he had decided to publish his course, and had turned over the material to Wilson, allowing him to use his own judgment in preparing a book suitable for students in geometry and physics.

Gibbs's work checked with the linear associative algebra which Benjamin Peirce had presented in 1870. It provided superior symbols for multiplication, and, more important, a single differential operator for the three forms of the gradient, and divergence, and the curl. Leigh Page says that "the notation almost explains itself, and requires a minimum effort of memory on the part of the student." He speaks of the inertia which has kept many writers, particularly in England, using the outworn symbols, which are not only clumsy, but meaningless.

The work of the Peirces in dyadics, of Heaviside in vectors, and more recent work in tensor analysis, are all closely related to Gibbs's method. Tensors have come in with relativity, and in their language a scalar (a magnitude) is a tensor of zero rank, a vector a tensor of first rank, and so on. There are ranks higher than Gibbs's notation will allow, in tensor analysis; but Leigh Page notes that "ordinary theoretical physics rarely requires the use of more complicated quantities than scalars, vectors and dyadics. In this field Gibbs' notation is preeminent, whether the student is concerned with the three-dimensional space of Galileo and Newton, or with the four-dimensional space-time of Einstein's special relativity."

As far as the public was concerned, nothing had been presented. But Irving Fisher, the economist, as a pupil of Gibbs found the course on vector analysis the most interesting course he had with Gibbs. Fisher, who has applied not only Gibbs's ideas of equilibrium, but his vector analysis as well, to exchanges of money and goods, was surprised to find when he went to Germany that it was felt that the method was—as Professor Schwartz at Berlin said—too *willkürlich* : arbitrary. Gibbs had broken too many of the fundamental rules, according to the Germans. When Fisher took the story back to New Haven, Gibbs's comment was that "all depends on what your object is in making those sacrosanct rules for operating upon symbols. If the object is to interpret physical phenomena and if we find that we can do better by having a rule that $a \times b$ is equal not to $b \times a$ but to minus $b \times a$, as in the multiplication of two vectors, then," he said, "the criticisms of the Germans are beside the point."

There was much more on vectors later, when the correspondence began. But, for the next two years, Gibbs was publishing three papers on the electromagnetic theory of light. These papers, appearing less than ten years after Clerk Maxwell's two volumes on *Electricity and Magnetism*, applied Maxwell's theory to the propagation of light through crystals. Double refraction, as through Iceland spar, which returns two images, is considered, as are dispersion and rotary polarization. Gibbs's concern here is with electrical equilibrium—in metals, for example—and he says, in a characteristic tone, that the objection is the same as one of Lord Rayleigh's, that the apparent mechanical explanation of the thing is illusory.

All this points to the same conclusion—that the ordinary view of the phenomena is inadequate. The object of this paper will be accomplished, if it has been made clear how a point of view more in accordance with what we know of the molecular constitution of bodies will give that part of the ordinary theory which is verified by experiment, without including that part which is in opposition to observed facts.

In this year, 1882, Helmholtz, working without knowledge of Gibbs's great paper, was dealing with calculations of electromotive forces of reversible galvanic cells, which may easily be derived from Gibbs's equations, so that Helmholtz' is a natural result. Gibbs had actually laid down the basis of electrochemical thermodynamics, and now the long stream of re-discoveries was beginning. As Donnan writes, "Nothing in the history of science is more remarkable than the way in which Gibbs in 1878 provided the electrochemical science of the succeeding generation with its thermodynamic *Principia*."

An observatory was at last set up at Yale. Swift's comet had been watched in 1880; and Newton had been working hard for this day. It arrived at last, on May 1, 1882, as the corporation voted to establish the observatory; and a new period of Newton's activity began.

In 1883 Gibbs published a short letter in *Science*, to correct the notion of an exception to the second law, which Professor H. T. Eddy had offered as a suggestion to transfer heat from a colder to a hotter body. The day of the perpetual-motion machine was over by a ruling of the Academy in France; the day of the machine to reverse entropy had just begun. But actual work on Gibbsian lines was going on. Planck showed that as the familiar principle that "the pressure in a gas-mixture is equal to the sum of the pressures which the component gases would exert" separately, with the same volume, at the same temperature; so is this true of the entropy. This was a use that Gibbs had made of Dalton's law in his passage on Fundamental Equations of Ideal Gases, in the great paper. Planck proved it with the use of a semi-permeable membrane, a method which is now of great importance in physical chemistry. It can be demonstrated with pistons, or different permeabilities, as in machines that have three spaces with pressure at any stage in them.

The two major works which were before him were now in preparation. The year 1884 saw the publication of an abstract of one short page, "On the Fundamental Formula of Statistical Mechanics, with Applications to Astronomy and Thermodynamics." This had the kernel of a concept which is still only half-used, and which takes its place with relativity and quantum theory, according to Henry Margenau. Here is the entire abstract, as it appeared in the *Proceedings of the American Association for the Advancement of Science*:

Suppose that we have a great number of systems which consist of material points and are identical in character, but different in configuration and velocities, and in which the forces are determined by the configuration alone. Let the number of systems in which the coordinates and velocities lie severally between the following limits, viz. between

$$x_1 \text{ and } x_1 + dx_1,$$
$$y_1 \text{ and } y_1 + dy_1,$$
$$z_1 \text{ and } z_1 + dz_1,$$
$$x_2 \text{ and } x_2 + dx_2,$$
$$\text{etc.,}$$
$$\dot{x}_1 \text{ and } \dot{x}_1 + d\dot{x}_1,$$
$$\dot{y}_1 \text{ and } \dot{y}_1 + d\dot{y}_1,$$
$$\dot{z}_1 \text{ and } \dot{z}_1 + d\dot{z}_1,$$
$$\dot{x}_2 \text{ and } \dot{x}_2 + d\dot{x}_2,$$
$$\text{etc.,}$$

be denoted by
$$L \, dx_1 \, dy_1 \, dz_1 \, dx_2 \text{ etc. } d\dot{x}_1 \, d\dot{y}_1 \, d\dot{z}_1 \, d\dot{x}_2 \text{ etc.}$$
The manner in which the quantity L varies with the time is given by the equation

$$\frac{dL}{dt} = -\Sigma \left[\frac{dL}{dx} \dot{x} + \frac{dL}{d\dot{x}} \ddot{x} \right],$$

where t, x_1, y_1, z_1, x_2, etc., $\dot{x}_1$, $\dot{y}_1$, $\dot{z}_1$, $\dot{x}_2$, etc. are the independent variables, and the summation relates to all the coordinates.

The object of the paper is to establish this proposition (which is not claimed as new, but which has hardly received the recognition which it deserves) and to show its applications to astronomy and thermodynamics.

"Mathematics *Is* a Language"

A review in the *Nation* had caught Gibbs's eye some time before he had worked out the ideas which held him now. It was in many ways a remarkable issue, this *Nation* of September 22, 1881. The death of Garfield, only three days past, was the big news of the issue; but there was also an article on the Abbé Galiani, whose letters from Naples and Paris—"the café of Europe"—were becoming quite fashionable, although nobody remembered his prophecies; there was a bit about the new catalogue of the office library of the Surgeon-General, at Washington. Surgery and medicine had really come up since the Civil War. *That* was the science that was the slut of war; it never failed to profit, and learn the lessons of bloodshed. And then there was the review, unsigned, as all reviews were, of two new textbooks on algebra, one by Simon Newcomb, and another by Wentworth. It spoke of Grassmann, "one of the greatest mathematicians who ever lived," and his high-school algebra, published in 1861; of how he followed the example of Isaac Newton and called it *Arithmetik;* but, the review added, a boy of sixteen could not teach himself algebra with the help of Grassmann's book. He could teach himself with Newcomb. Contrasted against this clarity and height—the highest algebra appeared in the *Ausdehnungslehre*, that was made plain—was the other side, represented by the second book. Todhunter is quoted as speaking for that side; he "regards mathematics as a clear-headed stoker who, by long and faithful service, has worked himself up to the position of engineer, regards an engine." And the caginess of this second author defied all comment. One need only quote a little statement in his preface : "To avoid trespassing upon the works of recent American authors, no American text-book has been consulted."

There was one sentence in the review that remained with Willard Gibbs. It was the voice of his social conscience; it spoke for him more clearly than he was speaking for himself. It said : "The human mind has never invented a labor-saving device equal to algebra."

Labor-saving devices! They were the rule of life, as America entered upon the Gilded Age. Charles Francis Adams, who was just becoming President of the Union Pacific, might see the whole railway system as a labor-saving device, or a wide exhibit of labor-saving devices, sowing cities from the Atlantic to California.

Edison was a factory in himself, and his plants were spreading. George Bernard Shaw and Samuel Insull were working for him in London, demonstrating telephones. Shaw was a poor young flaming-headed Irishman, just arrived in London. And Thomas Davidson was striding in the Adirondacks with William James, laughing as they walked with lanterns on the dark mountains, and calling James "stuffy" and "academic." Shaw was about to return to London, and the evenings at his rooms in Chelsea provided the glow and impulse to ethical socialism in England. His Fellowship led to the founding of the Fabian Society; and it was here that Shaw found his voice. But now he had not heard of Thomas Davidson, or of Sidney Webb; he had heard about Tyndall and Helmholtz, and his London job led to the creation of the central figure in his novel, *The Irrational Knot*. Shaw says, in the preface to this engaging and early work:

. . . This book is not wholly a compound of intuition and ignorance. Take for example the profession of my hero, an Irish-American electrical engineer. That was by no means a flight of fancy. For you must not suppose, because I am a man of letters, that I never tried to earn an honest living. I began trying to commit that sin against my nature when I was fifteen, and persevered, from youthful timidity and diffidence, until I was twenty-three. My last attempt was in 1879, when a company was formed in London to exploit an ingenious invention by Mr. Thomas Alva Edison—a much too ingenious invention, as it proved, being nothing less than a telephone of such stentorian efficiency that it bellowed your most private communications all over the house instead of whispering them with some sort of discretion. This was not what the British stockbroker wanted; so the company was soon merged in the National Telephone Company, after making a place for itself in the history of literature, quite unintentionally, by providing me with a job. Whilst the Edison Telephone Company lasted, it crowded the basement of a huge pile of offices in Queen Victoria Street with American artificers. These deluded and romantic men gave me a glimpse of the skilled proletariat of the United States. They sang obsolete sentimental songs with genuine emotion; and their language was frightful even to an Irishman.

"Mathematics *Is* a Language"

Shaw tells of the American energy that insists on being slave-driven by Americans, and despises the British. He writes scaldingly of the American workmen who sweated themselves for their employers' benefit instead of looking after their own interests, and sums up his own position as he discharged the duties of lecturer "in a manner which, I am persuaded, laid the foundation of Mr. Edison's London reputation." The Edison Effect had been dropped where the inventor patented it, but J. A. Fleming was working with the rest of the London staff; and when his thermionic valve was added, the third step—to be made by Lee De Forest, a student of Gibbs's at Yale—would produce the radio tube. Edison was establishing workshops now where he could find them, and Menlo Park was a huge laboratory-plant. Two experimental electric locomotives were built, at the order of Henry Villard, who wanted to adopt them for his Northern Pacific Railway. Engineers said at the time that the idea was "absolutely and utterly impossible." The engineers and the physicists were teaching that knowledge had come to a close; that electric machinery was impossible, that a heavier-than-air flying engine was impossible; that future advances in physics were impossible. But Edison was applying for his patents, at the rate of three hundred patents in four years; and the electric railway was soon being used on the New York Central and New Haven roads.

The Franklin Institute, in Philadelphia, responded logically to the storm of electrical equipment. William P. Tatham, the president of the Institute, wrote to Gibbs in July 1884, asking him to join the board of examiners in preparation for a huge electrical exhibit. Gibbs answered him :

New Haven, July 15, 1884

Wm. P. Tatham Esq.
      President of Franklin Institute
DEAR SIR,
   I regret that I am unable to undertake the responsibilities of the position to wʰ the Board of Managers of the Franklin Institute have honored me by an appointment.
   Such studies as I have made in electrical science have been so entirely confined to the theoretical side of the subject, & I am so unused to laboratory practice, that it would be impossible for me

to discharge properly the duties of an Examiner at the International Electr. Exhibition.

Very truly yours,

J. WILLARD GIBBS

A week after this refusal, a letter arrived from Frelinghuysen, the Secretary of State, informing Gibbs that "the President has appointed a scientific commission which may in the name of the United States Government conduct a national conference of electricians in Philadelphia in the Autumn of 1884."

The list included Prof. H. A. Rowland, who was appointed chairman, Prof. M. B. Snyder, Prof. J. Willard Gibbs, Prof. John Trowbridge, Prof. C. A. Young, Prof. G. F. Brackett, Dr. W. H. Wahl, Prof. Simon Newcomb, Prof. G. F. Barker, Prof. E. J. Houston, Prof. R. A. Fisk, Prof. Francis C. Van Dyck.

Gibbs answered at once :

New Haven, Conn., July 30, 1884

To the Hon. F. T. Frelinghuysen
    Secretary of State
SIR,

I have the honor to acknowledge the receipt of your communication of July 23, enclosing my appointment to the National Conference of Electricians at Phila.

In accepting this appointment, I desire to express my grateful appreciation of the honor w^h has been conferred upon me.

I am, Sir, with respect,

Your obedient servant,

J. WILLARD GIBBS

The Exhibit was a huge success, and the lights glared from the windows of the Institute as the hundreds of electrical appliances announced another age. The Conference brought together, for the first time, some of the most important of American and English scientists. Here Gibbs met Sir William Thomson and Oliver Lodge, and again saw Rowland and Simon Newcomb.

Gibbs presided at one of the meetings of the group. He spoke only twice from the floor; one recorded speech goes back in its interest to the early paper on weights and measures, and speaks for the point he made again and again in his life and work : that science is, above all, communication. Rowland was talking about the term "watt," which had not yet been legalized, and which had not been recommended in Paris at a general naming of units. These were the first days, when the scientists were arguing for and against "metric horse-power" and similar terms; the patriots had proposed giving the name "henry," after Joseph Henry, to the thousand-watt unit, on the grounds that not a single American name had been applied. Gibbs answered characteristically :

In regard to the names, especially of the units, there are two things which are most important; one is that they shall be universally adopted, and the other is that they shall be universally and easily understood, especially that they should not be liable to misinterpretation and misapprehension. With regard to the general adoption of this unit, I believe it has been suggested to you before that there is some little hesitation on the part of the French and on the part of the Germans. I do not know that we care particularly for a name which is to be confined to our language. We want words in the present state of science which will be adopted by all the important nations of the earth. Of course I am unable to express any opinion as to the probability of the adoption of it by the other nations if it is adopted by the English and ourselves.

. . . It seems to me it would be an advantage if we would continue in the scientific world as we have begun, to name the electrical system of units after electricians. That is much more important in work or power than in anything else, because there is danger of misunderstanding. There is nothing in the name of this unit of power to indicate that it belongs to the electrical units. It strikes me that that is an objection, perhaps a very slight one, to the name; but I should like to have the names to be as far as possible such that one who does not hear or read of them very often, and whose memory is not very good, will be able to place them at once in the proper list. Otherwise it would be necessary to have a pocket dictionary to refer to, because the number of names threaten to become somewhat extensive.

And, during the last five minutes of the Conference, Gibbs spoke in answer to a proposal for the electrical investigation of structural metals—an answer which throws back in the face of his critics the charge that he was not aware of the implications of his own work for precisely that—structural metals, whose deep knowledge has been provided by Gibbs's own "remote" laws. He said :

We have had a very interesting subject introduced to us by Captain Michaelis. It seems to me that a subject of so much novelty requires a little more thought before we can take such definite action as this [it had been proposed that a committee of seven bring the matter up before Congress]. He has brought forward many points to reflect upon. Some of us may have something useful concerning them in the future. In the infancy of a work like this it seems like putting a heavy duty upon the chairman to ask him to appoint a committee which should carry to any successful result an investigation of this kind, or suggest to Congress what could be done in a matter of so novel a character.

His caution and his foresight were the mixture one might expect of Gibbs; his view carried the motion, and the Conference adjourned. But the exchange of letters that is the best indication of Gibbs's personality came after the Exhibit. The following March, a letter arrived from the United States Electrical Commission in Baltimore, saying :

DEAR SIR,
Prof. Rowland requests me to inform the members of the U.S. Electrical Commission that some three thousand dollars still remain in the hands of the Commission of the fund appropriated by Congress, and that he is desirous of ascertaining the opinion of the Commission as to what should be done with this balance.
The original idea was to carry on a series of tests on dynamo machines at Philadelphia, but the Franklin Institute discouraged this.
I remain, very respectfully and truly yours,
ARTHUR S. HATHAWAY

Gibbs's answer went straight back to Baltimore. It is the most pungent and direct response he could have made :

New Haven
Mch 31 1885
Dear Prof⸱ Rowland,
If there is no proposition before the Commission for the employment of the balance of our appropriation, I think that it had better be returned to the U.S. Treasury.
Yours truly,
J. W. GIBBS

In the same month, Gibbs was made a corresponding member of the British Association, and on the first of September, he was notified that he was to be Vice-President of Section A, in Mathematics, for the next meeting of the American Association for the Advancement of Science.

"Mathematics *Is* a Language"

At that moment a young student who first saw the name of Gibbs in Maxwell's *Theory of Heat*—which he had read the year before—was in Berlin, working with Helmholtz; and Michael Pupin discovered that Helmholtz was studying the same problems of caloric and chemical behavior of bodies which Maxwell said had been solved by Gibbs. He tells the story :

> When I saw that von Helmholtz was interested in these problems, I decided to consult the original essays of Gibbs. I knew where they were, because Maxwell in his book gave the original source, namely, *Transactions of the Connecticut Academy of Sciences*. I found the essays, and I studied, studied, and studied them, and finally I understood them, thanks to my eighteen months' training in mathematics at the University of Cambridge. They were difficult from a mathematical point of view but with a little mathematical training they were not so very difficult. I told Helmholtz about it. "Everything you have done," said I, "and everything the physical chemists are doing today, is apparently all in Gibbs." He said, "Look it up very carefully and make a report," which I did.
>
> Every American who goes to Europe has two ideas in his head; one is to get as much knowledge in as short a time as possible, and the other is to get his doctor's degree, go back to the U.S., and get married. My doctor's dissertation was suggested by my study of Gibbs. It related to a physical concept first revealed by Gibbs, the Free Energy concept. Now in this doctor's dissertation, which I still have, I said, in substance, "This whole theory of physical chemistry was made in the State of Connecticut and not in Germany," as was supposed at that time. This statement was admitted to be correct by Professor von Helmholtz, who knew about these theories more than anyone else in Germany, otherwise he would not have permitted me to make use of it in my doctor's dissertation. I admit, however, that he had to check me in order to prevent me from giving offense.

At home, in New Haven, Gibbs was preparing for a journey to Buffalo. A story is told of him, the one story that anyone remembers of Willard Gibbs at a faculty meeting. He would come to meetings—these faculty gatherings so full of campus politics, scarcely veiled manoeuvres, and academic obstacle races —and leave without a word, staying politely enough, but never speaking.

Just this once, he spoke. It was during a long and tiring debate on elective courses, on whether there should be more or less English, more or less classics, more or less mathematics. And suddenly everything he had been doing stood up—and the past behind him, his father's life, and behind that, the long effort and voyage that had been made in many lifetimes—and he stood up, looking down at the upturned faces, astonished to see the silent man talk at last. And he said, with emphasis, once and for all :

"Mathematics *is* a language."

On August 18th, he spoke on Multiple Algebra in Buffalo.

The paper, presented only a short while after the Haymarket meeting in Chicago, when feeling had reached a new high, after the article in the Chicago *Alarm*, beginning : "DYNAMITE! Of all the good stuff this is the stuff . . ." And Spies and the others in Chicago, Most and the others in New York, the Knights of Labor everywhere, with their current membership of over 700,000, were in the headlines. It took a mind that ignored and selected and faced the social will to speak as Gibbs spoke in August.

He began with the line from the *Nation* :

"It has been said that 'the human mind has never invented a labor-saving machine equal to algebra.' If this be true, it is but natural and proper that an age like our own, characterized by the multiplication of labor-saving machinery, should be distinguished by an unexampled development of this most refined and most beautiful of machines."

And he went on to the history of this broader algebra, to the failures of Möbius, Hamilton, Grassmann, and Saint-Venant to make a proportional impression, which is the most conspicuous evidence "that the times were not ripe for the methods which they sought to introduce." This algebra "was not sought for or invented;—it forced itself, unbidden, upon the attention of mathematicians, and with its rules already formed.

"But the idea . . . once received, although as it were unwillingly," must have suggested other possibilities.

He chalks in the history : Hamilton, Möbius, Grassmann, Cauchy, down to 1870 and Benjamin Peirce's work, subsequently "developed and enriched by his son, Professor C. S.

Peirce." The early work was lithographed; Gibbs notes that even at so late a date the work had only a limited audience. And he notes the many remarkable papers by Sylvester.

"It is not an accident that this century has seen the rise of multiple algebra," he goes on, preparing to discuss matrices. And after mentioning the difficulty in algebra, he speaks of geometry. "If we were asked to characterize in a single word our modern geometry, we would perhaps say that it is a geometry of position." Position, he explains carefully, is a multiple quantity, and he points out how much more easily and naturally relations could be expressed in this way. He cites Lagrange: "It is indeed the real beauty of Lagrange's method that it is not so much an analytical artifice, as the natural development of the subject."

He speaks in terms of nature and ease throughout. He speaks of a geometer tangled in artifice, who needs a new artifice to extricate himself. "I do not mean that his genius might not possibly be equal to the occasion, but I do mean very seriously that it is a vicious method which requires any ingenuity or any artifice to express so simple a relation."

He produces examples to show that modern geometry is tending to "results which are appropriately expressed in multiple algebra," and he quotes Clebsch and Clifford on the past and future of multiple algebra.

"I do not know that anything useful or interesting, which relates to multiple quality, and can be symbolically expressed, falls outside of the domain of multiple algebra," he says, turning from its history to the process itself. "But if it is asked, what notions are to be regarded as fundamental, we must answer, here as elsewhere, those which are most simple and fruitful."

He speaks of multiple quantities, like ten apples+seven oranges, three miles northward+five miles eastward. And he explains that as the number 12 acts as an operator to change 1 mile into 12 miles, in multiple algebra an operator would act in more than one way to change, say, 10 apples+7 oranges into 50 apples+100 oranges, or one vector into another vector.

To go back for a moment, "Algebra, as a formal science, may rest on a purely formal foundation. To take our illustration again from mechanics, we may say that if a man is inventing a particular machine,—a sewing machine, a reaper,—nothing is more important than that he should have a precise idea of the operation which his machine is to perform, yet when he is treating the general principles of mechanics he may discuss the lever, or the form of the teeth of wheels" (there is an overtone of memory here, as one remembers the title of Gibbs's thesis) "which will transform uniform motion, without inquiring the purpose to which the apparatus is to be applied." And so with algebra, we ask the questions of its purpose. Given only the law, we may found a science, we do not need the other definiteness of conception. "Nor will such a science be merely a pastime for an ingenious mind," he says, as he exposes one after another of his own views and open beliefs. And he launches into a discussion of Grassmann and products.

In closing, he speaks of the applications of multiple algebra.

"First of all," he says, "geometry, and the geometrical sciences which treat of things having position in space, kinematics, mechanics, astronomy, physics, crystallography, seem to demand a method of this kind, for position in space is essentially a multiple quantity and can only be represented by simple quantities in an arbitrary and clumsy manner." He speaks of our spatial intuitions, and how the fact that they are well developed leads us to these methods. "Here, Nature herself takes us by the hand and leads us along by easy steps, as a mother teaches her child to walk."

Möbius and Grassmann disseminated the ideas of this algebra; Maxwell did much to bring quaternions in. "I wish that I could say as much of astronomy. It is, I think, to be regretted, that the oldest of the scientific applications of mathematics, the most dignified, the most conservative, should keep so far aloof from the youngest of mathematical methods; and standing as I do" among astronomers, he says, though not of them, he speaks for the method as applied to their subject.

The concept is a space-concept as distinguished from a point-concept. One needs to think in terms of space, and to understand one of Gibbs's most effective phrases : "In mathematics, a part often contains the whole."

He speaks for a few minutes more about the advantages and the applications of this method, and concludes : "But I do not so much desire to call your attention to the diversity of the applications of multiple algebra, as to the simplicity and unity of its principles. The student of multiple algebra suddenly finds himself free from various restrictions to which he has been accustomed. To many, doubtless, this liberty seems like an invitation to license. Here is a boundless field in which caprice may riot. It is not strange if some look with distrust for the result of such an experiment. But the farther we advance, the more evident it becomes that this too is a realm subject to law. The more we study the subject, the more we find all that is most useful and beautiful attaching itself to a few central principles. We begin by studying *multiple algebras;* we end, I think, by studying MULTIPLE ALGEBRA."

CHAPTER FOURTEEN

The Rosetta Stone of Science

W HEN THE American Academy gave Gibbs the Rumford Medal, no evaluation of his work was made; it was left to him to describe his paper in a letter of acceptance. But the invitation to foreign membership in the Société Hollandaise des Sciences, in Haarlem, carried with it the beginning of an interest that was to spread its contagion until it reached down to students and factory workers who had never heard of Yale, and surely never of Willard Gibbs. It was Clerk Maxwell's enthusiasm that had struck the American Academy; that was made clear in the presentation speech. But, in this country, there was nobody who was willing to cut through the "bristling quickset" of seven hundred equations to find their application. G. W. Hill, at Nyack, was too close to Gibbs in temperament; he was working alone, as Gibbs was; and Benjamin Peirce worked in curves, functions, and forces, and analytical mechanics for a generation that worshipped Sir William R. Hamilton; and beyond the fact that Peirce's own interest lay only in pure mathematics, for which he did less than Gibbs did for physics and chemistry, he had spent a great deal of time before his death in 1880 in proving the work of Adams and Leverrier unsound. Peirce was as influential in his way as Silliman had been in a more popular scene; but neither Hill nor Peirce was able to relate Gibbs to the future of their interests. It took a different range of vision : Maxwell had that necessary range, and Lorenz, and so, in Holland, did J. D. van der Waals.

Van der Waals, working in Amsterdam on the study of condensation in a mixture of gases, saw the deep significance of Gibbs's great paper. He had been proceeding along lines followed by Andrews, and, as Gibbs began to publish, he had obtained an equation for variations in imperfect gases. Van der Waals immediately undertook to incorporate Gibbs's discoveries in his own group of applications, and he drew the attention of a young chemist, Bakhuis Roozeboom, to these papers. Roozeboom was a student of Bemmelin's, and was in Leyden at the time, but he later moved to Amsterdam, and the nucleus of a Dutch school of physical chemistry prepared itself to develop the phase rule.

In Germany, Öttingen mentioned the existence of this paper to Wilhelm Ostwald, the young chemist who, with Ernst Mach, was working on many of the same problems of science and ideas with which William James was occupied at Harvard. Ostwald heard of the paper only generally. Öttingen said provocative things about it; but all that Ostwald really knew was that there was a significant work on thermodynamics by an American physicist; he knew, too, that it was difficult to follow. The whole story piqued his interest at once, for he was deep in the theory of chemical affinity, and he felt that thermodynamics was the mightiest instrument that could aid his purpose. He began to hunt down a copy of the "Equilibrium of Heterogeneous Substances," and he found it as hard to get a copy at Dorpat as John Aitken had at Darroch. The search was tantalizing; almost before he succeeded, he felt that he was on the trail of something whose obstacles only meant that there was great importance here for him. And as he began to study the paper, as he found the going hard, even if he made full notes while he went along, its unquestionable significance opened up before him. He saw that he was really translating as he read, working at the tense, dry style of this unknown American. But that was by far the best idea!—he would translate the paper. What he read matched what Öttingen had told him; there was no way to condense it, since it was already written in a flaming line of concentration. Abbreviation was out of the question; there was nothing to leave out. He could see that the close attention that he would have to give the work would help him. Hardly anyone had read the paper, it seemed; Maxwell and Lorenz had mentioned it, but that was all; and a German translation would really bring it to light. The review in the *Fortschritte der Physik* should have been very important; it should have made the name of the writer; but, in fact, it was like the Boston speech. It merely listed the contents of the paper; and it appeared too late to seem enthusiastic. No, thought Ostwald; here is a neglected masterpiece; we can use this here; and he wrote to Gibbs from Riga in 1887. He was starting, in collaboration with another editor, a young Dutch physical chemist—J. H. van't Hoff—a journal that would go on in the tradition of Poggendorff's long history of publication, the *Zeitschrift für physikalische Chemie*, and in this letter of April 26, Ostwald asks Gibbs to contribute to the new journal. He asks, also, that Gibbs allow him to use his name on the masthead; and then makes a proposal :

I take this opportunity of expressing the wish, shared by many colleagues, that your great memoir, which is fundamental to the application of thermodynamics to chemical problems, be made more readily accessible. Could you not bring yourself to republish it in expanded form, illustrated with specific examples, of which there is now no lack? I must admit that your work is very difficult, particularly for the chemist, who is seldom conversant with mathematical reasoning. I would like it best if you would agree to a German edition. I would be glad to arrange for its publication and to take care of the translation. In this way the study of this domain would be greatly intensified, especially in Germany.

Three months later Gibbs wrote :

Dr. W. Ostwald,
MY DEAR SIR :
Please accept my apologies for my delay in replying to your very kind letter. Some points required a certain consideration (the more, as at that time I had not yet seen your valuable journal), and when I had laid your letter aside, the pressure of other engagements prevented me from returning to it.

I am very glad that you have undertaken a journal of this character, for which there seems to be an abundant opening. The subject is one in which I have felt a lively interest, and to which, although my time for the last years has been given almost exclusively to other subjects, I have always hoped to be able to return. Nevertheless I am not able to make any engagements, but can only assure you of my

good wishes for your undertaking and my grateful appreciation of your kind interest in my own work.
I remain,

Yours very respectfully,
J. WILLARD GIBBS

Then—and, as John Johnston sadly says, the correspondence has clearly not been preserved complete—there is a gap, during which Ostwald obviously asked for a copy of the memoir and was helped by Gibbs to get one. His next letter, in the following year, is a letter of thanks to say that he has the work. He goes on to ask again :

Would you be willing that I publish a German translation of your fundamental paper? It is so inaccessible, and contains so much that is important, that such an undertaking seems to me to be very useful.

This time Gibbs answered in three weeks, with characteristic modesty and hesitation, but at the same time with the opening simple statement that discloses his real feeling :

Professor W. Ostwald,
MY DEAR SIR :
I should be very glad to have my essays in thermodynamics made accessible to a larger circle of readers. Yet I should have feared that the call for a German edition would hardly justify the labor and expense of the translator and publisher. If, however, you think differently, I should be glad to hear from you more definitely in regard to what you would think practicable.
With thanks for your kind interest in my work, I remain,

Yours truly,
J. W. GIBBS

During these years, the first wave of re-discoveries arrived. Re-discoveries, or rather independent discoveries of material that had lain unknown among the mathematical obstacles of the great paper. Konawalow's theorem of "indifferent points" was announced in 1881; in 1882, Helmholtz worked out a relation—now known as the Gibbs-Helmholtz equation—which relates values in a galvanic cell. In the last four pages of the "Equilibrium of Heterogeneous Substances," Gibbs had made the first clear statement of the operation of a reversible galvanic cell, says MacInnes. "If these pages had been digested by later workers in the field, a vast amount of error and misapplied energy would have been avoided." Gibbs showed that the electromotive force of the cell is determined by what is now named the Gibbs Free Energy. The prevailing belief was that it was determined by the total energy. The equation that he used, and that Helmholtz later reached, is "one of the most important equations in physical chemistry and is the basis for much of the recent work."

At the same time, a young chief of laboratory at the School of Physics and Chemistry in Paris was spending a lot of his time, aside from his classroom demonstrations, in working on the theory of crystalline physics. Pierre Curie was beginning to formulate the principle of symmetry, and, going past this to more research—on magnetism, this time—obtained in 1885 the result which is Curie's law of crystal habit. This, also, was implicit in the equations of the great paper.

Forty years before, working with photography, Draper had seen that the physical change in a substance can be produced by the light rays *absorbed by* the substance only. Light acts as another variable in this conception of a thermodynamic system; $n+3$ phases are required for an invariant system, as in any other system to which the phase rule may be applied. A beam of light may be treated as though it were homogeneous; and this line of attack—the use of the phase rule—has been the most promising one in photo-synthesis or plant-synthesis.

Gibbs himself was devoting much of his attention to the study of light. In 1882 and 1883, he published the three notes on the application, to light propagated through crystals, of Maxwell's electromagnetic theory. In 1886, two reviews of his appeared in the *American Journal of Science*: one was of astronomical papers prepared by Newcomb and Michelson, on *The Velocity of Light in Air and Refracting Media*; and the other, of E. Ketteler's *Theoretische Optik*.

A short paper in *Nature* (April 22, 1886) dealt with the velocity of light as determined by the revolving mirrors in an experiment of Foucault, calling attention to "the important fact, that while the individual wave rotates the wave-normal of the group remains unchanged." To get a picture of the phenomenon, Gibbs says, "we may imagine that we are able to see a few inches of the top of a moving carriage-wheel. The individual spokes rotate, while the group maintains a vertical direction."

Two papers in 1888 and 1889 compared Maxwell's theory of

light with other theories—elastic-solid ether theories, and the quasi-labile ether theory which Lord Kelvin had just advanced.

In connection with his work in optics, Gibbs put together an apparatus at home, and carried out an experiment. Kraus was told that nobody knew the nature of the experiment, but Hastings says that the explanation which Gibbs was using involved certain actions in reflection which had never been "seen or, at least, recorded":

As it did not seem to him that such negative evidence was conclusive, he constructed an apparatus with his own hands so perfectly adapted to the end in view that his observations afforded the proof sought. A striking light is thrown upon the character of the great physicist by the fact that no reference to this theory, which must have cost much critical study, appears in his writings, nor is it known that anyone except the present writer ever saw the apparatus and made the experiment for which it was designed.

When Gibbs really needed equipment to test his beliefs, he made his own. This machine actually tested the compressural wave system; but he never used it again, he never referred to it, and its only effect is buried among his equations, in which he added this reinforcement to his conviction of the truth of the electromagnetic nature of light.

A short paper on electrostatic force appeared in 1896, beginning, "As we may have to wait some time for the experimental solution of Lord Kelvin's very instructive and suggestive problem concerning two pairs of spheres charged with electricity, it may be interesting to see what the solution would be from the standpoint of existing electrical theories."

In the papers about other theories, the *Commentary* points out, Gibbs "emphasizes the fact that the electrical theory is not obliged to invent hypotheses to account for the phenomenon of light, but needs only to apply the laws furnished by the science of electricity." The success of the other theories depended on device and assumption, and finally physicists were led back to Maxwell's theory, as Gibbs defends it.

One of the stories of Gibbs's modesty is told of the publication of his letter to *Nature* on electromagnetic theory. "Oh, did they really publish it?" he asked in surprise to the friend who told him of it. These stories are not really ever tales of shyness or modesty, although they seem to be; they are evidences of Gibbs's unwillingness to make any assumptions whatever in regard to the physical world. He expected nothing; *nothing*, from outside. He was sure of himself, and trusted himself. Later, he trusted one or two of his pupils; and there was always his family. But even the little anecdotes tell of a nature that was cautious to a terrible fault; suspicious to the smallest detail; these were the faults of an experimental scientist, but they served him ill outside of his work, and even his work has been a disappointment to those who are unwilling to draw their own conclusions from it. For he would make no assumptions even after a fact was accomplished; he would *not* believe in publication; that is, acceptance. And he had tragic reason for this disbelief.

During the '80s, Gibbs was also preparing the computations of elliptic orbits from three complete observations, which were later verified by Beebe and Phillips. This classical work, says Langer, "has achieved an immense saving in astronomical calculations." It brought him even closer in activity to his friend next door, his tutor, his adviser with his thesis, his confidant in the Johns Hopkins affair, the man with whom he could leave off in the middle of a sentence and return the next morning to complete it— Hubert Anson Newton. Newton's plan, the College observatory, was prospering, and the new development was the most exciting. An amateur astronomer announced in the local newspapers that he had obtained, by accident on the same plate with the picture of a star, a clearly shown track—the track of a large meteor. He asked in the notice for observations from anyone who had seen the meteor. The correspondence, and the plate itself, were given to Professor Newton, and he was immediately fired with the possibilities for the observatory of having a camera set up. The National Academy granted funds, and in time a battery of cameras was mounted. Gibbs had been interested, not only in his friend's activities—his work at the observatory, his popular lectures, on "The Story of Biela's Comet," "The Relation of Meteorites to Comets," "The Worship of Meteorites," and an article on the fireball in a Madonna of Raphael's—but also in the idea of the relations between three positions in an orbit as vector relations. His paper determined an orbit from three complete observations by solving the equations which stood for elliptic motion. He limited himself to short-spaced intervals between the three observations, since he could then substitute simpler relations between the unknown factors. He writes :

The Rosetta Stone of Science

The problem is not entirely determinate, for we may lay the greater stress upon simplicity or upon accuracy; we may seek the most simple relations which are sufficiently accurate to give us any approximation to an orbit, or we may seek the most exact expression of the real relations, which shall not be too complex to be serviceable.

Hubert Anson Newton is described by Gibbs :

Professor Klein has divided mathematical minds into three leading classes : the logicians, whose pleasure and power lies in subtility of definition and dialectic skill; the geometers, whose power lies in the use of the space-intuitions; and the formalists, who seek to find an algorithm for every operation. Professor Newton evidently belonged to the second of these classes.

His natural tastes were gratified by the development of an abstract system as well as by investigation of "the concrete phenomena of nature as they exist in space and time." Newton's great pleasure is in his reply to the award of a gold medal : "To discover some new truth in nature," he said, "even though it concerns the small things in the world, gives one of the purest pleasures in human experience. It gives joy to tell others of the treasures found."

"In spite of his studious tastes and love of a quiet life," Gibbs also writes of Newton, "he did not shirk the duties of citizenship, serving a term as alderman in the city council, being elected, we may observe, in a ward of politics strongly opposed to his own."

Willard Gibbs had only one taste of conflict in politics. He was a solid Republican all of his life, and voted Republican at every election but one. The exception was the Blaine-Cleveland election of 1884, when a great group of independents swung against Blaine. This year was a forward-looking time : the opening of the Brooklyn Bridge alone (the grace of whose strong lines and the curve of whose suspended cables were derived, as Mumford says, from an elegant formula in mathematical physics —the elastic curve)—this alone would have been an indication. The election was another. Blaine, the sensitive and attractive past, had hats thrown in the air for him; but Cleveland, for all his plodding gracelessness, belonged to the transition; his phrases passed into the language, and he got the votes, including that of

Willard Gibbs, so much greater a figure of the transition than himself.

The treasures found were shared by Gibbs. He walked through the side path to Newton's house, with the gardens of both houses lying bright in summer and white in the middle of the college year beside the path. And in the dark-furnished study, among the heavy books, Newton was waiting with the sentence he had left unfinished, or the joke of the day. The walls of this house were different from all other walls. Newton used slides for his lectures : the delicate and graceful pictures of meteor-tracks and the orbits of comets. Here, on the steady grey background of wallpaper, stylized in pale gold, curved the tracks, twined in all-over patterns of the most graceful curves imaginable—fireballs and comets twisting in variety through every room, so that Newton's daughter Josephine, who was a little girl when Gibbs used to come over every day, can take out the slides and say : "Do you like that one? That used to be the wallpaper in my room."

She remembers Gibbs coming in, with his poet's head held high, and her father coming out of the study to meet him in the hall, with a book in his hand, perhaps, and how they went together into the study—"into the fourth dimension"—to laugh obscurely, as the children listened in the hall. They laughed about "lines and points," she remembers, and particularly about one mathematician who was making children and mathematicians laugh, everywhere that English was really understood.

One book of Lewis Carroll's, in particular, made the laughter billow in fine waves of pleasure from that study. The chess-puzzles of *Alice* were an enduring joy; the straight-faced proposals delicious, as of—

a narrow strip of ground, railed off and carefully leveled, for testing practically whether Parallel Lines meet or not : for this purpose it should reach, to use the expressive language of Euclid, "ever so far."

This last process, of "continually producing the Lines," may require centuries or more : but such a period, though long in the life of an individual, is as nothing in the life of the University.

But the particular book was *A Tangled Tale*. And in this strange Victorian house, with the comets plunging over the dado and fire leaping in the hearth, they would compute and speculate while New Haven was lost beyond the window; and stop their work to laugh, as they turned to this most mathematical game, and read riddle after riddle. Entropy and the heat-death and the infinities reduced to tea-time, over :

"And what made you choose the first train, Goosey?" said Mad Mathesis, as they got into the cab. "Couldn't you count better than *that?*"

"I took an extreme case," was the tearful reply. "Our excellent preceptress always says, 'When in doubt, my dears, take an extreme case.' And I *was* in doubt."

"Does it always succeed?" her aunt inquired.

Clara sighed. "Not always," she reluctantly admitted. "And I can't make out why. One day she was telling the little girls—they make such a noise at tea, you know—'The more noise you make, the less jam you will have, and vice versa.' And I thought they wouldn't know what 'vice versa' meant : so I explained it to them. I said, 'If you make an infinite noise, you'll get no jam; and if you make no noise, you'll get an infinite lot of jam.' But our excellent preceptress said that wasn't a good instance. *Why* wasn't it?" she added plaintively.

And every physical demonstration became nonsense at the seashore, as in :

Suppose a solid held above the surface of a liquid and partially immersed : a portion of the liquid is displaced, and the level of the liquid rises. But, by this rise of level, a little bit more of the solid is of course immersed, and so there is a new displacement of a second portion of the liquid, and a consequent rise of level. Again, this second rise of level causes a yet further immersion, and by consequence another displacement of liquid and another rise. It is self-evident that this process must continue till the entire solid is immersed, and that the liquid will then begin to immerse whatever holds the solid, which, being connected with it, must for the time be considered a part of it. If you hold a stick, six feet long, with its end in a tumbler of water, and wait long enough, you must eventually be immersed. The question as to the source from which the water is supplied—which belongs to a higher branch of mathematics, and is therefore beyond our present scope—does not apply to the sea. Let us therefore take the familiar instance of a man standing at the edge of the sea, at ebb-tide, with a solid in his hand, which he partially immerses : he remains steadfast and unmoved, and we all know that he must be drowned. The multitudes who daily perish in this manner to attest a philosophical truth, and whose bodies the unreasoning wave casts sullenly upon our thankless shores, have a truer claim to be called the martyrs of science than a Galileo or a Kepler. To use Kossuth's eloquent phrase, they are the unnamed demigods of the nineteenth century.

It was Lewis Carroll who, hating as Gibbs hated to be drawn into discussion of the philosophical meaning of his work, answered to such an invitation :

> And what mean all these mysteries to me
> Whose life is full of indices and surds?
> $$x^2 + 7x + 53 = \frac{11}{3}$$

Gibbs did not allow himself to be drawn any nearer to "these mysteries." He flinched before assumption, and the special audacity that it takes to make assumptions is necessary before one can enlarge a philosophy; he flinched before assumption as before experiment. In his own work lie immense generalities, but they are not wholly made; he only shows that they are possible to make. But the importance of that "only" cannot be overestimated. When Ostwald, as a student in his twenties, complained—and his complaint was of the greatness of Gibbs, because it was unknown—and there were only a few men who had spoken of him : Maxwell, Lorenz, Lord Rayleigh, van der Waals —one could see that here was a freak explorer. He was in a tragic, an almost godlike, relation as pioneer. He was the pioneer of dream who seems to float into an unmapped country. When the first trappers and farmer arrive, they see no footprints. But if—in this dream—they look above their heads, they see indelibly the blazes on these strange trees, to tell them that someone has already been here and seen this visionary landscape.

For example, in the papers on the theory of light, as Bumstead says, it is likely that the points they make would have been enough to establish the theory firmly, without a more direct proof.

But that proof was offered, when Heinrich Hertz in 1887 made the experiment, twenty years after the theory appeared first in Maxwell's papers. Using an induction coil, with the spark struck from it and its oscillating current, Hertz discovered electric waves in space. He placed a metal surface parallel to the spark gap, and detected the neutral lapses between waves; from there it was a simple step to determine wave-length; and this was the parent experiment to all of wireless telegraphy.

Hertz was acting on an analogy : sound is produced in the same way as these electric products. If you close a pipe at one end, sprinkle the inside length with powder, and tap the pipe, the powder will form ripples which outline the shape of these waves. The basis of the experiment—beyond its personal history, which traces the line of Faraday, Maxwell, Hertz—is in a metaphor of waves as old as history. The metaphor itself had been given flesh.

The metaphors of energy were being given flesh. The German scientists had a source of wonder, as the first young experimenters worked over Willard Gibbs, published in a provincial journal in Connecticut. Ostwald, in Riga; Mach, about his writings in phenomenalism; Karl Pearson, in London, having gone through branches of knowledge as rapidly and with many of the same biases as William James; and James himself at Harvard—were closing in on these new meanings.

Karl Pearson, of Yorkshire yeoman stock, was born in London the year before Gibbs graduated from Yale. He concentrated in mathematics at Cambridge, but, fascinated by philosophy and religion, worked in these fields as well as under his illustrious teachers—Clerk Maxwell, Cayley, Routh, Stokes, Todhunter. During his four or five years in Germany, he studied law, but once there he saw fossils of culture in fifteenth-century customs, and strayed off into folk-lore, into studies in Luther and Spinoza and language. It seemed straying, but it was no more purposeless than William James's painting or the suicidal seasons abroad, or the first reading of Renouvier; it sent Pearson back to London, lecturing in mathematics, lecturing to workingmen's clubs on socialism, on Marx and Lassalle, editing two books that established him as a mathematician, and building up a foundation for his work in statistics. Statistics was a synonym for civilized life. Pearson saw chance as obedience to law. "Where we cannot predict," he wrote, "where we do not find order and regularity, there we should now assert . . . that something else than Chance is at work."

In 1892 Karl Pearson published the first edition of *The Gram-*

mar of Science, the book from which Willard Gibbs said he got most help.

Raphael Pumpelly, the golden-bearded, restless voyager, was the boy who had gone to General Russell's school in New Haven, and celebrated the Burial of Euclid and climbed the basalt columns of West Rock. To Cambridge and Washington, he was the wide breath, the space of the world; in Arizona as a mining engineer, and in Michigan, he had advised anyone who would listen to buy iron instead of gold, showing the meaning of his science for industry and business. He swept through the East with tales of the loess-fields of China, of the thousands who would come here and should be given work; these were his hardest facts, but there were also his prints and jade and adventures. Van Wyck Brooks, in a dramatic description of him, says he was the Pied Piper who led to the cave of darkness, usually a darkness of money. He led Henry Adams in a different direction; for when he passed through Washington, "on his way to Central Asia," he was the man Adams needed. He cared about travels; and, as Adams says, "Of all the travels made by man since the voyage of Dante, this new exploration along the shores of Multiplicity and Complexity promised to be the longest." Adams and Pumpelly talked of these things; and Pumpelly "helped the winds," telling Adams how Gibbs felt about Pearson's book. With this result :

To Adams' vision Willard Gibbs stood on the same plane with the three or four greatest minds of his century, and the idea that a man so incomparably superior should find help anywhere filled him with wonder. He sent for the volume and read it. . . . Adams could see in such parts of the "Grammar" as he could understand, little more than an enlargement of Stallo's book already twenty years old. He never found out what it could have taught a master like Willard Gibbs. Yet the book had a historical value out of all proportion to its science. No such stride had any Englishman before taken in the lines of English thought. The progress of science was measured by the success of the "Grammar," when, for twenty years past, Stallo had been deliberately ignored under the usual conspiracy of silence inevitable to all thought which demands new thought-machinery.

Stallo, the Cincinnati judge, caught in the same conspiracy and lag from which Gibbs was now suffering, said he was making a "contribution not to physics or metaphysics but to the theory

The Rosetta Stone of Science

of cognition." As Mach was now doing, as James was now doing. Pearson brought to this war another tempered weapon : the civilized use of statistics, that is, a scientific method and the imagination to make it fertile.

Gibbs's old teacher in Berlin, Du Bois-Reymond, who had also been the teacher of William James, argued that these ideas of force and matter and the complexities they bred were all abstractions. He added his word as the battle-cry of the other side; it was *Ignorabimus!*

Pearson fought. With Galileo, he flung back in their faces, "Who is willing to set limits to the human intellect?" Everything might be unknown; but all his audacity rose, and he refused to accept an unknowable. The last forty years of science had forced a rewriting of history, that would gradually modify our theory of life and change our own conduct and habits to suit the new ideas. There was obscurity in this new world, because science, like a skillful general, was hiding his own deficient organization. We are to criticize, for criticism is the life of science. We are to learn these languages; to understand that material science is coextensive with our whole life, and the whole physical and mental life of the universe. If there are facts and sequences, there is science—if there are none, there is no knowledge at all. But beyond the formal process of reasoning fixed by these facts and their sequences, there is an element in our being which is not satisfied, except by the free imagination. Even here, scientists have shown more imagination, says Pearson, and used their gifts more beneficially, than any other group in his generation, even than the poets. Rich in these gifts, it is up to the men of science to grasp the relation of scientific progress to the social movements of their time—and so far, it has been only the rare Huxley or Clifford who has afforded the bridge between them. The scientific attitude is as applicable to social as to physical problems; and the scientific man has learned, if he has come to his work with the spirit it deserves, to eliminate himself in his judgments.

These must have been strokes to the heart of Willard Gibbs. Everything that he and the most generous resources of his background stood for reached an articulate speech in the writings of Pearson; and beyond this, the man combined in himself the gifts of language and science, the freedom of the individual and the appropriate language in which to communicate the methods of freedom, which had come to Gibbs's attention. Not only what he meant, but what his father had meant, was reflected in Pearson's essays, for after the *Grammar of Science*, whose name alone would have struck home to Gibbs, came *The Chances of Death*, with its fascinating researches in statistics and science, *Biometrika*, Pearson's magazine, and the valuable work in statistics, biometrics, and many extensions of the work of Dalton and Quetelet. Pearson brought to his work the excitement of the person who identifies his life and all thought : when he speaks of Death and chance, he tells how the theory of chance is bound up with dice and gambling through all its history, beginning with a fifteenth-century Italian commentary on Dante's lines :

> When from their game of dice men separate,
> He who hath lost remains in sadness fix'd
> Revolving in his mind, what luckless throws
> He cast . . .

"Of all the travels made by man since the voyages of Dante . . ." Henry Adams said. He was sunk in the pit of his voyaging. In 1885, soon after her father's death, Marian Adams poisoned herself. She drank potassium cyanide, which she had used to develop her photographs. When Henry Adams came home from his Sunday-morning walk, his wife was dead. He could not bear to live in the red house which Richardson had built in Lafayette Square for him and his wife. Keeping the six packets of stinging, highly colored letters of this keen woman, he burned his own correspondence and notes. His life had fallen away from him. Adams left Washington, commissioning Saint-Gaudens to prepare the unnamed monument over his wife's grave in Rock Creek Cemetery; he began to move over the world, longing now for further complexity to cover the single unalterable fact of suffering : Mexico, Cuba, the West, and finally to Japan and Hawaii.

Among the Americans drawn to Japan in the '80s, when the passivity and sacredness of its Buddhist teachings fascinated many —and particularly New Englanders, who would not loudly dissent, but were ready to withdraw quietly whenever they could from the Gilded Age—was Addison Van Name, who was known as an Oriental philologist. His house grew more and more beautiful, as he collected the fine-glossed woods, the delicate prints, and the silk paintings of the East. He had three children now reaching their early adolescence.

Willard Gibbs and Anna went to Keene Valley or to Canterbury, where Professor Brush and his daughter Eliza used to visit them. "He sat down at the melodeon in the farmhouse parlor," she remembers, and played to them.

Brush was always a good friend of Gibbs's; he told about the National Academy meetings in Washington, when Gibbs (as Margaret Whitney relates) asked Brush to stand by when he was reading one of his papers on light. He was growing famous, in a small and dismal way. The members were coming to know him for the forbidding quality of his papers, and they were likely to slip away during the reading. Brush was loyal; he sat in the front row with Simon Newcomb, and this time he leaned over and asked, "Are you following this?" "I did," said Newcomb, "for the first twenty minutes. Since then I have been lost."

On the way home, Gibbs visited Johns Hopkins, on the invitation of the trustees, who knew what they had lost in losing him. He stopped to go through the Physical Laboratory there.

In New Haven, the neighbors' children missed him. He seemed to neglect them for his niece and nephews, and they had lost the lovely drives with this kind man. But he had not forgotten; he was not slighting them; he only loved Julia's children best. When Marian Whitney injured her leg—and, as her sister says, she was then a well-grown girl of thirteen—"Cousin Willard Gibbs used to come day after day to take her out to drive, and that included carrying her downstairs and carrying her up again."

They knew he was not frail, but strong, although he was slight of bone. They knew he was not shy; they saw him come back from the meetings of the National Academy, whose very name was impressive to these streets, and they heard with respect that he had presided. "A really very shy man would not have presided," they said. "In the world of ideas he knew his way around; in the world of people he was sometimes ill-at-ease unless he considered a matter necessary or important."

If it was deeply important, he would praise. When Clausius died, on August 24, 1888, the American Academy asked Gibbs, who had chosen him for master, for a notice. His answer to that request is a portrait of the writer—Crowther speaks of the "profound knowledge and judgment, generosity, humor, sensibility and modesty" as well as the sensitive understanding of this response. It also illustrates a characteristic evasiveness, which in a truly evasive person would have been followed by a refusal, but which Gibbs followed by generous and positive action.

New Haven June 10/89

Professor J. P. Cooke
My dear Sir,

The task which you propose is in many respects a pleasant one to me, although I have not much facility at that kind of writing, or indeed, at any kind. Of course, I should not expect to do justice to the subject, but I might do something.

There are some drawbacks : of course it has not escaped your notice that it is a *very* delicate matter to write a notice of the work of Clausius. There are reputations to be respected, from Democritus downward, which may be hurt, if not of the distinguished men directly concerned, at least of their hot-headed partisans.

Altogether I feel as if I had to take my life in my hands.

Without making a positive engagement at this moment, as soon as I can get a little relief from some pressing duties, I will look the matter up and see what I can do, and will communicate with you further.

Yours truly
· J. W. G.

Crowther remarks that this letter "was followed by one of the most remarkable obituary notices in scientific literature, which contains the classical statement of the origin of thermodynamics, and the extent of the contributions by the various founders." It is not surprising, he adds, that Gibbs was beloved by those who had achieved his friendship.

The six and a half pages of the paper on Clausius chalk in the state of thermodynamics when Clausius published his first memoir, in 1850, a date before which materials had existed for such a science, but "truth and error were in a confusing state of mixture," and it was only with Clausius' memoir that the foundations were laid, the definitions were fixed, and the boundaries of thermodynamics traced.

"The constructive power thus exhibited," Gibbs says in his definition of greatness in science, "this ability to bring order out of confusion, this breadth of view which could apprehend one truth without losing sight of another, this nice discrimination to separate truth from error,—these are qualities which place the possessor in the first rank of scientific men."

In the development of consequences—in the application, that is—"Clausius was rivalled, perhaps surpassed, in activity and versatility by Sir William Thomson." His attention was directed toward the nature of molecular phenomena. The laws with which he dealt were an expression of that nature.

Gibbs reviews the mathematical form of the second law, and the equation for the molecular *vis viva* in relation to absolute temperature. There was no demonstration for Clausius' equations; Gibbs admires the insight which led him to anticipate the ultimate form of the theory. He summarizes Clausius' work in kinetic theory of gases, in the conception of the *virial,* and in mean values, as well as later papers on electricity. And he concludes with the classic sentences, which have so often been used to describe Gibbs himself :

"But such work as that of Clausius is not measured by counting titles or pages. His true monument lies not on the shelves of libraries, but in the thoughts of men, and in the history of more than one science."

If it was deeply important, he would fight. The subject of vectors was the head of a long battle between Tait and Gibbs. Garrison tells of the controversy :

Apart from his work in mathematical physics, Gibbs made several important contributions to pure mathematics, notably in his theory of "dyadics," a variety of the multiple of matricular algebras which Benjamin Peirce classified as "linear associate." The tendency of his mind was always toward broad, general views and the simplifications that go with such an outlook, and here mention should be made of his charming address on multiple algebra and his innovation of vector analysis, a calculus designed to give the student of physics a clearer insight into such space relations as strains, twists, spins and rotational or irrotational movements in general. Maxwell, who once declared that he had been striving all his life to be freed from the yoke of the Cartesian coordinates, had already found such an instrument in the Hamiltonian quaternions, the application of which he brilliantly demonstrated in his great treatise on electricity and magnetism. Quaternions are elegant, consistent, concise and uniquely adapted to Euclidean space, but physicists have latterly found them artificial and unnatural to their science, because the

square of the quaternionic vector becomes a negative quantity. The
Gibbsian vectors obviate this difficulty, and while seemingly uncouth, furnish a mode of attack more simple and direct and adapta-
ble to space of any dimensions. Their capacity for interpreting
space relations was amply tested by Gibbs in his five papers on the
electromagnetic theory of light and his application of vectors to
the calculation of orbits, since incorporated in recent German
treatises on astronomy. The fact that vectors tend to displace the
quaternionic analysis of Sir William Rowan Hamilton involved our
author in a lengthy controversy with Hamilton's best interpreter,
the ingenious and versatile Tait, who looked upon Gibbs as "one of
the retarders of quaternionic progress," defining his system as "a
sort of hermaphrodite monster compounded of the notations of
Hamilton and Grassmann."

Gibbs did not answer the charge with any epithet. He was a
Connecticut puritan, and there was no question of mentioning
monsters, hermaphrodite or other. But the cutting edge of his
argument is stronger than Tait's; it looks toward the future, and
it lashes out at the snobbery of any discipleship. He says :

It seems to be assumed that a departure from quaternionic usage
in the treatment of vectors is an enormity. If this assumption is true,
it is an important truth; if not, it would be unfortunate if it should
remain unchallenged, especially when supported by so high an
authority. The criticism related particularly to notations, but I believe that there is a deeper question of notions underlying that of
notations. Indeed, if my offence had been solely in the matter of
notation, it would have been less accurate to describe my production as a monstrosity, than to characterize its dress as uncouth. . . .

He speaks of the resemblance of his work to Grassmann's,
rather than to Hamilton's; "but this is a matter of minor consequence. It is more important to ask, What are the requisites of
a good notation for the purposes of vector analysis?" . . .
"Everyone will naturally prefer the methods with which he is
most familiar"; but, he goes on, the advantages of the rival form
are usually doubtful or very trifling. When he was asked what
the first duty of the vector analyst was, he was quick to answer :
"It is to present the subject in such a form as to be most easily
acquired, and most useful when acquired."
Usefulness, to him, was completeness. When one of his students
suggested that Gibbs's system could be restated in a form more

widely useful, Gibbs replied : "What is the good of that? It is complete as it is."

It is that point of view that makes the great imaginative genius, as against the person who over-simplifies continually and makes the excuse that he does it for the sake of use. The most useful *idea* is very likely to be the most complete idea; the compactness of Gibbs is for the sake of completeness, and to him, completeness and simplicity are the same thing. It is only a man like that who can say, "The whole is simpler than the sum of all its parts."

He was being attacked violently. It was the one fight in the thick of which he found himself. In a curious way, what the *Amistad* case was to his father, the vector fight was to Willard Gibbs. He was lashed at—"Gibbs gives a good many equations— theorems I suppose they ape at being," says the most vicious attack, by C. G. Knott. Gibbs thought that Heaviside was with him, but Heaviside was marking his copy of Gibbs's article on notation : "I do not like it."

The defense was, for Gibbs, a defense of the essential, a strong cry for the organic in thought. The other method was an independent plant; it had been called that by its partisans. Gibbs asks :

Can we wonder that mathematicians, physicists, astronomers, and geometers feel some doubt as to the value or necessity of something so separate from all other branches of learning? Can that be a natural treatment of the subject which has no relations to any other method, and . . . has only occurred to a single man? . . .

I believe, however, that if what I have quoted is true of vector methods, it is because there is something fundamentally wrong in the presentation of the subject. Of course, in some sense and to some extent it is and must be true. Whatever is special, accidental, and individual, will die, as it should; but that which is universal and essential should remain as an organic part of the whole intellectual acquisition. If that which is essential dies with the accidental, it must be because the accidental has been given the prominence which belongs to the essential. For myself, I should preach no such doctrine to those whom I wish to convert to the true faith. . . .

There are two ways in which we may measure the progress of any reform. The one consists in counting those who have adopted the *shibboleth* of the reformers; the other measure is the degree in which the community is imbued with the essential principles of the reform. . . .

Willard Gibbs

Now I appreciate and admire the generous loyalty toward one whom he regards as his master, which has always led Prof. Tait to minimise the originality of his own work in regard to quaternions, and write as if everything was contained in the ideas which flashed into the mind of Hamilton at the classic Brougham Bridge. But not to speak of other claims of historical justice, we owe duties to our scholars as well as to our teachers, and the world is too large, and the current of modern thought is too broad, to be confined by the *ipse dixit* even of a Hamilton.

Garrison continues in his passage on vectors :

But Gibbs did not regard his method as strictly original; he was only concerned with its application in the task of teaching students; and when, after testing it by twenty years' experience in the classroom, he reluctantly consented to the publication of his lectures in full, the task was confided to one of his pupils, our author declining, with a characteristic touch of conscience, to have the work appear under his name or even to read the proof. In the controversy with Tait there is, as in most controversies, an amusing element of human nature. The name of Hamilton is undoubtedly one of the most illustrious in the history of science, and Tait and his adherents seemed to regard it as an impertinence and a desecration to his memory that any other system than quaternions should be proposed. . . . In 1893 Heaviside, an English vectorist, reports "confusion in the quaternionic citadel : alarms and excursions and hurling of stones and pouring of water upon the invading hosts." The vectorists were denounced as a "clique" and ridiculed especially for their lack of elegance, their alleged intellectual dishonesty and the fact that their pupils were "spoon-fed" upon mathematico-physical pap. But some of the notations held up to ridicule turned out to be things like Poisson's theorem or the difficult hydrodynamic problem "given the spin in a case of liquid motion to find the motion," which Helmholtz solved with one of his strokes of genius, and which Gibbs showed could be understood and interpreted by the average student without genius by a simple application of vectorial methods. The real point at issue in the controversy, the fundamental difference in the ideals of European and American education, lies here. Both have their relative advantages and defects, but the object of one has been to bring the best to the highest development, while the other is concerned with increasing the efficiency of the average man. One has been exclusive, aiming at the survival of the fittest; the other is democratic and inclusive, and aims, in Huxley's words, to make the greatest number fit to survive.

The Rosetta Stone of Science

The merits of the case are well summed up in Gibbs's final statement : "The notions which we use in vector analysis are those which he who reads between the lines will meet on every page of the greatest masters of analysis, or of those who have probed deepest the secrets of nature, the only difference being that the vector analyst, having regard for the weakness of the human intellect, does as the early painters who wrote beneath their pictures 'This is a tree.' 'This is a horse.' " This view is in perfect accord with the recent trend of mathematical teaching, European or American, which is to emphasize the meaning and interpretation of equations and formulae rather than their demonstrations or manipulation; in short, to substitute visualizing methods, the art of thinking straight and seeing clear, for what is conventional and scholastic.

William James wrote one of the masterpieces of this trend; he emphasized meanings in the book on which he had been working since the summer of his marriage, the "ballad-like" summers in Keene Valley, and the long Harvard years. *Principles of Psychology* was ready only after eleven years, so that James could write to his brother of Howells' latest novel : "With that work, your *Tragic Muse*, and last *but by no means least*, my *Psychology*, all appearing in it, the year 1890 will be known as the great epochal year in American literature."

This book had been written against a resistance which William felt Henry James knew nothing about. It had nothing to do with romantic restlessness, and he had long ago identified his brother with that quality; this was against "the resistance of *facts*, to begin with, each one of which must be bribed to be on one's side, and the resistance of other philosophers to end with, each one of which must be slain. It is no joke slaying the Helmholtzes as well as the Spencers."

If the *Principles* alone had appeared just then, it would have been an important time. But Emily Dickinson's poems were appearing, Mark Twain's book that is in curious contrast to Henry Adams' work—*A Connecticut Yankee*—had just come out, this study in the multiplicity of a far past and the multiplicity of the present. Mark Twain used social symbols rather than the religious and aesthetic ones that Adams was to find at Chartres and Mont-Saint-Michel, and found no unity. He believed in a mechanistic universe, and he lived in the materialist

America of H. H. Rogers, Standard Oil, and Gilded Age apparatus. Adams was working towards a defense against his period; at the moment, it took the form of the *History*, part of which had already been published. Emily Dickinson had her own, and it resembled Gibbs's defense, in many ways.

William James was building up a system, the only possible defense for those critical minds which approach the world with love. That love almost inevitably develops into a wish for order; and that requires a system that can combine science and humanism. This book, which C. S. Peirce called "probably the most important contribution made to the subject for many years," was not written from a sense of isolation : James felt that his allies existed among the scientists, and he named Mach, Karl Pearson, Ostwald, and Henri Poincaré.

Helmholtz visited James at Chocorua, in the White Mountains, soon after the *Principles* appeared. There is no record of a visit to Gibbs.

These were curious years for Gibbs. He lived his life quietly; but that other Gibbs whom New Haven would not acknowledge lived, the Gibbs of reputation, had strange adventures.

When a new university was founded, the president went abroad looking for professors. He arrived at Cambridge, found J. J. Thomson, and asked whether Thomson knew of anyone to fill a chair in Molecular Physics. When Thomson said, "You need not come to England for that; the best man you could get is an American, Willard Gibbs," the newly elected president answered ingenuously, "Oh, you mean Wolcott Gibbs," mentioning the widely known chemist.

"No, I don't," Thomson retorted, "I mean Willard Gibbs," and he began to tell the man about Gibbs's work. Thomson watched him as he sat and thought for a moment and then said, "I'd like you to give me another name. Willard Gibbs can't be a man of much personal magnetism or I should have heard of him."

Wolcott Gibbs must have been haunted by this greater name, which was so like his that he was mistakenly, several times, offered medals and positions meant for the man sealed up in New Haven, and, according to Ostwald, given an ovation once in Germany when the town heard that Gibbs, "the newly discovered star," was among them. Nobody was more surprised than he himself was—but at this moment, Ostwald was still working on the translation that was to announce Gibbs's name to Germany.

Gibbs himself was at home. He was honorary member of a committee in Germany that was raising funds for a monument to Gustav Adolph Hirn, who in 1857 established a tolerably approximate equivalent value for heat. He was advising Percey F. Smith on his thesis, considering a trip to England for the Faraday lectures, in the same month—May 1891—that he was made an honorary member of the Royal Institution. He was receiving all the official honors : from the Cambridge Philosophical Society, the Royal Academy of Sciences in Amsterdam, the Victoria Institute, the International Electrical Congress and the Columbian Exposition in Chicago, the London Mathematical Society, the American Philosophical Society, the Literary and Philosophical Society of Manchester, Dublin University. He was given a Ph.D. at Erlangen, and an Honorary Doctorate of Letters at Williams. But many of these signs of prestige depended on Ostwald's translation.

Lee De Forest, inventor and pioneer in wireless, has been recognized as a brilliant and courageous leader, whose life has been a drama of service to the point of martyrdom. He writes in a letter about his year as Gibbs's pupil :

Even as a senior at Sheffield, I had begun to absorb from my professors and instructors something of the admiration which these former students of Professor Gibbs had themselves derived. To study under Gibbs I saw was a noble ambition; to be able to pursue his courses, the final test of a man's mathematical acumen. There developed, therefore, an intense desire to follow their example, a determination to sit at the feet of Yale's Great Man. Accordingly, I find this diary entry :

"September 28, 1890—I began work in the Lab 16 hours. 7 hours lectures. Math. with Clark, Pierpont and Gibbs. The latter is a great man with whom I want to be, as much for his ways and thought as for lessons and thoughts. Wrote Tesla for advice in this; he congratulates me on the attention Gibbs is giving me. So I told Gibbs of my aim with Tesla."

My lecture notebooks in Vector Analysis reveal that I was soon deeply entangled in the Gibbian forms of Hamilton quaternions, linear vector operators, bi-vectors, bi-scalars, curls, $\nabla.\nabla$, dyadic dyads, "dots," "double dots," and the like.

Willard Gibbs

Later, in his terrific courses in Thermodynamics and the Maxwell theory of light, were found the "jot," "Pot," "Max" (for Maxwellian), "Lap" (Laplacian), volume integrals embracing all space, infinite discriminants, operational equations, solenoidal, irrotational. Gibbs' formulas and methods of analysis were extremely condensed, designed for abbreviated short cuts in procedure, deceivingly simple in appearance, but in physical application demanding a very special ability. His interpretations were always those of pure intellect, clear, concise, non-physical. His mind seemed infinitely discerning, intimately dealing with imaginaries.

Often he would remark in that quiet peculiar voice, almost lost in his beard of sandy gray, "We shall pretend we know nothing about this solution from Nature." And with most of us this was more than pretense! It was an event when my notebook recorded any reference to a physical example, a piece of laboratory apparatus. I find this admission in my diary :

> "My vector analysis and thermodynamics are in a bad state of misunderstanding. Professor Gibbs, great man though he is, but little satisfies me with his peculiar vector analysis, a tool very difficult to handle, and one, for me, never suited to working in any physical problem."

But at the close of my second year under Gibbs I wrote :

> "My mathematical training this year I find already of the greatest practical value. Without such, and every bit of it, I could not read these books leading up to Maxwell. I want another year, still higher. Then I can expect to deal intelligently with light and wave phenomena, along which lines I see lies the great future of electrical advance . . . the higher theory of waves and oscillations, and a transmission by these means of intelligence and power." And later : "Now my next year's life is settled—mathematics with Maxwell and Gibbs to perfection!"

After my first year's study under Gibbs, I wrote in sophomoric enthusiasm :

> "My very soul burns with desire, is enflamed with unspeakable zeal to learn, and is consumed with a fire for scientific research. I must learn these truths. I must master the means of research, familiarize myself with the methods by which the evidence is found, probe deeply into these new fields, that fascinate beyond all else by their weird truth, by their unreal

[*308*]

The Rosetta Stone of Science

realities. I feel then that we tread in the spirit realm, that we are on the universal highway that leads to all—before, behind, at hand and far away. By this route, we hold communion with the misty past far down the dimmest dawn of the world's first mornings, and out to the farthest stretch of ultimate futurity, where suns are cold and gray and still in the Death of Matter.

"Who can dare to dream the depths to be illumined by the new found light, who so bold to place a limit to its ultimate achievement—even to the making of man's mind akin to God's? In the presence of this great discovery thought is overpowered with the beauty and the awe. At a step we merge from our physics into the vague, vast and tenuous land of spirit. At a stroke, we emerge from Earth to Heaven, from the temporal to the infinite."

Professor Gibbs was, I am sure, nothing of a metaphysician; nothing in his teaching had such slightest indication. Yet the influence of his noble and gigantic intellect may have been largely responsible for such an outburst from one of his younger and worshipful pupils. "Mathematics as Revealer of the Deity!" I exclaimed. "Some day even theologians, and women (!), will admit to evidence the highest and the noblest product of our universe—the *evidence of thought*, the value of the *intellect*." . . . "With thoughts and readings such as these all base desires seem unknown. At such times how beyond all price seem the opportunities of this coming year." (I had then determined on a third year under Professor Gibbs—his study of Maxwell and Electro-magnetic Theory of Light.) "How inconceivable appears any thought of other work or occupation—not discouragement nor fate in any form, scarce death itself, could keep me from this purpose, this great prize. I wish that I might study without rest or sleep, losing not a wrack of all the jewels I may gather in." Surely I had been set afire by the radiations from that inspiring soul.

The name of J. Willard Gibbs, even in my day at Yale, had acquired an almost legendary greatness. This, notwithstanding and perhaps in part because of the fact that then the recognition of his transcendent achievements in Thermodynamics and nature of solutions had scarcely extended beyond New Haven. As an undergraduate, I had heard with awe rumors of the Gibbs Tradition; that the *summum bonum* of a Yale career in Science was to have studied under him.

His students admired, revered this strange, quiet man, never seen on the campus and seldom outside of his classroom in the old Sloane

Laboratory. He became almost a tutelary god, to be worshipped by those sufficiently fortunate, or gifted, to come under the aegis of his intangible aura.

With long acquaintance I found him a kindly, human soul. When I required, for my Doctorate, an additional course he volunteered to give me his special course in Orbits. There, very solemnly for one hour each week, we sat facing each other while he discoursed on the paths of comet and asteroid. In that course at least I proudly led the class—I was his only pupil!

Through Professor Wright, Gibbs followed, by remote control, the progress of my Thesis work on Hertzian waves along wires. I still recall the eager pride I felt when the great teacher finally entered my basement laboratory, where I outlined to him the work I was there conducting.

I can fervently say that it was Willard Gibbs' influence and inspiration which so firmly resolved me to continue my post-graduate studies for the second, and finally the third, year, to master as fully as I might the theory of electro-magnetic waves, thus thoroughly to prepare myself for that project of research and invention which I had determined should be my life's work.

At home, Gibbs and Addison entertained their class. At an earlier reunion, they sang the old song, with the lines :

> What's done we partly may compute,
> But know not what's resisted.

That day had started with an excursion to the athletic grounds, and then lunch, with cold meats, coffee, and lemonade. In the afternoon, the class went to the Harvard-Yale baseball game. "No chairman was elected, no speeches were made, and no songs were sung, as our poets had all passed away."

This year was better. "Mr. and Mrs. Van Name, and Gibbs having very kindly invited the Class to their beautiful home on High Street to dine, the evening from six o'clock was passed very delightfully."

And one of his students, now in Germany, was finding a prompt and delightful recognition. "When I studied in Berlin in 1893," says Irving Fisher, "and was asked under whom I had studied in America, I enumerated the mathematicians at Yale. To my mortification not one of the names was known to those Berlin professors, until I mentioned Gibbs, whereupon they were loud in his praises. '*Geebs, Geebs, jawohl, ausgezeichnet!*' " "Indeed, distinguished!"

Two letters of Gibbs to Sir Oliver Lodge as the secretary of the Electrolysis Committee of the British Association for the Advancement of Science have been called his most important contributions to the theory of electricity. He had stated his theory of the galvanic cell—with which the experimental work of Raoult, Bosch, and others agrees, and from which Raoult's law may be derived—and Helmholtz was only now developing the new step with a series of brilliant experiments. But the two letters were as far away from experimental procedure as can be imagined. Helmholtz was talking about cells and measurements; Gibbs now showed how in the perfect, or reversible, cell, an equation will give you the answers about force and heat *without your having to set up a cell.*

In his first letter, Gibbs refers to the great paper. "Essentially the same view of the subject I have given in a form more general and more analytical, and, I fear, less easily intelligible, in the closing papers of a somewhat lengthy paper on the 'Equilibrium of Heterogeneous Substances,' . . . of which I send you the Second Part, which contains the passage in question. My separate edition of the First Part has long been exhausted. . . . The definition of the *potential for a material substance*" is found in the enclosed synopsis, he writes; and adds, "I cannot say that the term has been adopted by physicists. It has, however, received the unqualified commendation of Professor Maxwell," and he notes, with a quiet touch of pride, the conference at South Kensington in 1876; "and I do not see how we can do very well without the idea in certain kinds of investigations.

"Hoping that the importance of the subject will excuse the length of this letter . . ."

Sir Oliver Lodge asked whether Gibbs was not regarding a galvanic cell as "too simply a heat engine" and making several assumptions. Gibbs was the last person to make an unwarranted assumption, or, indeed, an assumption of any sort where it could be avoided, and he answered that "in supposing such a case we do not exceed the liberty usually allowed in theoretical discussions. But if this should appear doubtful," he continues, and proceeds to re-define his terms; showing that "these results are in complete accordance with Helmholtz's differential equation," and proving that Helmholtz's work could have been naturally derived from his own earlier papers. Garrison says :

The accuracy of his reasoning is sustained by such developments of the subject as the "Peltier effect," in which it is demonstrated that the thermoelectric effect in systems of conductors, in which no chemical action takes place, is still proportional to the absolute temperature at any junction. In general, the properties of a thermoelectric system are determined by the entropy function, and the entropy and energy in a thermoelectric network are not, as previously supposed, stored in the conductors, but, as we see in the electric transmission of motor power from a waterfall like Niagara to an engine or railway car, actually travel with the moving charge of electricity itself.

According to this exposition of a fictional cell, entropy is in the electric charge, and can be located.

These letters were both, as another famous letter was, elaborations on the last four pages of the great paper. MacInnes says :

Another subject dealt with in the same four pages on the galvanic cell is that of the effect of gravity, and, by implication, of centrifugal force, on the galvanic cell. The relation given by Gibbs is the basis for work by Des Coudres and by Tolman who fully verified the original deductions of Gibbs.

Still another relation, at least implicit in the deductions of Gibbs, is the effect of pressure on the potential of a galvanic cell. Gibbs' deductions are fully verified by modern work on the subject.

MacInnes has already mentioned that the galvanic cell is—

a most important tool in the investigation of the theory of solutions, particularly of electrolytes. By the use of such cells it is possible to draw conclusions concerning reversible processes occurring in solutions. G. N. Lewis has re-defined the chemical potential as the partial molal free energy and in so doing has limited it to only one of its properties. By a simple equation, also given, in form at least, by Gibbs, the *activity* may be obtained. This has led, step by step, to the modern theory of electrolytes, culminating in the interionic theory of Debye and Huckel.

The power of this work is that of the writing on other subjects; it is that, actually, *subject* itself is done away with as completely as possible at the time, and that process and principle are dealt with, so that the conclusions are not true for particular substances, but, as MacInnes says, "for all substances and all machines." The work was to go out, to have its effect on research, and slowly and namelessly, on industry.

Dr. W. R. Whitney, vice-president in charge of research of the General Electric Company, speaking of the enormous influence which the work of Gibbs has on the electrical industry, says :

Looking into the experimental facts deeper than others had done, he was able to express in new forms, in simplicity, in diagrams and in words those regularities which are to be of ever-increasing significance to scientist, chemist, physicist and engineer. His Phase-rule was part of this orderliness. To the layman, it is clear that he saw further into the mechanics of natural processes than others of his time, and discussed relations and regularities which escaped less meticulous observation. Adhering strictly to observational facts, and under no theoretical guiding star of wishful thinking, he thoughtfully analyzed related facts. . . . Take the expression: $de = tdn - pdv$.

Countless pages of comprehensive and useful science have been constructed around the skeleton-structure. Probably all that most of us need know about it, is the time-table of our train or the cost of our aero-flights; which, in the minds of the local creators, depend upon that, to them, simple equation of Gibbs.

. . . Walter Lippmann has said: "Where all think alike, no one thinks very much." Gibbs and Einstein have thought as specialists who peered into Creation's complexities and brought back their individual pictures.

Over a long time, it was said that less than a dozen men understood Einstein, except in the very general way that he was dealing with such fundamental things as matter and energy, space and time. Gibbs was also pretty well out in front. I remember hearing Ostwald in Leipsic remark upon the fact that for years some most important contributions to "matter and energy" had remained buried in an obscure Connecticut publication. He undertook the translation of this fundamental, increasingly obvious group of mathematico-physical expressions of measured facts which Gibbs had so scientifically coordinated.

The reprints of the first half were exhausted; there were only a few left of the second half. In 1892, a new edition appeared that was to change European industry. Ostwald wrote, in the preface to *Thermodynamische Studien, von J. Willard Gibbs*:

The importance of the Studies in Thermodynamics by Willard Gibbs cannot be better characterized than by the fact that a great part of the relations discovered in the meantime by various researchers in the province of chemical as well as physical statics— and leading to a very remarkable development in this province— can be found, explicitly or implicitly, in these papers. That in spite of this fact a re-discovery of these statements has become a necessity is probably due to the inaccessibility of these studies.

The difficulty is twofold: external and internal. To this day, the papers have been published only in the *Transactions of the Connecticut Academy*, and the limited circulation of these *Transactions* has prevented them from coming to the knowledge of wider circles. On the other hand, one cannot deny that the study of these researches offers inner difficulties, as well. Actuated by a wish for the greatest possible universality and plainness of expression, the author has chosen a mode of presentation which calls for an unusual attentiveness and devotion on the part of the reader, owing to the abstractness of the form and the difficult presentation.

Ostwald says that he has been able to remedy the first difficulty, and time may have removed part of the second, since the ideas of the book have become more familiar to the scientific world than they were at the time of its publication.

The material of the work is still of direct importance at the moment, and the interest in it is not historical. For only a small part of the almost immeasurable results which are contained and suggested here have as yet been realized. There are still hidden treasures of the greatest variety and importance here for the theoretical, and most of all for the experimental, worker.

Since we know many of the values of energy and entropy for solutions and gases, part of the work has already been re-stated, but the far greater part is still waiting to be fulfilled.

That re-statement has taken many forms. In Holland, the school of Roozeboom and Schreinemakers, with the help of this translation and Meyerhoffer's book, *Die Phasenregel*, were to begin a new chapter of research and industry. "The principles first enunciated by Gibbs became a veritable Rosetta stone," says F. G. Cottrell, of the U.S. Department of Agriculture. Boltzmann, who announced, "The struggle for existence of

The Rosetta Stone of Science

living matter is a war for free energy," also said that Gibbs's work was the greatest synthetic achievement in science since Newton's achievement of the theory of universal gravitation. In glimpses, far away from New Haven, single workers could see that here was not only a rule that could be applied to countless mixtures, but that all the materials of the world, all common objects—the common and rare things which we use to survive—the elements, our blood, plants, metals, an almost infinite number of combinations—could be "managed efficiently." Here was a principle which had made a clean sweep, not only of its science, but of a whole way of thinking. An entire structure had been erected by one man. If he was remote, if in his achievement of a general language he had withdrawn to bear the penalties of discovery, there was nothing remote about his gifts. They were common and everyday gifts of the greatest imaginative power. It was beginning to be possible to see concrete results from the shadow of this man and his equations; and there was no end to the immense prospect.

CHAPTER FIFTEEN

The Shadow and the Factory

THE CENTURY filled in across America, to its end more desperate and contradictory than any other hundred years. Ill-equipped and grasping, romantic and wasteful, tinkering with the details of the democratic state and ignoring the vast hope and invention that would have to come before that state could be confirmed, the last quarter was reaching its end, with the gaps wider than ever before. The farmer and the railroad millionaire were farther apart socially and economically than ever; the pressure groups and actual mass protest could be seen as worlds apart when three or four Western papers had the full responsibility for the campaign for silver; but even farther apart—and this is clearest in the case of Gibbs—were the domains of influence and recognition. To those few who could see their lives as education, and search untired for causes, believing in causes and effects whose relationship could be found, these secret powers left spoors on every lesser power. But the kind of person who was emerging from formal nineteenth-century education was not that kind at all. The expert was advancing as technical knowledge rose in value.

And the expert was not likely to be merely a trained man with special abilities in one field, and an ordinary interest in the rest of the world. He was likely not even to be an expert in his line, and a mass-man in all others. He was, most often, a skilled detail-worker who was highly conservative—reactionary, indeed—because there was nothing in his training to let him see where, in society, his own skills became mixed with all other knowledge.

[*316*]

The Shadow and the Factory

The professors of literature were turning out little critics, with appetites as broad as hairlines for democracy; the economists were turning out disciples in economics; and the technical schools beginning to flourish were turning out a new man in the world—highly surfaced, confident only of the limited knowledge he recognized in himself and was aware that his colleagues recognized, and almost without earned opinions about anything else.

The Adams family, in this generation of Brooks and Charles Francis and Henry, summed it up. Some critics have accepted a superficial view of this family in terms which these Adamses themselves used in the self-weariness that is bound to arrive in clans which have touched great power. But they had a relationship to power itself which we need to have. Their parents and grandparents had been power itself. They kept the old attraction to the hand on the lever. Henry Adams was drawn to Pumpelly for that confessed reason. Power in their own family had been misunderstood and hated, and Jackson's aggressive rise had been seen as pure anti-Adams. To a race of tycoons and senators, it might look as though the Adamses had thinned out and been degraded—as energy—all the way down. But the relationship to power had become almost more important than power itself. And it was gaining in importance, for it foreshadowed the future.

There was little with which to face the year 1900, it seemed, that was not on the surface. Inventions, and aptitudes, sprang up overnight, and their techniques with them. Edison and Tesla, low and high frequency—that was something a whittling boy could follow, and claim. The horn of plenty, and the gilded age. They seemed to speak wealth. Broadness should follow. But this was a technical cleverness; nobody was being trained to administer; one section was being inflamed and over-stimulated, and the rest of the people were falling into hungry anger, or into the appeased after-dinner surfeit that this glamor of gadgets pulled down over their eyes.

Brooks Adams spoke the need. "Apparently modern society, if it is to cohere," he wrote, "must have a high order of generalizing mind—a mind which can grasp a multitude of complex relations —but this is a mind which can, at best, only be produced in small quantity and at high cost. Capital has preferred the specialized mind." It was only in science and mechanics that the standard of training was being lifted.

Even so, in these years, the country lifted up freshness and hope, a frontier brightness as the frontier passed. That line had wandered West as the equilibrium of America changed—indeed, as an image, the country might be seen as one of Gibbs's mixed fluids, with the frontier, a barrier of single molecules, drawn down the map as a surface of discontinuity. The hope was always there : a lawless hope, since no one could predict the future of this system, unless they worked as Gibbs was working, frankly with partial knowledge, toward great and partial ends. Sumner, Powell, Morgan—they were making experiments and accumulating material.

It was with a sense of loss that the hope of America made itself clear, to the invalid, the expatriate, in sensitivity and longing. William James's sister Alice, ill and neurotic and of intense bravery, was dying in England of that frightful nervous strain which James himself had stopped at the moment at which he reached his belief in the freedom of the will, and whose cure he had confirmed in his marriage. Alice was dying, and the American friends who visited her struck her to the heart with memory. She wrote of such a visit :

What a tide of homesickness swept me under for the moment! What a longing to see a shaft of sunshine shimmering through the pines, breathe in the resinous air, and throw my withered body down upon my mother earth, bury my face in the coarse grass, worshipping all that the ugly, raw emptiness of the blessed land stands for,—the embodiment of a huge chance for hemmed-in humanity; its flexible conditions stretching and lending themselves to all sizes of man; pallid and naked of necessity; undraped by the illusions and mystery of a moss-grown, cobwebby past, but overflowing with a divine good-humour and benignancy, a helping hand for the faltering, an indulgent thought for the discredited, a heart of hope for every outcast of tradition.

One may not speak of "outcasts of tradition" in connection with Yale. The traditional terms are in themselves too strict. Here is a wealthy University, thriving on New Haven tax-free real estate. Its unreal estate is not in tradition; but the temptation is to think it is. Powerful Sumner, even after his breakdown in 1890, was the dominant, stamping man who knew the value of use, rather than reason. He was the type, rather than frail-seeming high-voiced Gibbs, whose classroom Wilbur Cross passed one spring morning, with all the windows open, to hear the shrill voice with its complaining tones, until young Cross stopped, thinking someone was suffering. "That's Gibbs's classroom—that's his usual voice," a student happening by told him.

Gibbs was New Haven. That was enough to stamp him. A city festival was held, and Professor Whitney's name was up in the street. Two men stopped before it. "Why is Whitney up there?" one of them asked, and the other replied, "He was born here, wasn't he?"

And, on the other hand, Gibbs was recognized. He had come into his fame. It has been one of the strangest kinds of illustriousness that any man ever received. For his influence has been felt, with enormous and bewildering impact; he is revered in his own field. But his name is completely unknown to the lay person; as point after point makes clear, if he wished his work to be popular and recognized—and, although his students and critics say he did not, his own plain statements contradict them—he is buried in more ways than he bargained for.

The stories about his classroom and his study grew in the '90s. Half of them were the crank stories that are one of the New England crops; some of them the pathetic stories of misunderstanding and ignorance; and one or two the evidences of his sweetness and the noble simplicity of his mind.

The few students who were prepared for his teaching loved him. Irving Fisher remembers walking out of his classroom with Percey Smith, who turned at the door and said, "What a *gentle* man he is!"

But then, William Lyon Phelps still has the nickname "Gibes" ringing in his ears, along with the memory of Gibbs as a quiet-tempered man, with a beautiful head and face. He tells of one boy who had been plagued by his undergraduate courses beyond endurance. He could not stand a great many things about Yale; and by and by he was expelled. He knew he was to leave that day, but he took one last fling, and went to Gibbs's classroom. Once class had started, he began the wildest clowning he could think of. He muttered, and said fierce things to his neighbors, and finally threw something across the room; and when Gibbs turned on him and asked, still in comparative mildness, "What is the meaning of this, sir?" he got to his feet with one last look around the classroom, then said loudly, "Oh, go to hell, Gibes," and stamped out.

That was a public scene. The story that is a real index of Gibbs as teacher, after all the opinions—he was a gifted lecturer, he was impossible, nobody understood him, he had brilliant students—is a private story. Charles Studin arrived as an undergraduate, fresh from two years at the University of Colorado, applying for a transfer to Yale. He was told that he would have to take an examination in mathematics in order to enter; and when he showed up for his examination, it was to take place in a room down the hall, where he would find his examiner. He went down the college corridor, trembling with scholastic anxiety; put his hand on the door, and went in. There, at the desk, was a man with white hair and a great face. He was later told it was Gibbs. The examiner waited for him to be seated and then said, gently, "You have had two years of mathematics at Colorado?" He looked at the student with a kind and searching look; and when the answer, "Yes," came, he took out his watch and held it in his hand. Looking down at the watch, he said, "This examination will last one hour," wound the watch, and set it down on the desk before him. The student looked up at him as he sat there. The student waited for the questions to begin, but there was silence. And, as his bewilderment grew, and then a growing sense of an academic miracle, the minutes ticked away. Not a word was said, until at the end of the hour, Gibbs rose, and said, quietly, "You have passed the examination."

During these years, he was teaching seven subjects, of which three were two-hour courses, and the others one-hour, a week. Vector analysis, thermodynamics, and electromagnetic theory of light were the longer courses; there were also advanced vector analysis, multiple algebra, statistical mechanics, and potential theory with theory of electricity. Not all of these were offered in any one year. His lectures were given as his books were written, without notes. His processes were clearly going on inside of his head, as the class listened and made its own notes. Yale had had enough of the other methods. There are letters complaining about one tutor who said that he "was not familiar with

The Shadow and the Factory

the subject but would make it as interesting as possible," and one professor who made it clear to his class that all he wanted, after having written his textbook, "was to hear again the exact words in his book." Gibbs became a legend to his classes as the man who let the simplest things go wrong, like his demonstration of the Carnot cycle, but who, when he was asked a complicated question about the experimental proof of one of his findings, tilted his head back, closed his eyes, thought a little, and finally said simply, "Yes, that would be true."

He went down to Princeton to receive his Doctorate of Laws at the Sesquicentennial in October 1896. That year he had also been invited to be a member of the Victoria Society; and when he arrived at Professor Magie's home in Princeton, he found a letter informing him that he had been elected honorary member of the Cliosophic Society of Princeton. The days of the celebration included the huge reception on October 20th, with President Eliot speaking for the American universities and J. J. Thomson for the European; the concert that evening in Alexander Hall, with Walter Damrosch conducting a program of Brahms and Bach and Schubert, Wagner, Weber, Saint-Saëns, and Tschaikowsky.

That winter he finished a paper on semi-permeable films and osmotic pressure, which was published in *Nature*. Going on with this work in the great paper, he went from the conditions of equilibrium to a statement for the potentials of the solution. The equation he reached, he said, "may be regarded as expressing the property of the solution implied in van't Hoff's law." At the time the great paper was published, not enough experimental data had been collected to allow Gibbs to make a full statement; he had made a partial statement, for gases, and added that "the law expressed by these equations has a very general application." The facts, again, were direct consequences of the laws of thermodynamics which were his only assumptions. In the end, there is only one assumption that anyone can make, in science or philosophy. That is the assumption of a logical relation between cause and effect. Gibbs, who withdrew from assumption, being well aware that the simplest system in nature was infinitely more complicated than the fictive systems he had set up, was willing only to make that magnificent single assumption. In holding back, he contributed more to the methods of making average generalizations from partial knowledge than he might have with any more reckless gesture.

Van't Hoff had inferred his law from experimental work; Gibbs worked, as usual, deductively, with results that led to very important fields. Donnan, writing about osmotic pressure, says : "When we consider the part played by the concept in the earlier and very important development of the theory of dilute solutions, we cannot but feel the greatest admiration for the investigations of Gibbs in this field"; and adds the inevitable : "If later investigators . . . had gone back to the work of Gibbs, much confusion and error would have been avoided."

Gibbs had already "created a new branch of science, namely, the thermodynamic theory of capillarity." The work he did in all of these branches has led up to fearfully significant and branching changes : a fountain of results, reaching in war and peace, not only to our moment, but to the future. Whoever touches his work here sees that it is at once proper to speak of him in terms that reach far out beyond us. His work is just begun.

At this same time, he published a short paper about the infinite series of Fourier, noting a convergence which came to be known—after it was so called by Maxime Bocher—as the "Gibbs phenomenon." This was a contribution in the tradition of mathematical rigor that led from Fourier through Weierstrass to Gibbs. Riemann, Dedekind, and Cantor worked in this series also, until, three years after this paper of Gibbs was published, Henri Poincaré, the flashing and gifted French scientist and writer, could say, "Mathematics, as we say, has been arithmetized. . . . We may say today that absolute rigor has been attained."

Other kinds of recognition besides the academic meetings and degrees were reaching Gibbs. In Ithaca, at Cornell, Wilder Bancroft and J. E. Trevor founded the *Journal of Physical Chemistry*. Its first issue appeared in October 1896, and during all of its early years, its articles and reviews were full of Gibbs's name and work. The latest advances were checked against the suggestions in which Gibbs's papers were rich; reviews of books judged them according to their recognition of Gibbs's contribution. Ostwald's new book on electrochemistry and Woldemar Voigt's *Theoretical Physics* included full sections on Gibbs, and were commended for it; but Mach's *Wärmelehre* was sharply criticized for one detail—"the magnificent works of Gibbs were little more than cited." Trevor spoke of Ostwald, whose *Lehrbuch der allgemeinen Chemie* had thirty-five pages on Gibbs, as "one of the very few people who have read Gibbs' paper without skipping a single word." Bancroft reviewed van't Hoff's latest work, and said caustically that it omitted the phase rule. In 1893, van Rijn van Alkemade had used Gibbs's method; Roozeboom was going on with the work in a long series of effective papers on equilibrium, graphical methods, liquid layers, vapor pressures of ternary mixtures, and crystals—the same set of subjects which Gibbs had dealt with theoretically was finding its practical material, until there was little to do but add further examples. Bancroft was talking about the triangular diagram, too —Gibbs's invention of a three-axis graph to be used for a three-component, or ternary, system. These diagrams have been of particular value in the knowledge of alloys. The composition of an alloy can be seen by measuring the distances to the sides of such a triangle. If its corners A, B, and C, each represent a pure metal, a point on the side of the triangle, which has one hundred units in each side, gives the composition of a binary alloy combined from two adjoining "corner-metals." A ternary alloy, inside the triangle, is easily measurable.

This magazine, and a whole trend in Dutch science, were indicating the early awakening to Gibbs's value. In France, Le Chatelier was preparing a French translation of the great paper; and in a damp workroom, the Curies were beginning their heroic collaboration, working all through the summer and fall of 1898 on the long elimination, element by element, of pitchblende, until in July they announced that they believed that they had extracted a metal not yet observed, *polonium*—named patriotically by Marie. At the end of the year, her daughter notes, after an entry in her diary about her little girl, Irène, who can now "walk very well, and no longer goes on all fours," appears another note, announcing the new element, radium, the "metaphysical bomb," as Henry Adams called it, that was to distort ideas of matter into a new explosive arrangement, its balance of order and chaos to shine with something of the luminous wonder of the element itself.

Ideas of order were wished for, as the century drew to its

close. It was clear in Gibbs that balance, order, and chaos itself might be seen approaching one principle of larger and purposive equilibrium. The French translation was finished; the preface could speak for Gibbs, as he himself would never do :

. . . Gibbs was able by a truly extraordinary effort of the scientific imagination and logical power to posit all the principles of the new science and to foresee all its ulterior applications. . . . To Gibbs belongs the honor of having fused the two sciences into one, chemical mechanics, of having constituted a completely defined body of principles, to which additions may be made in the future, but from which the progress of time can take nothing away.

His method, like that of Newton, Fresnel and Ampère, consists in starting with a small number of first principles or hypotheses, and searching out all the necessary consequences of those principles, without ever introducing in the course of the reasoning any new hypotheses or relaxing the rigor of the reasoning.

Willard Gibbs, in New Haven, was little touched by this delayed entrance of his work into the world. He went on in the ways he knew so well : along High Street, to Sloane, where now he worked into the evenings, to the meetings of the Mathematical Club, which he had founded; to the meetings of the Connecticut Academy, with which his work had been bound; to the trustees' meetings of Hopkins Grammar School. He was treasurer of Hopkins now, as well as trustee. A shrewd, efficient treasurer he turned out to be, making sound investments with Hopkins money, as he did with his own. He sent letters out to trustees, informing them of meetings, held in his office at Sloane Laboratory at seven-thirty or eight in the evening. He was involved in school politics, worried as the rate of attendance dropped sharply during the '90s, wrote his tart letters about money matters, like this early one to Lounsbury :

Dear Professor Lounsbury,

I am sorry to cause you any trouble or annoyance, but I feel compelled to call your attention to one or two points.

I have never been authorized by the Board to receive any contribution in the premises. The matter was entirely a private one, with w^h the Board, as such, has nothing to do.

I thought at the time, & I think still, that in returning the money I followed the only course w^h was open to me,—that I did the only thing w^h any gentleman would think of doing under the circumstances.

In fact, if I were inclined to take the matter seriously, I should now feel constrained to persist in the same course.

Nevertheless, as the discussion threatens to enter upon a ludicrous phase, I acquiesce, in the interest of economy of paper & ink, in your desire that the money should be applied to the object proposed.

Truly yours

J. W. GIBBS

That letter appears to contain the only use of the word "phase" outside of his scientific work, and one smiles at the way it happens, in this stiff reminder of an old, forgotten school issue.

As for the new European interest in his work, Gibbs held back from that. He did not like the idea of sending Ostwald a picture of himself to be used in a foreign publication. He did not know that many Yale boys, graduating from college without ever hearing of him, would have to study his work abroad; and that others, trying to place themselves with German professors, would recite the names of their New Haven teachers without producing a flicker of recognition, until they reached the name of Gibbs.

He was cut off in the same way that the country at large was cut off. America was reaching the end of self-sufficiency, but to a great extent she produced her own climate, and responded only to what she produced; one statesman could say that, until the Spanish-American War, there was no reason for any American but the Secretary of State to be aware of the outside world. Deep within this isolation, he had his own stern and creative loneliness. There is no climax in Gibbs's life, and in that it is like the world itself. By suggestion, by particles of intense life, the darkness of wish and love and abstract thought may be seen, and all the struggles in which they are caught. His compulsion was great and conflicting, but his own steadiness is best seen, as his life is best seen, in his work, which flowed; his interests ran on, in a flicker of creative motion; no maze of experiment ensnares him, no device acts as a bridle. Other men—Lord Kelvin is the prime example—felt the failure of their apparatus as the century turned, and the new horizons opened; they were the people saying that physics was coming to a close; that, for example, there could not be a flying machine; it could be proved impossible.

Willard Gibbs

Gibbs went on, increasing his thought as he increased his mountains. He did not go to Keene Valley or Bethlehem, where he had summered. Now he spent his summers among the highest of the White Mountains, at Intervale, above which Mount Washington marshals its snows and clouds. The fast Saco winding in its wide motion through the valley, the light among the birches, the light on the water, the light of the immense sky, leaping as the eye leaps over these mountains; he lived among these. He walked here, with his look, so unseeing toward passing people, quickened to the bright valley.

It seems impossible that he should not see William James. James lectured at Yale in 1896; he might have met Gibbs in Berlin, at Heidelberg, or Keene Valley, or at last here, since James knew Helmholtz and was in touch with Ostwald. The tragic waste of the nineteenth century seems to have kept apart just those who most needed each other's ideas; and there is no record of a meeting. But James's son Henry remembers talk of Gibbs, although it was during his childhood, and he has only "a vague memory—very vague." This is the painfully unrecorded wandering of ideas. The meanings needed each other. And, so short a time after, there is no way to place a meeting : around a fire on these starry nights, on the windy mountainside, or simply coming together with a note or a friend for introduction. As for the scene itself, in full September and unpopulated, the second Henry speaks for himself and, one feels, a word or two for Alice, dead now and eternally expatriate. This is Henry James on one of his brief trips home, writing of the valley which holds Jackson, North Conway, and Intervale :

. . . The old informal earthy coachroad was a firm highway, wide and white—and ground to dust, for all its firmness, by the whirling motor; without which I might have followed it, back and back a little, into the near, into the far, country of youth—left lying, however, as the case stood, beyond the crest of a hill. Only the high rock-walls of the Ledges, the striking sign of the spot, were there; gray and perpendicular, with their lodged patches of shrub-like forest growth, and the immense floor, below them, where the Saco spreads and turns and the elms of the great general meadow stand about like candelabra (with their arms reversed) interspaced on a green table. There hung over these things the insistent hush of a September Sunday morning; nowhere greater than in the tended woods enclosing the admirable country home that I was able to enjoy as a centre for contemplation : woods with their dignity maintained by a large and artful clearance of undergrowth, and repaying this attention, as always, by something of the semblance of a sacred grove, a place prepared for high uses, even if for none rarer than high talk. . . . The rich, full lapse of the river, the perfect brownness, clear and deep, as of liquid agate, in its wide swirl, the large indifferent ease in its pace and motion, as of some great benevolent institution smoothly working; all this, with the sense of the deepening autumn about, gave I scarce know what pastoral nobleness to the scene, something raising it out of the reach of even the most restless of analysts. The analyst in fact could scarce be restless here; the impression, so strong and so final, persuaded him perfectly to peace. This, on September Sunday mornings, was what American beauty *should* be; it filled to the brim its idea and its measure—albeit Mount Washington, hazily overhung, happened not to contribute to the effect. It was the great, gay river, singing as it went, like some reckless adventurer, good-humored for the hour and with his hands in his pockets, that argued the whole case and carried everything assentingly before it.

That is the valley as one walks by the bends of the Saco. But to anyone who has gone up these turns by canoe, to anyone who has climbed Washington, gone up the Notch or the other way, across the range of the Presidentials—Madison, Adams, Jefferson, and on up—the challenge and the air of Intervale has other potencies : the sting and summer sweetness of the highest mountains.

They saw Gibbs walking here as they saw him at home : "head in the air, tall, uplifted, the very semblance of a poet," said Hubert Newton's daughter, and one girl who was a student in his vector-analysis class said she knew he wrote poetry. The traces of his influence are in the theses with which he helped. The following list includes the theses on which he presumably advised : In 1885, the thesis of Eliakim Hastings Moore, who said when he left to teach at the young University of Chicago that he hated to leave a place that had two men so alive as Newton and Gibbs; in 1891, Percey Franklyn Smith, and in 1898, George Pratt Starkweather, both in the Mathematics Department at Sheffield; in 1900, Herbert Edward Hawkes, Professor of Mathematics at Columbia; in 1901, Edwin B. Wilson, of Harvard. During the years from 1896 on, Gibbs was receiving, at last, his full salary, $3,250. In the six years after, there are five theses on which Gibbs's help is acknowledged. They are those of Shum-kichi Kumira, who became wireless engineer of the Naval Electrical Laboratory in Tokyo; Henry A. Bumstead, who later helped to edit Gibbs's papers and whose biographical note on Gibbs is printed with them; Arthur W. Ewell, who taught physics at Worcester Polytechnic Institute; Lee De Forest, the inventor and pioneer in the fields of radio, sound film, and television; and L. P. Wheeler, of Sheffield.

There are other instances of help from Gibbs. Two of these are in Carl Barus' note about Gibbs's suggestions to him on geophysical research, in which he remembers Gibbs's cordiality and his enthusiastic writing out of a plan of attack. Unfortunately, Gibbs was too chary of print for the project ever to have been completed.

The other memory is J. McKeen Cattell's. The scientist and editor writes :

I regard Willard Gibbs as the greatest American man of science. It seems that Benjamin Franklin and Joseph Henry did not reach his stature. I had the great pleasure of knowing him and of learning to appreciate his personal qualities even more than I could his great contributions to science, which I could only judge by what Ostwald and others said. On one occasion he very patiently helped me in solving certain applications of mechanics to psychology.

The work in which Gibbs kindly helped me was on the problem of the measurement of physiological energy, in connection with an invention by me of an ergometer in which the energy was measured by a spring instead of a lifted weight, intended to replace Mosso's ergograph. It takes more effort to lift a ten-pound weight one inch ten times than to lift the same weight ten inches.

Known to physical chemists and to those who intelligently asked his help as the kindest of men, who would always use his own time to help a friend or student work out a problem, Gibbs was unknown to the people about him, who were beginning to hear rumors of some achievement, dimly realized, and not, as it seemed, capable of being described. The stories grew in New Haven. One tale was of a student who went to see Gibbs in his office. He asked him about a diagram which had been explained in class; and Gibbs, to explain, began to draw imaginary lines across the floor. The lines grew more complicated. They reached up the walls, to the ceiling, across the door; and, as the student left exhausted, he saw that Gibbs was still standing in the center of the floor, hopelessly enmeshed in his own diagram.

Another story is about the *Transactions of the Connecticut Academy*. Word got about that an article by Gibbs had appeared there, saying that of course the moon was not made of green cheese—this is according to Henry Seidel Canby—but that if it had been, these are the laws it would have obeyed, and then working out an impossibly abstruse set of laws.

There was no green-cheese article. But there was a speech made to the Mathematical Club. Gibbs had just bought a horse, and his next paper, presented before the Yale Mathematical Club, was on the "Paces of a Horse." Irving Fisher writes, "Probably no one else ever put a horse through his paces as scientifically or amusingly as Gibbs did in that paper."

Still another anecdote comes, says George Eaton, the secretary of the Connecticut Academy, from "one of New Haven's older and highly respected bankers. As a young man he was present when Gibbs consulted a real estate agent about a proposed sale of land. Gibbs tried to calculate the hypotenuse of a right-angled triangle from the other two sides $\sqrt{a^2+b^2}=c$ and confessed that he had forgotten the rule for finding the square root!"

"He lived only a few doors from my house in New Haven," wrote William Lyon Phelps, "and I used to see him taking his solitary walks; and I thought what an exciting life he really must be leading, away out on the remote frontiers of speculative thought. For, as Henry James said, 'There are no adventures like intellectual ones.'"

His intellectual adventures were leading him farther on, as those closest to him fell behind, dying. Hubert Anson Newton died in August 1896, and Gibbs wrote a note on his life to be read before the National Academy of Sciences the following spring. Newton, his closest friend, had been asked whether he followed what Gibbs was saying, at a lecture; he had answered; "I saw how the second equation was derived from the first, and the third from the second; after that I was lost." He had advised Gibbs on his thesis, helped him publish his papers, sat with him in his rooms where comets darted golden on the walls, laughed over Lewis Carroll, walked among the iris garden's color. And, in this sixteen-page paper, Gibbs lovingly spoke of his life, summing up Newton's qualities in words that have often been applied to Gibbs himself :

But these papers show more than the type of mind of the author; they give no uncertain testimony concerning the character of the man. In all these papers we see a love of honest work, an aversion to sham, a distrust of rash generalizations and speculations based on uncertain premises.

And he concludes the description :

In all these relations of life, the subject of this sketch exhibited the same traits of character which are seen in his published papers, the same modesty, the same conscientiousness, the same devotion to high ideals. His life was the quiet life of the scholar, ennobled by the unselfish aims of the Christian gentleman; his memory will be cherished by many friends; and so long as astronomers, while they watch the return of the Leonids marking off the passage of the centuries, shall care to turn the earlier pages of this branch of astronomy, his name will have an honorable place in the history of the science.

The year after, the deepest blow fell. With Anna's illness and death, the house must have changed profoundly. There is no way of knowing how the household balance was altered, or what this parting meant. Anna was buried between her father's and Emily's graves, and on the pyramid was written

EMILY NOV. 15, 1841–MAR. 4, 1864
ANNA LOUISA JUNE 18, 1831–JULY 13, 1898
THEY WALK O LORD IN THE LIGHT OF THY COUNTENANCE
DAUGHTERS OF JOSIAH WILLARD & MARY ANNA GIBBS

In Washington, Henry Adams read Stallo, whose work has been considered as a theoretical anticipation of the work of Willard Gibbs. Stallo's "There is no physical constant" announced the laws of change; to Henry Adams, looking for "streaks of order" in the universe, there began to recur certain facts. He wanted a pattern here, an idea of probability, at any rate. The throw of the dice was fixed by law; if you did not know the answer, throw by throw, you could learn averages and possibilities. Adams' search dated from before he wrote that "any science of history must be absolute, like other sciences, and must fix with mathematical certainty the path which human society has got to follow." It went back to his Quincy childhood, to the power in his family, to his grandfather calling in the same way for a clue to order.

The Newtonian concepts of his family's past had not been broken until now; but here were the splinters, and Adams "wanted to ask Mme. Curie to invent a motor attachable to her salt of radium, and pump its forces through it," in much the same way that Mark Twain said he could approve of sun-worship if a rope tied to the worshipper's neck could move with his moving head and do work connecting his exertion to a machine.

Gibbs had been thought of as such a sun-worshipper, no doubt, by many. But if he was a shadow walking through New Haven, there was light seen radiating from him. In Holland, Roozeboom was using him to interpret the properties of steel as a two-component system. The tremendous industrial possibilities began to emerge. There had been no proper knowledge of alloys; here was a key that could turn metallurgy into a modern science.

Bancroft's book on the phase rule was beginning to be read. It appeared in 1897, and it spoke more directly to physicists and chemists both than the paper itself could possibly have done. The Americans who were flocking to European schools could find Gibbs's paper; and while there had been altogether 150 Americans before 1850, now there were yearly two hundred Americans in the three universities of Göttingen, Berlin, and Leipzig alone. Industry in Germany and Holland—particularly in Germany—was fit to accept theoretical advance. In 1871, when Bismarck had unified Germany, he knew that one of the most important sources of unity would be industry, and he had set about to unify German industry. Step by step, the industrialization of empire had taken place. The old prophecy of the Abbé Galiani that Europe would be a center of manufacture, as India was in 1771, had come through, and that knife was being twisted again. Brooks Adams wrote of the industrial revolution in England : "For nearly a century the inventions of Hargreaves, of Crompton, of Cartwright, and of Watt, enabled Lancashire to supply Bombay and Calcutta with fabrics, as, in the seventeenth century, Surat and Calicut had supplied London . . ." And a prophetic German chemist, back in 1862, had set another mark of prophecy—and this was the turn of the knife indeed—by saying that England would be the greatest color-producing country in the world, sending coal-blues to indigo-growing India, tarcrimsons to the Mexico of cochineal, and substitutes for quercitron and safflower to China and Japan.

The turn of the century was proving how deep a revolution was taking place. Probability, chance, the huge chance. There were other turns the knife might take.

Many suffered revulsion as the changes came. Greatness can withstand that, except in those lives whose pattern is oscillation. Gibbs was a still center of violence, the most profound violence thinkable out of such silence. He was able to withstand all change; he was going ahead.

Henry Adams entered the twentieth century like one who has prepared all his equipment for a final outcome, and is at the last moment filled with the foreboding of the prisoner at the bench, the soldier before battle, the subject entering the operating room. He wanted to make answers to life, but he saw the pressures; and dimly saw their climax ahead. He wrote from Paris to Cecil Spring-Rice:

. . . Make your own answer to Life as it asks its questions, and hang on to one fact : that that particular question is (The Republic or the Empire! Both are Progress! Or are they not?) only another form of the kinetic theory of gases, of which your German problem is an illustration. Do you know the kinetic theory of gases? Of course you do, since Clerk Maxwell was an Oxford man, I suppose. Anyway, Germany is and always has been a remarkably apt illustration of Maxwell's conception of "sorting demons." By bumping against all its neighbors, and being bumped in turn it gets and gives at last a common motion, which is, and of necessity must be, a vortex or cycle. It can't get anywhere except round a circle and return on itself. It has done so since the time of Varus and his legions. The struggle between the industrial and the military impulses was at the bottom of the Reformation. It has been at the botton of every political change since Merovig. We can pretty well measure the possible x which is the ultimate quantity we want to eliminate. Another generation will have the figures, and the limit of ultimate concentra-

tion will then be calculable—barring war, which may of course
delay, or wholly defeat, further vortical movement. The point to
study is, however, not primarily the social movement, but the industrial, and I am always wondering at my own ignorance and at the
European conspiracy of silence on that point. What is the rate of
progress of the creditor nations in exports and in capital? What is
the rate at which credit increases with reference to its base, if it has
one, in exchange? What is the rate of production compared with the
possible markets? I can get absolutely no serious information as to
the amount of credit now existing, or its equivalents in previous
decades. With these two elements : the industrial and the capitalistic,
I think I could fix approximately the elements of the human orbit,
which is necessarily limited by the same conditions of mass, etc.,
which limit the orbit of the planet.

But this is something approaching thought, and our intelligent
classes now permit no one except Jews to think. Beware how you
betray such a vicious tendency. All governments particularly regard
it with jealousy, and Universities and Society are very shy of all who
indulge in the habit. Only Socialists and Anarchists can afford to
think. . . .

Adams had not found a possible beginning to his solution. He
was not aware of the work of Gibbs. And no University would
believe that Gibbs had anything to do with the industrial movement or the human orbit, any more than the specialists would
believe he had anything to do with their specialty. Lord Kelvin,
for example, was writing hesitating letters to Lord Rayleigh :

I feel very doubtful as to the merits of Willard Gibbs's applications
of the Second Law of Thermodynamics referred to by J. J. Thomson. Do you attribute merit to them?

and later, of this man whose mark is now on all chemistry,

I find no light or leading for either chemistry or thermodynamics
in Willard Gibbs.

He would change his mind long before his visit to New Haven.
The Royal Society members changed their minds more slowly.
Lord Rayleigh worked to secure recognition for Gibbs, saying
everywhere that the phase rule, "with all its implications, concerned many of the ways in which the different sciences inter-
sect, i.e., biology and chemistry." But the chemical members of
the Council said that the phase rule was "not chemistry."

[*333*]

Willard Gibbs

His field of operations was not yet found. Time's arrow had not been named; nobody yet had claimed that the mind itself was a system of vectors. There was intense fear before a great deal of Gibbs's work; thermodynamics suggested to laymen—if the word itself, at which they bogged, suggested anything—the petering-out of the universe. William James, at the end of the marvellously suggestive *Varieties of Religious Experience*, answers the threat of the heat-death in the only way he could even bring himself to face it :

God's existence is the guarantee of an ideal order that shall be permanently preserved. The world may indeed, as science assures us, some day burn up or freeze; but if it is part of his order, the old ideals are sure to be brought elsewhere to fruition, so that where God is, tragedy is only provisional and partial, and shipwreck and dissolution are not the absolutely final things.

There was a link between that answer and Adams' concern with orbits. It was a huge link of the imagination. Changes were coming; only a great imaginative scientist—Henri Poincaré, for example, knotting up science and reality and the illumination of both—could supply the link for God and Germany, violence and change and the explosion and blending of forms.

Gibbs, in New Haven, lectured on *Values* to the Mathematical Club. That lecture might have a clue. But it was never written down; no notes are at this point available, and there is no reliable memory of what he said. He found destruction and burial here, too. And it persists. He was writing letters and giving other help. His correspondence with Ostwald is in the hands of his nephew—unavailable. Langley wrote to him about his early experiments with the airplane, asking for help and finding it. That letter is unavailable. These patterns persist, for the mind is indeed a system of vectors, and the century was at its beginning ready with evidences of magnitude and direction.

Henry Adams entered the twentieth century consciously, aware of changes of form and freaks of force, with this first year a critical point. Knowing process more and more clearly, he was looking for a change that he knew would have to take place in himself. Gibbs entered the year with the consciousness of a great work, not behind him, but growing with him, and ready for a new summary, among all the other earth-shaking summary announcements. The ions discovered through work in solutions, the rays that first Röntgen and then Becquerel had found, with the work leading to the explosive history of radium, and the quantum theory devised by Planck just at the turn of the century—these were all heralds of entrance. The majority of physical scientists were not preparing for change They were holding onto their ideas of mechanism while they could. They lived in a reliable scene, they felt; they could prove what they needed to prove, and the only thing that might be moved was, perhaps, the last decimal. No other extension was visible. But the last years had thrown open the horizon.

Now the foundation would shift, everything would rock and totter, the old ideas would be re-tested in this storm of change.

Willard Gibbs was summing up much of his lifework in a last book. Between the autumn of 1900 and the summer of 1901, he was writing, without notes, out of the results of fourteen years of preparation and teaching of the subject, the book of a new science. Maxwell, Clausius, and Boltzmann had worked here before him, but it was Gibbs who was bringing it to a form that could be reconciled with the new physics, reconciled with the twentieth century. It was Gibbs, too, who would give the science its name : *Statistical Mechanics*.

The book was written while Gibbs carried his full teaching schedule, in nine months of work which expressed the accumulation of his lifetime. All during that winter and spring, his students saw the familiar light in the second-floor study of Sloane, burning through the dark afternoons and into the white evenings of snow and the green spring. The body of the book was finished at Intervale that summer, but the preface—that concise and beautifully written testament—was added at home in New Haven the following December.

This book is about possibility and blending, about the tendency of the universe. The uniformity presented here is not the final sameness we contemplate with dread, the likeness of every particle with every other—that heat-death which is the end of horror and the last shipwreck—but it is that blending which outdoes our senses. If we were not gross, and limited, our infinite eyes could see the distinctions among grains, seeing each particle as single and original; variety is there so long as our perceptions match it. Variety remains if our perceptions become more acute as the random mixing goes on. It is the limitlessly perceptive sense we long for; the keen eye which will not be fooled by a trick of the world. In this sense, mathematics throws a sop to our weakness, providing sharpness for our blindness, that we cannot see; our clumsiness, that we cannot intervene.

Poincaré gives the vivid example of a drop of wine falling into a glass of water :

Whatever may be the law of the internal motion of the liquid, we shall soon see it colored of a uniform rosy tint, and however much from this moment one may shake it afterwards, the wine and the water do not seem capable of again separating. Here we have the type of the irreversible physical phenomenon : to hide a grain of barley in a heap of wheat, this is easy; afterwards to find it again and get it out, this is practically impossible. All this Maxwell and Boltzmann have explained; but the one who has seen it most clearly, in a book too little read because it is a little difficult to read, is Gibbs, in his *Elementary Principles of Statistical Mechanics*.

Again, there were hardly any assumptions. There were the laws of probability, the universal shuffling—applied to the flowing of matter through time. People had dealt with particles, Gibbs would deal again with the whole. He invents a vast mechanical system which is already defined, and multiplies that past count. Dealing with examples taken at random from such lists, he applies everything he has been concerned with—the ideas of phase and space and chance, the vectors moving in a new kind of space, a phase-space whose balance he will describe and models for which he will make. He launches these models into space. He adds dimensions. They are no longer the statues, solid as mountains, whose shadows and timber-lines may be read as a map is read. They are subtler maps of many dimensions. The charts and diagrams of conservation have become even more fictional; ghostly and more real at the same time. This is an ideal world that does not reckon with atoms and molecules, or even gases and liquids; but with creations invented only *because* they can be applied. The most sensitive analogies are here, and they lead on. From this book of two hundred pages, says Langer, "emerged in fine succession all the basic laws of heat as they are embodied in the science of thermodynamics."

The Shadow and the Factory

The *Commentary* devotes three hundred pages by Arthur Haas to the book and its background, and 120 further pages by Paul S. Epstein to appreciation and discussion of Gibbs's method in quantum statistics, up to the Einstein-Bose statistics of 1924.

Gibbs gave a fifty-year-old science its first comprehensive treatment in a work which, "like a monument in the history of physics, marks the separation of the two centuries." It stands at the highest level of the nineteenth-century classical method and "will at the same time serve as a guide in the treatment of the new problems."

His own preface sums up the work. Gibbs opens by speaking of the usual point of view in mechanics, according to which the attention is given to the changes taking place in any one system. Given the condition of the system at any time, the problem is to find its condition at any other time, and to express the changes taking place. Sometimes this may be made easier by the invention of other states not too different from the states "which are regarded as actual."

For some purposes, however, it is desirable to take a broader view. We may imagine a great number of systems of the same nature, but differing in the configurations and velocities which they have at a given instant, and differing not merely infinitesimally, but it may be so as to embrace every conceivable combination of configuration and velocities.

This great number of systems is called an *ensemble;* it is dealt with collectively. The problem now is set : not to follow a particular system through its voyage, but to determine how the whole number of systems will be distributed at any time, if we know the distribution for some one time. It is a picture of the massing of *systems* along a curve of probability—the gathering of atoms, of constellations.

"Such inquiries have been called by Maxwell *statistical*," Gibbs continues, citing the work of Clausius, Maxwell, and Boltzmann, and saying that their researches applied to particles of a system, rather than to independent systems, and subsequently to phases of systems.

But although, as a matter of history, statistical mechanics owes its origin to investigations in thermodynamics, it seems eminently worthy of an independent development, both on account of the elegance and simplicity of its principles, and because it yields new results and places old truths in a new light in departments quite outside of thermodynamics.

Moreover, this study "seems to offer the best foundation" for thermodynamics and molecular physics.

The laws we have empirically determined express the behavior of systems, Gibbs notes—their *probable* and *approximate* behavior, "or, more precisely, they express the laws of mechanics for such systems as they appear to beings who have not the fineness of perception to enable them to appreciate quantities" as small as these, "and who cannot repeat their experiments often enough to obtain any but the most probable results." The laws of statistical mechanics are exact. This does not mean that their results apply to the individual case, but there are exact results for the average. They are not more difficult to establish than the limited approximate laws.

The reverse is rather the case, for our attention is not diverted from what is essential by the peculiarities of the system considered, and we are not obliged to satisfy ourselves that the effect of the quantities and circumstances neglected will be negligible in the result. The laws of thermodynamics may be easily obtained from the principles of statistical mechanics, of which they are the incomplete expression, but they make a somewhat blind guide in our search for those laws.

Gibbs feels that this may be the main reason why the science has moved so slowly, while rapid applications were being made all the time. Also, students have never yet been familiar with the fundamental notions of this branch of mechanics. "We may confidently believe that nothing will more conduce" to the clear understanding of relations between several branches of science than this study.

"Moreover, we avoid the gravest difficulties," he writes, when we make these inquiries without talking about the constitution of matter.

In the present state of science, it seems hardly possible to frame a dynamic theory of molecular action which shall embrace the phenomena of thermodynamics, of radiation, and of the electrical manifestations which accompany the union of atoms. Yet any theory is obviously inadequate which does not take account of all these phenomena. . . . Certainly, one is building on an insecure foundation, who rests his work on hypotheses concerning the constitution of matter.

Difficulties of this kind have deterred the author from attempting to explain the mysteries of nature, and have forced him to be contented with the more modest aim of deducing some of the more obvious propositions relating to the statistical branch of mechanics. Here, there can be no mistake in regard to the agreement of the hypotheses with the facts of nature, for nothing is assumed in that respect. The only error into which one can fall, is the want of agreement between the premises and the conclusions, and this, with care, one may hope, in the main, to avoid.

That paragraph is the expression of Gibbs's approach, the caution that defined him and at once marked his greatness and his limits. With its understatement, the hesitating rhythm of its close, the exclusion of error if the end agrees with the beginning, it marks his idea of truth. Truth is, according to him, not a stream that flows from a source, but an agreement of components, an accord that actually makes the whole "simpler than its parts," as he was so fond of saying. It is truth flowing through the world, depending on an accord in great complexity. Not originality, but order, becomes the important factor; the point of view and the arrangement may be different, he says of this. "These results, given to the public one by one in the order of their discovery," were not arranged before he seized them and discovered their pattern. This arrangement turns them into a tool, a new science.

In dealing with a system of, say, N molecules, we must know the position of these N molecules if we are going to know how they are massed in groups. Three coordinates are needed in space —x, y, and z. So that we have 3N coordinates of position, in all—three degrees of freedom in the system. Then, also, there are three components of momentum to each molecule as it moves in the coordinates. There are 3N components of momentum, in all. The motion and grouping of the system at a given moment will be decided by 3N and 3N magnitudes—6N magnitudes, determining the state of the system.

These 6N coordinates, then, are the structure of a space of 6N dimensions. This is called *phase space*. It is an artificial and imagined space invented to suit requirements. In it, a point **P**, determined by the 6N coordinates, is called the *phase point*. If you know the position of this point at any instant, you are able to define the whole system and its condition in the phase space. As the system changes, the point P will move. It can only move in certain ways : its freedom depends on the container of the system, and on the laws of the system, which is defined as conserving energy. The energy keeps its value, which in turn makes certain conditions for the particles. The phase point begins to move, and the ground it covers outlines a surface existing in phase space. As D'Abro writes, the "phase points stream through a limited volume of the phase space. The volume cannot be visualized exactly on account of the large number of dimensions of the phase space," but it looks a little like the space produced when a tin can is put inside of another only slightly wider can. It is the space between the walls of the two tin cans.

When the phase points stream between the two cans like the molecules of a fluid, the equations are working. These are equations that cannot be solved. But Gibbs proved that the *phase fluid* streams like "an incompressible fluid in steady motion."

Gibbs shows the steadiness of the motion. The flow does not vary in time.

There are two famous theorems to express the fluid. They are ideas of conservation : one deals with "extension in phase" and the other with "density in phase."

Various *ensembles* are used; this is a way of dealing with many kinds of things in changing arrangements on their flow towards *statistical equilibrium,* which is the state of *maximum probability*, or *maximum entropy*. At this level the blending is complete; the glacier of motion has slipped down the slope of time. There is permanent distribution.

The makers of this theory had to show that it was not absurd here; the thermodynamic laws could be demonstrated to agree with the kinetic theory. In the limits which can be imagined to possibility, heat may become a meaningless idea, and so may temperature. D'Abro says : "Suppose, then, that by some chance all the molecules in a certain region should happen to be moving simultaneously in the same direction." These molecules go as fast as rifle bullets. Now a hundred-mile hurricane will tear trees up by the roots; here we have a storm of much greater strength, capable of the blasts of catastrophe. If the molecules of the air blew together, the heat energy would all be mechanical, and there would be no definite temperature. In short, "heat energy is disorganized random mechanical energy"; regular mechanical energy is "directed, ordered."

Thermodynamic theory always said that entropy increases. The kinetic theory said that systems pass from less probable to most probable states. Now the point was to prove that maximum entropy was the most probable. And here the answer to the conception of degradation arrives. D'Abro continues :

The kinetic theory requires, however, that we abandon our belief in the absolute validity of the principle of entropy. It shows that occasionally a less probable state may arise, and that even when the most probable state of statistical equilibrium is reached, there is always a possibility that some of the subsequent states will be among the highly improbable ones. The fact implies that the entropy may decrease of its own accord—a conclusion which contradicts the law of entropy when viewed as a law of absolute validity. The contradiction may be avoided, however, if we regard the law of entropy as a law of only approximate validity, expressing probabilities and not certainties. Such was the attitude championed by Maxwell, Boltzmann, and Gibbs; today it is universally accepted.

This theory of Gibbs was conceived when nobody was ready to receive it, and the public was looking at meteors of ideas. This was a glow that at first was hardly visible. Margenau talks about this half-used theory :

After three decades of continuous growth it has reached the proportions of a true and enduring luminary, and yet its rate of growth is still increasing. The state is reached where no one will deny Gibbs' greatness, although his theory of statistical mechanics, which is undoubtedly his noblest achievement, is studied and understood by relatively few.

There is hardly any choice between the denial of greatness because of lack of understanding and the accolade for the same reason. Gibbs hated device; he said that it was a vicious method which required any artifice or ingenuity to express a simple relation. But here, dealing with an unpopular idea, he had invented the "ensemble"; it looked like another device to a generation of scientists brought up on the simpler models of Lord Kelvin. Now these models have proved inadequate, the quantum theory in discarding them has shown kinship with this work of Gibbs, and attention is being directed to *Statistical Mechanics* as the forerunner of work in quanta.

Harold Urey, Nobel Prize chemist and Gibbs medallist, in a letter of tribute to Gibbs's intuition and foresight, writes :

I believe that the debt of modern physics and physical chemistry to the work of Willard Gibbs is greater than that to any other American scientist of the 19th century or earlier. It is probably true that very few scientists of the world have ever contributed as much enduring material to physics or physical chemistry as Gibbs.

The development of physical chemistry in the first quarter of the 20th century was almost entirely along the lines of thermodynamics. There has been little contribution to the methodology of thermodynamics since Gibbs, and it is probably almost correct to say that there has been no fundamental advance since his contribution.

In the past decade physical chemistry has used to an increasing extent the methods of statistical mechanics. It appears to be probable that this use will increase in the near future. Our fundamental notion of statistical mechanics is based almost entirely on the work of Gibbs.

The extraordinary usefulness of Gibbs' methods in statistical mechanics is the more uncanny because of his necessary ignorance at that time of the fundamental nature of atoms and molecules which go into the equations which he developed. It is a tribute to his unusual foresight that the Gibbs statistics required practically no modification with the introduction of the quantum theory.

A fact which is frequently lost sight of might be mentioned in this connection. The development of quantum mechanics was necessitated by a conflict between the predictions of statistical mechanics based on the assumption of the validity of classical mechanics, and the results of experimental observation. It was only due to the rigor with which the theory of statistical mechanics had been developed by Gibbs that it became necessary to alter the assumptions of the laws of classical mechanics. Thus Gibbs unwittingly played a role in one of the two great developments of the 20th century, that of the quantum mechanics.

That is the development of Gibbs's last book; and the end of this final expression is not in view.

The Shadow and the Factory

A. W. Phillips, at this time his closest friend, said that it was the sustained work on this manuscript that killed Gibbs. Phillips went with him to the express office to mail the package to Scribner's. As the publishing house writes:

. . . Statistical Mechanics, by Joseph [sic] Willard Gibbs, is one of the volumes in the series entitled *Yale Bi-Centennial Publications*, the publication of which was arranged for with the Yale University press some years ago. There was no correspondence between ourselves and the various authors in the series.

Although Gibbs's nephew and niece told a student of their uncle's that they felt Gibbs had recovered from the strain of the severe work by the autumn of 1901, Phillips said that on the way to the office Gibbs was well and walked with his usual elasticity, but that after they turned away, and from then on, suffering from the reaction after the completion of this book, Gibbs slumped—"he was a worn-out man, and never fully came back."

There was a little more for Gibbs, however. His lectures are full of vigor. One set of notes talks about Ostwald's *Klassiker*, jots down the remark that Pascal is not very vigorous, but does a great deal of talking. Willard Gibbs, himself prolific in the smallest possible space, mistrusted much talking and much writing, and left pages uncut when he found an unchecked rush of words. The notes on one lecture remind the student to check a set of reductions—"Prof. G. appears to have some doubts." In talking about some equations of light—possibly Fresnel's—Gibbs told the class it was a pleasure to read them, they were so easy, echoing his old assertion that whatever success he himself had had was due to the fact that he always avoided mathematical difficulty! The lecture on dyadics (often called Gibbs's most important contribution to mathematics) is marked "rather confusing." Few pupils were properly prepared, and few of those reached the appropriate excitement when Gibbs announced: "Our object this afternoon is to see what general relations hold between these thirty-two quantities." Students would copy down in alarm his opinion that Cauchy's physical theory "could hardly be called honest," and note with a kind of agonized delight that "he did not *prove* that the coefficients have this form, but said he 'didn't care to.' " The examples he uses are the seaport ones of a big swell coming from the sea, striking a dock with regularly placed spills—or beautiful corkscrew problems, or the quotation from Lord Kelvin about being able to prove the color of Columbus' cloak. And Gibbs would say, "The reasonableness of things will appear as we go on farther." He would give steamboat examples, the image of the little waves getting "lost," speak with great beauty about a vibrating helix, throw out to his class two symbols, and say that, given these symbols in space at this instant, the problem before them was to find the state of things after an hour.

Some of the students were profoundly excited. One said that Gibbs had a vision, and worked for the fun of it. One spoke of his charming and unworldly quality, his interest, and how it made him an inspiring teacher, who would show a student what had been missed, covering the board with figures in a rapid, almost a single motion, to prove the problem of why a cat lands on all four feet. Professor Richards' daughter remembers her father telling how the Mathematical Club was specially summoned to hear the same proof—"but the cat got away from them, too, as it had from Blanche," the student who had missed it in class.

He wrote, during this period, a letter to Bancroft, explaining a point in electrochemistry which Bancroft questioned. The letter has become famous, because in this slightly expanded version of a passage in the great paper, Gibbs explains and justifies himself, but at the same time shows what he has done to lay down new methods, founding careers for countless younger men who might choose to develop any tiny detail of what he says in this one letter.

He also wrote a letter to the editor of Klinkerfues' *Theoretische Astronomie* on elliptic orbits.

In 1901, Gibbs received the Copley Medal of the Royal Society. He was now a member of the Royal Academy of Berlin, a correspondent of the Institut de France; but this was the most open honor he could receive, and it brought home his achievement to not a few who had been blind to it. It had that effect. In the meantime, he had a new champion. The President of Yale who succeeded Dwight, Arthur Twining Hadley, let no opportunity slip to praise Gibbs, whose knowledge of mathematics he said began where that of other specialists left off. This final honor confirmed much of the praise, coming so late, so poignantly late. Sir Joseph Larmor notified him, sending a check when Commander Richardson Glover received the medal in Gibbs's place at the London presentation. And a letter came from Johns Hopkins:

614 Park Avenue
Baltimore

Nov. 16, 1901

MY DEAR GIBBS:

I read, with the greatest pleasure, that the Royal Society has awarded you the Copley Medal,—everywhere recognized the Blue ribbon of Science. On this proud distinction,—this well earned recognition, I congratulate you & all your household, and all Yale,—& my only regret is that you are not, as you might have been a Baltimorean!

Yours sincerely
D. C. GILMAN

That the correspondence has been lost is a waste which will go on growing in importance, as more interest in Gibbs is shown by those outside of the specialists who already know him. The correspondence of these years must have been full and important. There are stories now of visitors from abroad: of the German visitor who arrived with stories of Gibbs's place in Europe, and how his eyes filled, and he said, "If this had only come twenty years ago how much better work I should have done!" Of the French scientist who arrived with an interpreter, and struggled through half an hour of tortured communication, until Gibbs said (never explaining that first thirty minutes) that it was all right, he would speak French. There were visitors, and there were letters. A note to Anson Phelps Stokes bears witness to that:

DEAR MR. STOKES

I do not remember Rayleigh's or Kelvin's address. Will you send them to me here. If you have not them at hand, you can easily find them in the Report B. A. A. S.

Yours faithfully,
J. W. GIBBS

He attended the meetings of the Physics Club, which he founded in 1899, and organized a joint meeting of the Physics and Mathematical Clubs.

In these years, Gibbs was becoming, to the few, a sanctified legend. Henry Seidel Canby heard from Morris Hadley, the son of President Hadley, that a classmate of his father's was staying with him and decided to visit some of the Yale lectures. "When he came back, he told the president he had been to Willard Gibbs' course. Hadley asked him what had happened there. His friend replied, 'There were four students sitting with far-away looks like angels' on their faces, while Gibbs was drawing circles on the blackboard with tears streaming from his eyes.'"

The Yale pageant was only part of the celebration of the two hundredth year. A more relevant part, for Gibbs, was the visit of Lord Kelvin, who said publicly that the time would come when Gibbs would be considered the greatest man of science of his generation; and the visit of Sir J. J. Thomson a little later.

New Haven was sharply changed. The elms were ravaged by disease; there had been a trolley strike, and the students, volunteering as scabs, brought out more clearly than ever the split in this town—half industrial, half academic, and unresolved. The men of the striking company appealed to the president of Yale to call the students off; but he refused, and shots were fired in another town-and-gown fight. The story of that year is told : there was typhoid fever in New Haven, and the newspaper was attacking the water company bitterly. A man went into the office of the water company, and the entire force crowded around him when he said that he could *prove* they were not responsible. They offered him anything to prove that for them. "Why," he said, "that's easy. There's a waterfall right up near the source . . ." "That's right," they said, "what of it?" "Well," he went on, "it stands to reason : no microbe could get over those falls without breaking its goddamned neck!"

That was the level of the town. A little sketch of Gibbs relates some of his plans in June of 1902. He was talking to one of his students* about possible publication, and when he was asked why he had only given advanced courses, seems to have consented to let the student give an introductory course. He talked

*The student was E. B. Wilson, of Harvard University.

about his own plans for the future, saying that if he could live to be as old as Methuselah, he would study for several hundred years more, but that as it was he was going to prepare for publication, with one of three different approaches : there was more work to do on his thermodynamics; there was a contribution to multiple algebra; and he wanted to revise his method of computing orbits. He did not wait for an answer when he asked which it should be, but went on to say that astronomers were conservative, mathematicians were not impatient to have his ideas, and that he thought he would go on in thermodynamics, after a gap of twenty-five years without publication.

At the last faculty meeting Gibbs attended, William Lyon Phelps remembers that he voted with a minority for elective classes in modern languages for undergraduates, and against the strict compulsory requirements in classics.

His students gone—the favorite ones, the ones who were prepared—his niece and one of his nephews abroad—Gibbs seemed to give way in the spring of 1903. His digestion had always bothered him, and suddenly he suffered a violent and acute attack. It was diagnosed as an intestinal obstruction; there was nothing that could be done. Willard Gibbs died on April 28, 1903, at home. He was buried at the end of High Street, in the Grove Street cemetery, with its red gate and Egyptian butterfly of immortality. On the heavy casket-stone that marks his grave, now visited on many pilgrimages, are his name, his dates, and the words :

PROFESSOR OF MATHEMATICAL PHYSICS IN YALE UNIVERSITY, 1871–1903

He died intestate, leaving about $11,000 in real estate, $90,000 in personal property, and some choses in action. His estate, witness to his business ability, consisted of property and mortgages, mostly in New Haven, sound railroad and utilities stocks and bonds, a library of three hundred volumes, and other items coming to almost twelve thousand dollars.

His actual legacy to the people of the world—to whatever specialists can use his gifts for good or for evil, to whatever rulers can integrate the kinds of knowledge he sowed, carrying the tight and potent seeds within him locked—that legacy is not yet measurable. It may be indicated.

Willard Gibbs

As Willard Gibbs died, the few families who lived on a bright strip of Atlantic beach were gossiping and laughing about a couple of brothers. The silver wrecks of ships, the tides of the sea, were nothing to them. The Wright brothers were watching sea gulls, their flights, their wings, the structure of their bodies. By the end of the year, they would confound the physicists who had depended on their experiments : they would fly.

CHAPTER SIXTEEN
Three Masters: Melville, Whitman, Gibbs

THE LIFE OF SUCH A MAN as Gibbs does not end with his death. As he died, his gifts were but barely beginning to be taken. If his life was shadowy and imperceptible to many of those who make lives famous—the academic ones, the remembering friends, the writing ones who know a compartment for everything, the specialists who make a beehive, a *cloison* of the world, seeing the partitions only, and never how like these foods and colors are, cell after cell—then his death was only one more shadowy incident. We need pay no more attention to it than the Yale boys did, or the barons of industry, or the famous writers. There was nothing to be found among his papers, beyond a few notes for the supplement to the "Equilibrium of Heterogeneous Substances" which he had been preparing. Or, if there was anything, the tradition of secrecy persisting in the family, it has not yet appeared. Only two of the chapters which he lists for the proposed reprint are indicated in the notes. One is on the values of potentials in liquids, and ends in a disconnected jotting :

> Deduce Ostwald's law in more general form.
> Deduce interpolation formula.
> What use can we make of Latent Differences? $\mu_A, \mu_{AA}, \mu_B,$
> μ_{BB}, μ_{AB} all conform to law, I think.

The other is an abbreviated copy which he had kept of the famous letter to Bancroft of almost four years before. He had kept the first version of the letter between the pages of his new manuscripts. Bancroft had received the fuller draft—it had already gone to press in an article written by him for the *Journal of Physical Chemistry*. The letter dealt with the equations of electric motion, listed fourth among the chapter headings which are all the plans for the future which Willard Gibbs seems to have made. The others are :

On the fundamental equations of molecules with latent differences.
On the fundamental equations for vanishing components.
On the liquid state, $p=O$.
On entropy as mixed-up-ness.
Geometrical illustrations.
On similarity in thermodynamics.
Cryohydrates.

This life, that reaches unconsciously from the kidnapping of the African captives, whose slavery and struggle raised their lives to an image to bedevil fanatics and work upon prophecy, to the experimental trance of the Wright brothers, tracing the wingwork of gulls on the sky over Hatteras, is the lifespan of an age. Convenience had made its crazy changes, overthrown level after level to afford mastery to this man who could never break through himself. The time made him a phantom of science to haunt inventors who did not know his name, to overreach dimension, touching history and touching art—those expressions less varied and less rigorous than the sciences he professed. This seems a paradox. No art reins in the spirit as closely as mathematics, no art drains every spring of vigor into itself so deeply, emerging with less signature. For the name stands in these progressions as in the words of a poem, but the whole is confided to law. In interchange the world is made, and we begin to understand its levels. We touch matter, and transform many lives in an act of the spirit; are touched by spirit, and invent, beget, produce, in a material transport. Of these creative masters, we may trace the lines. Capable scientists will say that it is impossible, that Gibbs, that Einstein adhere in no way to their season, that, far from being an expression of the *Zeitgeist*, they cannot be provided with proper ancestry.

We look for ancestors as if the world were completed. It is constantly being torn away. Wars and suppression on every level tear it. The life of the world is in its living people, in those who express that life and the dynamic equilibrium which is its home.

Once that expression is made, the responsibility is to receive it : Gibbs failed far less than his time which could not take his word. The most profound and sympathetic of his critics spoke constantly of the need to translate his work; the little circle that published the *Commentary* ended its preface with this wistful acknowledgment : "Should our joint labors succeed in liberating the beautiful work of Gibbs from the abstract *tour d'ivoire* in which it has been for so long concealed from many students of science, then great will be our reward." When the world is hidden and torn away from itself, the secret great become in a real sense contemporaries. Pride enough, folly enough, to call them ancestors, when they worked on a world that must constantly be made! Now a whole generation of young men has grown up and made careers for themselves—as the teachers and historians of many "fields"—in this search for ancestors. At this point, it might be appropriate for women, who have rarely been deceived by superficial definitions of progress, to laugh. The young men will find the great dead who stood for the attitudes they think of themselves as continuing. When they find these sources, we are coexistent. It becomes time to fight hard and live hard, or the young men will die without having advanced the wish of the past one point, and die in their conceit still "young," in a special and horrible way.

The translations become evident in time of war and the breaking of orders. The impersonal pursuits are shown for what they are : human activity—and the private fantasy for what it is : human activity. Neither more personal or more fantastic than the other, but both to be judged as gifts of passion, for use. The use of these gifts is in what they in turn produce. If more use and more passion flow from them, or if they indeed preserve their moment, we may begin to know them. In art, the expressions that have best restored their own days to us have been the creations of the delighted intelligence—in Faure's phrase—that arranges the objects and confusion of desire. The great expressions of our past have driven relentless through sense and torment, into system; even if the system must touch order with its left hand and dissolution with its right.

The masters of the nineteenth century faced the difficulties of re-affirming freedom. Democracy had from the beginning carried its darkness and its threats. There was not enough democracy to meet these. The crime of the century in this country was the most complicated crime of waste that any country had yet committed. Tribes had been enslaved, and golden kings had trampled them; bloody Cochulas had been fought, and the plains had turned green again while the domed intricate churches rose like a jungle from the welter; the rifle and the water cure were not much as against the *peine forte et dure* and the ordeal by fire. But here the goal had been named. Even if the century betrayed it with every insult of waste and dislocation, it would be named again, re-discovered and re-affirmed. The re-affirmation is more painful than discovery. Then, we smelled land-breeze and saw the first branches rocking in the furrow. We knew with whom we sailed, and under what flag; we had reason to be sick of voyaging, and the strange-skinned natives were bright on the shore. This was to be something else. To know the shipmates and the flag, their breakdowns and failure, and to have made America from them and ourself. To see democracy falter, and sink, mutilate itself, and almost die; to see as the world's system evil and grief, the ignorance of despair; and still to say

Have the past struggles succeeded?
What has succeeded? yourself? your nation? Nature?
Now understand me well—it is provided in the essence of things
    that from any fruition of success, no matter what, shall come
    forth something to make a greater struggle necessary.

The three masters of that terrible time, when continuity snapped, were Gibbs, Melville, and Whitman. In 1900, the two poets had been dead for almost ten years. They had published their top work in the middle of the century. It had been rejected then, but it held good. The scientists protest that Gibbs is recognized in his own field; his name is unknown outside of it. Melville's novels lay in the warehouse and were burned in the Harpers' fire. Thirty or forty copies of *Moby Dick*, perhaps, would be sold each year; it might have been published in the *Transactions of the Connecticut Academy*, for all the readers it reached. Whitman was laughed at in the streets of Philadelphia; in Washington, he had waited a year and a half for his clerkship, during the Civil War, because of his obscene book, which in the end lost the job for him, too. And the policeman on the Camden ferry said to one of Whitman's rare visitors : "That old gas-bag comes here every afternoon." They are the ancestors, they walk silent in our streets, and they die without formal obituaries like any farmer. However, they speak to us. They wait for us in a great congregation to take each of them into our lives, until, as Viola Meynell wrote of Melville, "To know him is to be partly made of him forever."

Melville found in himself conflicting wishes that would in anyone, however small, tear at each other like wild beasts, until the person—the cage of such wishes—could understand that it was not the animals themselves, but the relationship, that could give him life or death. "Rushing from all havens astern," Melville fled. But in his fixed look at the vulture universe, the consuming, he unrolls before us the image of a system.

His affirmation is the word of the engulfed. Truth and her black billow balanced over him; however, the balance itself was an illusion. He knew the reality for a wave in motion; he knew where he stood; and he wrote that place. From where he lived, from the company he felt more clearly than his household—momentous men, fierce sheer-waisted sailors—and from the growing poverty of a writer whose books were hated after the first two had made a place for him—he wrote of the two equilibrated principles, freedom and evil. He was Herman Melville, Ecclesiasticus—orphic writing, poems of pursuit, tremendous lashings behind the mask of a century issued from him. *Moby Dick, Mardi, Billy Budd*, the poems, stories like "Bartleby"; with the travel books, we have a grasp and vision of the spirit which sets its own unit and its own hunt.

The unit is the ship on a sea of dissolution. In *Moby Dick*, the responsibility for the life of the ship—the world itself—rests on one monomaniac wish, as in "Bartleby," life rests on one withdrawal. But this wish is enlarged before our minutes, as we read, until it becomes in time the symbol for the conflicting energies of existence. Ulysses' wish took his sailors through chances as narrow as Captain Ahab saw; however, Ulysses drove his ship homeward. Ahab in himself concentrates many pursuits; his ship is not an individual, but an aggregation whose nature is determined by himself; and the two energies of the captain and the whale are not single, but clusters of forces working against each other. There is no compromise ahead. Whatever triumph there is, does not arrive at the end, but moment by moment during the chase. Ahead there is nothing but dissolution—the sea and death.

The logic of these balances lies in analogy. Melville knew, as well as any scientist, how far language falls short of these recognizable truths. "O Nature, and O Soul of man!" he wrote, "how far beyond all utterance are your linked analogies." The apprehension of mystery and its image in human bodies and in human wish gave him his clue. He touches in his work meanings palpably obscure, because they are alive. Everywhere the flame and appetite, the living flickering eye, gleams from the trough of darkness, the face of the empty sea.

If there were islands in that sea—if there were flowers and decoration anywhere about these meanings—the islands soon dropped under the wave horizon, the sweetness was to be cut down to "the standard of what is unchangeably true."

After the long, unbearable tension of writing *Moby Dick*, Melville again leaped toward an identification with that man to whom he felt more closely drawn, more kin, than anyone since he had left the sea. He wrote to Hawthorne, in one of a series of letters of courage, genius, and a wavering exultant hope for some intimacy, some profound recognition, more generous than any he had ever known:

. . . There is a certain tragic phase of humanity which, in our opinion, was never more powerfully embodied than by Hawthorne. We mean the tragedies of human thought in its own unbiassed, native, and profounder workings. We think that into no recorded mind has the intense feeling of the usable truth ever entered more deeply than into this man's. By usable truth, we mean the apprehension of the absolute condition of present things as they strike the eye of the man who fears them not, though they do their worst to him,—the man who, like Russia or the British Empire, declares himself a sovereign nature (in himself) amid the powers of heaven, hell, and earth. He may perish; but so long as he exists he insists upon treating with all Powers upon an equal basis. If any of those other Powers choose to withhold certain secrets, let them; that does not impair my sovereignty in myself; that does not make me tributary. And perhaps, after all, there is *no* secret. We incline to think that the Problem of the Universe is like the Freemason's mighty secret, so terrible to all children. It turns out, at last, to consist in a triangle, a mallet, and an apron,—nothing more! We incline to think that God cannot explain His own secrets, and that He would like a little information upon certain points Himself. We mortals astonish Him as much as He us. But it is this *Being* of the matter; there lies the knot with which we choke ourselves. As soon as you say *Me*, a *God*, a *Nature*, so soon you jump off from your stool and hang from the beam. Yes, that word is the hangman. Take God out of the dictionary, and you would have Him in the street. . . .

Of this truth, the only thing asked was that it be usable. That it fit into a tradition, make itself at once plain to many. The only use of truth, among human beings, is its communication. Melville made a gesture of liberation, proved by this stroke that he breathed air of freedom. And it was he who said, "Freedom is the name for the thing that is *not* freedom," insisting that it is what rules oneself, not what rules the state, that matters. The order is complicated always by one force, "though all evils may be assuaged; all evils can not be done away. For evil is the chronic malady of the universe; and checked in one place, breaks forth in another," with wars in which "peaces are but truces. Long absent, at last the red comets have returned. . . . Could time be reversed, and the future change places with the past, the past would cry out against us, and our future, full as loudly, as we against the ages foregone."

Against this weight of time, freedom's a single fighter. Janus-faced, this renaissance expressed in Melville sees all the past, like a woman in childbirth who may in one agony discover her mother and her child and be reborn. But this was 1850 : and with whatever love, with what passionate shock of discovery, he could be reborn to disenchantment only. Science, in this black sea, was a lightship turning its beam on water. There were impossibilities; and he required these of life, throwing himself with the "thought-divers . . . coming up again with bloodshot eyes since the world began."

The scientist he describes has something not quite serious about him, as in the brilliant portrait of Benjamin Franklin (in *Israel Potter*) setting him down as "all of a piece . . . labyrinth-minded, but plain spoken . . . a lady's man, a man's man, a wise man . . . a sort of handy index and pocket congress of all humanity . . . everything but a poet." Thought was to him an ocean waste, among which nations and single men were degraded. He needed some restoration. Democracy, he said, lops, lops.

There was a bridgeless space between himself and nineteenth-century America. He saw it everywhere : in his regressive flight from home, in Washington when he failed to get a consular appointment and watched Lincoln shaking hands like a man sawing wood, in finding the plain things the knottiest of all, in the bondage of his starveling family life, his failing eyesight as the '80s closed in; and long before that, as he sat at his letter to Hawthorne on an autumn Monday in 1851, writing :

. . . Whence came you, Hawthorne? By what right do you drink from my flagon of life? And when I put it to my lips—lo, they are yours and not mine. I feel that the Godhead is broken up like bread at the Supper, and we are the pieces. Hence this infinite fraternity of feeling. Now, sympathizing with the paper, my angel turns over another page. You did not care a penny for the book.

This was about *Moby Dick*. Infinite consanguinity was what he wanted, a consuming Kronos of a father. However, this Saturn was rich-bodied and rich-minded. Melville's wish could not stop; it must be translated in his life many times. Even translated into his version of suicide—"With a philosophical flourish Cato throws himself upon his sword; I quietly take to the ship";— subjugation that transforms itself into mastery and bitterness, until he could say :

Implacable I, the old Implacable Sea:
Implacable most when most I smile serene—
Pleased, not appeased, by myriad wrecks in me:

dread and guilt that would lead him to Hawthorne as they led him in Liverpool along his father's path; drive him to unchangeable Hawthorne, who cool and guilty could not match this pursuit. The whole drama was in him. There was no use in looking for a counterpart. It was true; he *was* large enough to include it all. He did feed on the world, as it fed on him.

The split between him and Hawthorne is as enlightening an antagonism as the enmity between John Quincy Adams and Jackson, or the visible balance between Edison and Gibbs, and it means as much to democracy, whose equilibrium depends to a

great extent on the inclusion of opposites. Melville had none of
the reflection of Hawthorne's lakes and mirrors, which F. O.
Matthiessen points out as fine analogies of his artistic concentration. He was his own remote reflected self, Narcissus in conflict,
but with the scope that made the twin images almost able between them to create a universe. Inclusive in hunger, inclusive
in sexuality and in power, he would forever find his needs
denied, until the terrible engendering desire to make fruitful
whatever he touched was burned down to the last masochism of
"a fierce, a cannibal delight in the grief that shrieks to multiply
itself." Rich, patriarchal in his genius, Melville mourned :

> Hate the censor pelted me. . . .
> At my shadow I cast a stone.
> When lo, upon that sun-lit ground
> I saw the quivering phantom take
> The likeness of St. Stephen crowned :
> Then did self-reverence awake.

He was able to translate the stoning into full consciousness. In
Billy Budd, his one important book that does not end in dissolution, he counters the death-sentence by one pure, tremendous
cry—the clear call of the sailor as he is hanged to the captain who
condemned him : "God bless Captain Vere!" It is the "wisdom
that is woe," the "Catskill eagle in some souls that can alike dive
down into the blackest gorges, and soar out of them again and
become invisible in the sunny spaces. And even if he for ever
flies within the gorge, that gorge is in the mountains; so that even
in his lowest swoop the mountain eagle is still higher than other
birds upon the plain, even though they soar." He was able to
reach this pitch and height within himself; but they were not
empty curves of air; they were fertile. He was able, knowing
himself fuller than cities, to make the fullness multiply.

He went past this wish of birth, into the wish of genius : to
create the creative.

The gifts of Whitman were as much at variance with the time
as were those of Melville; and the two never met. Matthiessen
writes, "It is another commentary upon the isolation of the

artist in America that Whitman and Melville, separated by only two months in the dates of their birth and by six in those of their death, both spending more of their time in the vicinity of New York than anywhere else, never came into contact."

They were both fatalists of democracy. It was necessary to purify the Jacksonian process, and their work raised individualism until it was as much identification with a principle as it was the single striding life. The profound acceptance of democracy in both of them defined their enemies, as well. And if, as Whitman had declared, it was the Universal that was to be spoken, the enemy would be the closer to the absolute of evil. There is no room, in the universe of space, once these beliefs are held, to hate the human being. The only thing that can be despised is a trait that may be identified with intellectual evil. The entire process becomes an analogy in which the most delicate judgment must be used. Every step must be tested, for we are surrounded, and this is quicksand. But it is on this shifting, tenuous film that we live; we are made of it.

The delicacy of this abundance was the concern of Whitman. It has been noted with what completeness he was able to include and absorb all the important ideas of his time. He saw, as Gibbs did, the importance of his belief to his own age, which would not admit it. Gibbs and Whitman are of the utmost importance to any industrial age, and neither of them dealt directly with an industrial framework. Whitman was completely conscious of the meaning of his work in relation to the republic. He wrote: "I look upon *Leaves of Grass* . . . as my definitive *carte visite* to the coming generations of the New World. . . . I have not gained the acceptance of my own time. . . . Beyond all that can be said, I consider *Leaves of Grass* and its theory experimental,— as, in the deepest sense, I consider our American republic itself to be, with its theory."

The unit with which Whitman dealt was a statistical unit. More than any poet until our own time, he was—however instinctively—expressing the attitudes of science in poetry. Beyond the bare statements, of which the lowest and worst is

Hurrah for positive science! Long live exact demonstration!

than which nothing can better express Whitman at his bottom level—and the positive

Three Masters: Melville, Whitman, Gibbs

Lo! keen-eyed towering science,
As from tall peaks the modern overlooking,
Successive absolute fiats issuing . . .

Yet again, lo! the soul above all science,

with its wish for the ensemble—to the directly personal poems that have more "exact science" in them than any of his windier slogan phrases. Whitman indicates a possible direction for the expression of scientific attitudes.

Poets before him had been alarmed; but, one suspects, more by the narrowness of scientific specialists than by the attitudes themselves. Even Coleridge had made partial statements about science as the antithesis to poetry, although the body of his work disclaims that balance; Poe's rationale is experimental with a difference, as if a chemist were to go to the laboratory doped and hallucinated, but remembering the procedure in his flesh; Keats's toast against Newton for destroying the poetry of the rainbow can only be matched by Newton's wonder at the taste for rhymers. These accusations sound each time like the partisan fury of the unrequited lover. If poetry has failed science, science has failed poetry.

Whitman could talk about "the bad majority," and did. But he said continually, "Identify." He felt of himself that he was the ritual, and that the dance was holy; that through it the dancer was on the way to holiness. His dilating rhythms were, as Matthiessen says, "the common property of the era which believed that, by breaking through the conventional restrictions of art, the writer could be invigorated by the elemental forces of nature." For him, language was to break through; language, the miraculous head which, battered against the wall, was the one head that might break it down.

His unit was the ensemble, used not with the looseness of his wild French, but with a meaning closely related to Gibbs's "Let us imagine a great number of independent systems, identical in nature, but differing in phase, that is, in their condition with respect to configuration and velocity." Gibbs himself, with his care for terms, footnotes the page on which that sentence appears with an apology for the want of precision of expression, allowing such language as he has just used "when the sense in which it is to be taken appears sufficiently clear," "to avoid tedious circumlocution." In Whitman, we have the catalogue, which may in mathematics be expressed by a symbol for series, but which becomes something very different in

The words of true poems are the tuft and final applause of science.

Divine instinct, breadth of vision, the law of reason, health, rudeness
   of body, withdrawnness,
Gayety, sun-tan, air-sweetness, such are some of the words of poems.

The sailor and traveler underlie the maker of poems, the Answerer,
The builder, geometer, chemist, anatomist, phrenologist, artist,
   all these underlie the maker of poems, the Answerer.

The words of the true poems give you more than poems,
They give you to form for yourself poems, religions, politics, war,
   peace, behavior, histories, essays, daily life, and every
   thing else . . .

They prepare for death, yet are they not the finish, but rather
   the outset,
They bring none to his or her terminus or to be content and full,
Whom they take they take into space to behold the birth of stars,
   to learn one of the meanings,
To launch off with absolute faith, to sweep through the ceaseless
   rings and never be quiet again.

The failure of his method, when it fails, is because he was not, like Gibbs, interested in the *relations* between these facts (or systems) so much as in the facts themselves. Emerson is quoted by Matthiessen in a passage which tests Whitman by his accuracy of symbols alone. Emerson had said, "Things added to things, as statistics, civil history, are inventories. Things used as language are inexhaustibly attractive." Matthiessen takes this up :

That furnishes an exact index both to Whitman's failures and to his triumphs. Despite his "Hurrah for positive science!" he was never rigorous enough to arrive at anything like comprehension of its methods; and though he talked about being "the bard of Scientism," his notes for such pieces as "Poem of Chemistry" gave promise of nothing more than a monotonous recital of the surface information he could have picked up in a magazine.

But, in Whitman's clumsy and factual manoeuvre after scientific information, he had absorbed, as he so often intuitively did, certain fundamentals which he could use in his own method, at his best. When he made myth out of this attitude, he reached his own height, and created the creative.

His political re-affirmation was made in sadness. The moments of gusto, the appetite and wish to believe, withdrew soon enough. They left him with the checks and measures of the industrial East, and a hope that was filled with premonition. The hurrying, distracted years were filling his life. Mark Twain wrote on Whitman's seventieth birthday that he had lived through the greatest seventy years—a bitter taste on his own tongue, and Whitman's. But, during those years, his causes had been really his own. Whatever the change was that made the ample, gross, and sensitive man out of the finicky boy, and whatever the ideas were that fed that change, the effort of will was honest. Imagination changed him; he designed a character for himself, chalked in a single work that would be at once his life and his poems. There is nothing as heartening about his life as Melville's life affords. This change of heart, this attention to the listed group, can only mean that he felt that he himself was amorphous, and his life is another proof. To know that Melville lived his twenty years in the New York Customs House is to know what kind of irritable heroism was possible after *Moby Dick* had been published and forgotten. The poems came after that—his cry of

O, the sailors—O, the sails!

long-drawn and private; and the brilliant, crystallized poem whose two short verses end :

Hidden in the cap
Is the anguish none can draw;
So your future veils its face,
   Shenandoah!
But the streaming beard is shown
   (Weird John Brown),
The meteor of the war.

It was that unprecedented faith in a veiled future that was the core of their re-affirmation. Whitman had nothing in his life to back it up; nothing for himself, that is. The returning Army of the Potomac had soldiers who dropped out of line to greet him as he stood on the curb, watching with the others; the doctors in the hospitals knew how many lives his affection had saved, as he came through the corridors with his oranges, when Washington was one huge understaffed hospital, and the soldiers called to him, "Walt!"

Burroughs wrote : "At first sight Whitman does not seem vitally related to his country and people; he seems an anomaly, an exception, or like one of those mammoth sports that sometimes appear in the vegetable world."

Many have said that about each of these three. But from their concerns their country profited. The values were not seen at once, in terms of headlines or numbers; but, in terms of history, their use came soon enough to prove that they were working along with their country's wish. That alone would fix their ancestry. And to say "their *country's* wish" is meaningless here; all the communicating generation must be included. Whitman's life was nothing in itself; he poured himself, like Proust, into his work. The attempt to realize himself through the ensemble may very well have issued from a realization that his *own* personality was shapeless, a speaking chaos; the attempt to know himself by dealing with an indistinguishable crowd led him into *Leaves of Grass*. Insubordinate lines! They set up Ensemble, Evolution, Freedom, as three stars. Finding Herbert Spencer and the theory of evolution was for Whitman one more step towards the unity which he demanded among the lists of things. The Law was in the Thing; naming an object was the first ritual step. If he had been a narrower person, with less faith and less insistence, his work might have been like Tennyson's, who drew on scientific material as he drew on music. But Whitman absorbed. To speak of the intellectual life is crazy here. With Whitman, with Melville, it is the life of the appetites, which finds strong meat in the intellect as in the senses, which feeds with a fierce and infantile demand. Burroughs declared that Whitman knew from the start what science could give, and what it could take away. He makes his own list of principles. That "all things are alike divine, that this earth is a star in the heavens, that celestial laws and processes are here underfoot, that size is only relative, that good and bad are only relative, that forces are convertible and interchangeable, that matter is indestructible, that death is the law of life, that man is of animal origin, that the sum of forces is constant, that the universe is a complexus of powers inconceivably subtle and vital, that motion is the law of all things"—he simplifies. "If we ask where is the modern imaginative work that is based upon these revelations of science, I answer *Leaves of Grass,* and no other. The work is the outgrowth of science and modern ideas, just as truly as Dante is the outgrowth of medieval ideas. . . ."

It was not his ideas that Whitman contributed. Ideas of a definable nature are to poetry what invention is to science. It was the faith and meaning behind whatever facts, whatever faces, he described. Science reached him during his lifetime mostly as biology, astronomy, steam-science. The passage he traced here and in his work was from simple to complex, in terms of human activity and invention. As for science, the slave-breeding dark mother, he may have picked up his facts in a magazine, as Matthiessen suspects. But he wrote, in "Democratic Vistas" :

Though little or nothing can be absolutely known, perceived, except from a point of view which is evanescent, yet we know at least one permanency, that Time and Space, in the will of God, furnish successive chains, completions of material births and beginnings, solve all discrepancies, fears and doubts, and eventually fulfil happiness—and that the prophecy of those births, namely spiritual results, throws the true arch over all teaching, all science.

The arch was over the ground he knew—

Land of unprecedented faith . . .

If he picked up his science in a magazine, part of that reason was because Gibbs, in New Haven, remained "untranslated."

Melville and Whitman had to do with the expression of the possible—the necessary, *because* it was possible. They were writers, at any rate. When the schoolmen look for the accent of their age, they will have to look to them. But in the fusion of history, when it becomes clear that the martyrs express just as much as the rulers, we find various martyrs. It has been pointed out as remarkable that Melville did not commit suicide after *Pierre,* or even after *Moby Dick.* In a century as inverted in values as this last, the inverted martyrdom is to go on living in it, to die, as these three men did, of old age and its complications; sons outlived, Jack Chase and Peter Doyle disappeared, Anna dead. There was, for all of them, a split between profession and practice at the most expressive point; guilt and tumult for Mel-

Willard Gibbs

ville, softness and tumult for Whitman, and suppression for Gibbs. They were the three points that may fix a curve in our culture. In their attitudes—Melville withdrawn from people, with the most passionate declaration concerning them, Whitman thinking of himself as intercessor for every person born, Gibbs never committing himself about people except in the formal obituaries; in their lives—Melville with his irritations over children and grandchildren, Whitman bragging of children with his pathetic lie, Gibbs with nothing; and in their expressions— antagonism, reconciliation, caution—they set the range.

When Whitman wrote

I will not make poems with reference to parts,
But I will make poems, songs, thoughts, with reference to ensemble

he needed the help that Gibbs could have given him at precisely that point, in another century, another America—another time that could never be, the past being what it was. If Whitman could not reach Melville, how much less chance did he have of reaching Gibbs! And there was no one in Gibbs's own acquaintance who might acknowledge that he stood beside these two in their relation to their contemporaries. Gibbs himself would have claimed that least. He had escaped more completely than any whaler. Not "rushing from all havens astern," but keeping his home about him like a shell, hiding the already hidden life.

And the split between expressions was deep enough. Helmholtz has traced it to the attack on Newton by the Hegelians, that capped the separating barrier:

The philosophers accused the scientific men of narrowness; the scientific men retorted that the philosophers were crazy. And so it came about that men of science began to lay some stress on the banishment of all philosophic influences from their work; while some of them, including men of the greatest acuteness, went so far as to condemn philosophy altogether, not merely as useless, but as mischievous dreaming. Thus, it must be confessed, not only were the illegitimate pretensions of the Hegelian system to subordinate to itself all other studies rejected, but no regard was paid to the rightful claims of philosophy, that is, the criticism of the sources of cognition, and the definition of the functions of the intellect.

Dampier says of this passage that Helmholtz, in deploring the attitude, was denying the broader claim of philosophy to attack "the deeper questions of the nature of reality and the meaning of the Universe." And Helmholtz was tracing only a recent deepening of an old cleavage. The symbols and myths of poetry and painting had their parallels in the symbols of science; the analogies are dangerous, again, but they are most dangerous when they are most usable. The danger has kept too many people away from these barriers. The meanings themselves cross the barriers which convention had put up to keep Melville and Whitman and Gibbs away from their own receiving audience. There is no reason to make a fetish out of the barrier.

Gibbs was a deep and powerful expression of his time.

He supplied a need of his age, whose purest cultural expression was not in any monument or book, but in the steam-engine. Efficiency, power, the understanding of systems were his far aims; the system was his unit, with all the unknown factors except consciousness, which he never faced. His dissolution was complete uniformity, the end of entropy, considered ideally; a perfect end which cannot exist where there are not perfect systems. He seemed to get beyond the language limits, as did Whitman; he was found impossible to read, as Julian Hawthorne found Melville "repulsive." He kept the relationship between parts, which Whitman so often destroyed; he did not interpose man as the individual falling and falling through the universe among laws whose equilibrium *he* destroys. His caution is perfectly clear in the wary statement, so like the ringing shout of Billy Budd facing his death-dawn and calling "God bless Captain Vere!"—that famous sentence : "In other words, the impossibility of an uncompensated decrease of entropy seems to be reduced to improbability." The difference between the two is a gap between cultures. But the age had two cultures; it was like the prediction of the old Abbé, that there would be two distinct religions, later on.

Gibbs was able to develop formulas that could be applied to substances and mixtures without any regard for their separate problems. His great contribution was in showing that "all cases conform to the same laws. . . . In one rough analogy, it is as though the farmer, who had made many observations about single crops, had had revealed to him the laws relating to the growth of all single crops and of mixed crops. Over a vast field Gibbs made it possible to know what results would follow given sets of conditions; only by such knowledge is man enabled to manage natural forces."

The key words are "possible to know." They are a key that belongs to art, science, philosophy, and religion.

The Renaissance, in subordinating art to science, lost to the scientist many of his powers, although the artist alone seemed to suffer. Art, in declining, let science drag it down, and the display of limiting power was a force that impoverished imagination wherever it was to be found. Science has vulgarized the idea of progress in its applications, and in an ecstasy of vulgarization, promised happiness, "as if," Faure writes, "happiness could be anything else than a state of unstable equilibrium, as if the first effect of science had not always been to destroy this equilibrium and illuminate cruelly the inmost recesses of our illusions!" Whatever these illusions are, and whatever surrounds their myth, there is no doubt that there is a "humanitarian religion of today, of which science constitutes the central myth. The pitiless development of science, that universal mechanization, fated as the course of a star," has worked on our environment with a ferocity which none of the older religions has matched. And swiftly, both in the external reality and in the individual consciousness, the effect has been visible.

That evil, traced to the mob, traced to the industrialists and inventors, was what in his way Gibbs tried to escape. He was escaping responsibility in every way. But at the same time he was assuming the loneliest responsibility of all; he was handing down the law. Moses on the mountain saw that scene, golden calf and all. The same distracted worshippers, the same deafness; but this Promised Land was the twentieth century.

It is Gibbs's power of "profound reasoning and extreme generalization" that raises him, until he becomes what Langer called him, one of those rare intellects from whom the race obtains its pictures of the world as a cosmic universe. Disjointed phenomena were organized in his mind. It was the organization that marked the advance, as it always is. "Mathematicians find peculiar satisfaction in the work of Gibbs, for in it is revealed the quintessential power of mathematics—spreading its net over the Cosmos and calling forth from it order, abstract form, and the law of science."

His business was with that law. It stood in the same relation to himself that the re-affirmation of democracy held to Melville and Whitman. Acceptance of the order of the day was an application that they could not make, any more than Gibbs could invent or predict inventions that would depend on his work. Ignorance kept his time from him. Ignorance kept him pure, in a very real sense. He stayed away from the problems of consciousness, keeping his own hidden; and he stayed away from the environment of consciousness, the world of invention. Even when he was dealing with the theory of light, Gibbs could say, "The object of this paper will be accomplished when we have expressed (explicitly or implicitly) the relations which subsist between the values . . ." In Gibbs's own phrase, the happy audacity of genius took him away and towards the relation between values, as near an absolute as we have come.

Practical people feel remorse when they see how Gibbs has waited. The factories and laboratories and plants are witness to this remorse. John Johnston, the director of research of the United States Steel Corporation, speaking of the debt to Gibbs, and the importance of the phase rule, adds :

The phase rule is but a part of Gibbs' work, whose quantitative expressions are only now beginning to be applied to the successful analysis of metallurgical problems. The second point is the long time, fully a quarter of a century, which elapsed between the birth of this idea and its extensive use as a tool in the interpretation and simplification of data which otherwise appeared so complex as to defy a useful or consistent interpretation. Let us therefore see to it that we keep our eyes and minds open for ideas which may assist us in solving our manifold technical problems, even though these ideas may seem to be somewhat highbrow and to have no immediate application to the improvement of our processes and metals. For there can be no doubt that the methods of thought originated by Gibbs have increased enormously our command over processes, enabling us to calculate their efficiency and thereby to get a much better yield of the thing we want; they have entered, directly or indirectly, into almost all lines of manufacture and have thus enriched the world immeasurably.

The enrichment of the world is the business of these three masters. That they happen to have emerged in the same region, at the same time, is more than compensated for by the fact that that region and that time could not understand the language they used or the meanings for which they created language. Whitman used a heightening of common and technical speech; Melville, a vivid and peppery Shakespearian; Gibbs shared the symbols of Helmholtz, Massieu, Clerk Maxwell. Their gifts are not national. They have nothing to do with the compulsion of the state. They are free gifts.

Clerk Maxwell had said, "Long ago I felt like a peasant in a country overrun with soldiers, and saw nothing but carnage and danger." All these men must have felt hemmed in by threats. They saw dissolution in their several ways; they were concerned in several degrees with the country, the peasants, and the soldiers. Gibbs, least of all concerned, has influenced the condition of the country most. He condensed, he re-discovered and re-affirmed, bringing a power to his work that has preserved it alive and given it an impetus that started almost at the time of his own death. Personal death had little to do with Willard Gibbs—as little as personal life, nationality, or region fame. He had taken a field not regarded as fertile, and had taught the laws of its fertility; this lean, laconic gardener still gives us harvest, and promise of more.

In taking least of all from the outside world, in paring down language to economize thought, he named relationships which were able to produce their own effects.

The single faces of Whitman's people, the faces of principle in Melville, the stars seen as the molecules of a great bubble of gas according to Gibbs, the furnaces pouring metal—these are linked.

Gibbs's attitude provides an important clue, in beauty and rigor reaching past barriers. He reached past order while the barriers faded; as he became more real, they could be clearly seen, phantom, untrue.

His work began its drive; he had created the creative.

CHAPTER SEVENTEEN
The Imagination of America

CREATIVE LIFE in this country had been completely absorbed in conquest. The roadbuilding and stripping and digging of the continent had built a nation that would worship applied science—"applied" anything, as the arts and philosophy also demonstrated. The fact, the document—that became the sceptre—if Success could be recognized as the bitch-goddess, surely her attribute was a symbol of the fact in action. There were many of those. Trumbull had painted his reverence for detail and the moment; Brady had converted that feeling into its true terms in his photographs. But even though they were to be found on living-room tables all over the country, Brady lived to an old age full of appeals to the government to take over his collection, and when he was finally asked where his negatives were, he had to say, "I do not know." And now the split came. If Eakins carried on this clear and careful fidelity to the reasonable eye, Albert Ryder answered in the terms of foreboding and pure energy, in his moonscapes, the turnings of his scenes of destiny, the rushing of his seas. He was almost forgotten, with all those whose care was not for the immediately functional. The restless royalty of this country rose from a power group of the wealth broken out of coal, steel, and every industry that could expand by applying science.

Bernard Jaffe writes:

There was no time or thought for pure theory when every value of science was expressed in terms of service or function. Theoretical speculation and contemplative philosophy were engulfed in the rush to subdue a land overflowing with material resources. In such an atmosphere as this the pragmatic philosophy of William James was born, and the guiding star of "learning by doing" rose under the leadership of John Dewey. These forces, reflecting an industrial revolution, made it very difficult to breed and sustain men who could be happy in the pursuit of science for science's sake. . . .

But things have changed and are still changing, altering the shape of things as they are, giving new form to things that are to come. The frontier days of the country are gone. Science now offers the excitement of new frontiers of discovery. Education at the same time is penetrating deeper and wider into the masses. Leisure will be more common and no American Copernicus will any longer have to take holy orders to find time for study. Our centers of learning are slowly changing their philosophy. Further emancipation from the load of teaching and the treadmill of class routine is giving our university teachers more time and clearer heads for contemplation and experimentation. Philosophy may still return after fleeing from the ogre of the frontier days and the machine age. Pure research is being subsidized as never before. It may be that our Keplers may never again have to sell horoscopes to keep alive.

Perhaps his fresh spirit has already brought us beyond the threshold of a new burst of scientific accomplishment. We may already be witnessing a Golden Age in American science. We can point to Morgan's Theory of the Gene, the greatest single theoretical conception we have as yet produced with the exception of the monumental contributions to thermodynamics of Josiah Willard Gibbs. . . .

That passage was published in 1935, when only Manchuria and Ethiopia had been invaded.

The split sides have tried again and again to recognize each other, and many times have been defeated. Early in the century, the practical scientists were hopelessly behind the theoreticians at many points; but in other, more dramatic scenes, they had outstripped the prophets so drastically that they could afford to have the completest contempt for theory. The Wright brothers and Langley flew their planes while the research workers still howled that the lift of a wing was proportional to the square of the angle; and only at the last moment saw that it was, rather, proportional to the angle of inclination of the wing. In 1905, Andrew Carnegie made a public statement, saying that he was convinced that the automobile was now perfected. There was good reason for the inventors to laugh at the theoreticians.

But in the meantime they had left the theoretical work untouched, believing the representative figures of nineteenth-century commercial science. Or, where they had touched them, they had accepted the easiest ideas. Dissipation of energy, degradation of any kind, could be seen as shortage. For example, in 1898 Sir William Crookes drew a dark picture of "near-famine for the entire world within a generation, because of the possible shortage of fertilizers containing nitrogen compounds for feeding the cereal crops." This prophecy was based on the belief that the Chilean deposits were the only source of nitrates.

There were other sources, and they could be found by work based on fundamental energy relations involved in the chemical system of nitrogen and hydrogen. These relations are to be found in the work of Gibbs.

Clifford Furnas, of Yale, writes : "Although he attached no measure of practicability to his work, Willard Gibbs formulated scientific relations which have had profound effects on the technological developments of the twentieth century." And Donnan said, in a memorable speech, that it is curious and interesting to observe how strongly "the great Dutch school of physicists and chemists has been inspired and influenced by the work of Gibbs. One might almost say that the experimental study of the equilibria of coexistent phases of matter is a Dutch science." The work of van't Hoff, Roozeboom, and after his death, Schreinemakers, "who, being a gifted mathematician as well as an experimental investigator, has been able to develop and apply the methods of Gibbs in the fullest possible manner," was the backbone of a tremendous structure of European investigation. This was to be used in many ways, according to the users.

Germany was emerging as a chemical power, whose early milestone was the discovery of synthetic indigo and aniline. As the century grew, the balance shifted; the old fortune-telling writers had spoken of the exchange of power between India and England, because of dyes. It was Germany who saw the applications here. A chemical industry would prosper Bismarck's dream. And a chemical industry might send its agents as benefactors—salesmen of dyes and aspirin—to any part of the world, to learn intimately these markets and these people.

Fritz Haber, a gifted chemist, was one of those who reacted sharply to Sir William Crookes's prediction. He says :

At the beginning of this century, the nitrogen question brought up a problem in which the imperative need of cooperation in theory and practice became conspicuous. General concern was caused by the doubt whether, in the long run, agriculture could be supplied with the necessary quantities of fixed nitrogen by the vast fields of Chile, which were practically the only natural deposits. I remember my vivid impression, when visiting (for the first time) the United States in 1902, on seeing the first industrial experiment station to be established, that of the Atmospheric Products Company. The idea of copying the process of the combination of nitrogen and oxygen by lightning in the atmosphere, and in this way producing nitrogen oxides that could easily be transformed into nitric acid and nitrates, fascinated the world.

Other instances appeared : Kuenen investigated evaporation and condensation in mixtures; Cohen investigated allotropic states of matters; and van der Waals and Kammerlingh Onnes made the practical applications of this field of Gibbs's work, to whose influence Donnan says there is no finer monument than the *Heterogene Gleichgewichte*, whose six volumes were begun in 1901 by Roozeboom and finished by Schreinemakers and Buchner. He cites books by Findlay, Clibbens, and Rivett, as well, adding, "but it is pleasant to recollect that the first book to appear in this field—and a very interesting one, too—was written by a fellow countryman of Gibbs, namely, Wilder Bancroft."

There is no need to speak of country in science, except where the applications are made for the sake of the state, and conflict between states uses these general gifts to destroy human liberties. There would be no reason to speak of recognition within a country if there were no problem of communication. But there is that problem, and the wish for communication finds one answer in the fact that Gibbs was translated into German and French in the century in which he wrote; the great paper was not reprinted in English until 1906—and then only in London. It was not until 1928 that Gibbs's work was collected and published in the United States.

Wilder Bancroft had issued number after number of the *Jour-*

nal of Physical Chemistry, reinforcing Gibbs's discoveries with critical papers and workings of detail. His direct communication with Gibbs consisted only of the famous letter of explanation written by Gibbs in answer to his question. But Bancroft, writing in 1905 on future developments in physical chemistry, spoke of the last ten years, during which Roozeboom and his school had brought the phase rule to the front "as a basis of classification and an instrument of research." He saw an increase in the next decade, as carbon steel and many alloys began to come into extensive use, as cement and clays were better understood, and as the work of the Geophysical Laboratory at Washington went forward. As for an application to organic chemistry : that was far off, but it was a possibility.

In the next years, he published many papers expanding these views. In 1906, he wrote of the phase rule as applied to photosynthesis. And in the thirty-five years after that, as van't Hoff, Arrhenius, and Ostwald made possible a theory of dilute solutions; as Guldberg and Waage's mass law equation was found in Gibbs; as work on solubility was done by Nernst and Lumsden; as the quantum theory and the third law of thermodynamics loomed over the entire scene of knowledge, and the work of Einstein, Planck, Rutherford and Soddy, Bose and Bohr issued in a new era of physics, Gibbs's contribution began to be seen in true perspective against a new horizon. Wilder Bancroft, in a letter, writes of his new work in determining coexistent liquid phases in dimeric systems, and of new work in enzymes, concluding, "A more exhaustive study of chemical potential is absolutely necessary and we see that it has been a mistake not to keep in close touch with Gibbs.

"The future development of chemistry depends in many cases on a better knowledge of chemical potentials, which makes this chemistry Gibbsian. Some thermodynamicists of my acquaintance think that Gibbs is something of a back number. That seems to me to be a sad delusion."

Einstein, in the patent office in Zurich, stood at the threshold of this era, in which the only process that was left found its symbol in entropy, called by Dampier "the one, all-important process of nature which corresponds with the remorseless march of time in the human mind." Pragmatism, which had made survival its final test, could be seen now as a part of mechanistic doctrine; and T. S. Eliot was yet to say, "A purely 'scientific' philosophy ends by denying what we know to be true; and, on the other hand, the great weakness of Pragmatism is that it ends by being of no *use* to anybody." The great civilized and humane man, William James, was caught in his fear of heat-death. Even his jokes showed it. Charles Peirce had wondered, not at his incompetence in mathematics, because he didn't quite believe in that, but in James's bragging, "laying it down," that he couldn't understand the *evident*. That kind of logic was deep in the American mind. Poe had said, before Baudelaire, "The highest order of the imaginative intellect is always pre-eminently mathematical; and the converse." A statement like that from a poet has more to do with process than with the forms; it comes from a man who, like Eliot, has been deeply sensitive to rationale, to truth itself. The analogy between truth and survival has been made many times.

William James made it, and wrote in his notes: "Ostwald, telling of his difficulties with consciousness in his energy-scheme, says that after a week of walking in his garden mulling over the matter, he felt a 'knock' in his mind, as when an umbrella turns inside out—and after that all was clear to him."

And Ostwald, speaking about identity and survival, said: "It is a strange thing indeed that by merely being associated with another thing of the same kind identity is lost. And still more strange is the fact that every being of this kind seems driven by an irresistible impulse to seek every occasion for losing its identity." He was speaking of a bit of mass, or of water, or of a personality. He was bringing the science of energetics into philosophy. He had maintained for ten years that the matter-and-motion theory (or scientific materialism) had outgrown itself. Another theory had replaced it—Energetics—and he asked in 1906, What has energetics to say about immortality?

The threats had not been of the mortality of energy, as against the mortality of elements. Radium had threatened energy in its conservatism, "not with mortality, but the contrary, a creation out of nothing." From what he knew of science, Ostwald said, he had the impression that energy would outlive everything else in the universe; he would not feel justified in saying more than that.

But he went on to speak of diffusion as the general aim of all happenings. This property might be observed in certain moments in man : in the happiness of love, for instance, in the enjoyment of art, during whose great moments one finds oneself relieved of "the burden of personality and carried away" as a drop of water is carried by the wave.

"While we are as sure as science can make us about the general validity of this law"—the second law—"as applied to the physical world, its application to human development may be doubted. It seems to me to hold good in this case also, if it is applied with proper caution." Here was the whole difficulty of the analogy, the delicate moment at which to throw the model away and venture out. There were immeasurables here : with what objective scale could we read sex and age, or the general standard of living, or wealth? How could we speak of heterogeneity or homogeneity in human affairs? "The accumulation of enormous wealth in the hands of a single man" indicated to Ostwald an imperfect state of culture, and culture was the only thing that tended to diminish the difference between human beings. Work seemed a common possession, a mark of culture—but again the language was lacking. Where were the measures for these values? Where were the words? What Gibbs could come, swinging a two-handed sword of words as Willard Gibbs had swung his dyadics, bringing a great gift as Gibbs had brought the phase rule, to bring over the poems and truths of energy into the laws of human death and existence?

It was empty to ask what Gibbs would come, when Gibbs himself was still unknown, his work diluted in application. There were, however, a few signs; although the most important were these symptoms of his beliefs in fields other than his own. G. N. Lewis, expressing in his notion of activities the chemical potential of Gibbs, took him farther in his strange, persistent life. Einstein's law of sedimentation equilibrium, dated 1906, and Perrin's work in 1908 acknowledged him. Larmor's article on Energetics in the eleventh edition of the Encyclopaedia Britannica spoke of "his monumental memoir" in 1910, saying he had "made a clean sweep of his subject" and tracing the entire history of his science through his work. Haber, lecturing on the thermodynamics of technical gas-reactions, explained how Gibbs, Helmholtz, Planck, and Mach had shown that "the theory of heat becomes simpler and more convincing when stripped of its atomistic clothing." But these were papers that, for the most part, were seen by the experts only; Gibbs's name was under its shadow; the conspiracy—part repression, part academic attitude and an inability to see past the experts—was confining him, drawing an artificial "field" for him. His gift was there; but, as its influence grew, taking on organic strength, the penalties of ignorance accumulated with his penalties of character, and became visible in the "outside" world.

As the influence of Gibbs's work grew, the tragic waste, directly or indirectly traceable to ignorance of the laws he had stated, became more dramatic. The most heroic appearance is the story found in full detail in the heartbreaking record of Captain Scott's expedition to the South Pole during the iron winter of 1912. Crowther repeats the belief that Scott and his party died through ignorance of the phase rule.

The entire journey was a series of desperate magnificence, from the first glimpse of a dark spot across the gleaming ridges of ice, as the men reached a place only a few miles away from where their calculations fixed the Pole. Within a few minutes, they saw that it was Amundsen's cairn and flag, and they knew beyond hope that the other expedition had been first of all the world to arrive at the South Pole. When they pressed on to find that it was true and that their glory—the aura of the discoverer for which they had staked their lives—was lost to them, they started the long journey back over the eight hundred waste miles to their base.

As they retraced the trail, they found in the white wilderness things they had dropped on the way out—a ski, a pipe, lying with strange personal emphasis on the gleaming impersonal snow. They found the depôts as they had left them—the rocks and the food and fuel-cans. But they had a moment of terror when they looked into an oil-can and saw that it was empty. And as they marched northward, they found this true again and again. Late in February, Captain Scott wrote :

Friday, February 23rd—Lunch. Beautiful day—too beautiful, an hour before starting loose crystals spoiling surface. Saw depôt and reached it middle forenoon. Found store in order except short-age oil—shall have to be *very* saving with fuel—otherwise have ten full days to go. . . . It is an immense relief to have picked up this depôt, and, for the time, anxieties are thrust aside. There is no doubt we have been rising steadily since leaving the Shambles Camp. The coastal Barrier descends except where glaciers press out. Undulation still but flattening out. Surface soft on top, curiously hard below. Great difference now between night and day temperatures. Quite warm as I write in tent. We are on tracks with half-march cairn ahead; have covered 4½ miles. Poor Wilson has a fearful attack snow-blindness consequent on yesterday's efforts. Wish we had more fuel.

Two days later, he makes the entry, "Fuel is woefully short," and just after that: "If next depôt is reached in time, oil will just about spin out."

The oil they carried with them was in tin cans, with solder containing tin, and leather washers around the stoppers. The cans had been left on the cairn-tops, exposed to the fearful cold and blaze of sunshine. At extremely low temperatures, the block tin of the solder may change phase and turn to powder. Even without the shrivelling of the leather, which was sometimes noticed, they saw that the oil was escaping when there was no apparent damage to the cans. They never understood this.

On March 2, Scott wrote : ". . . Misfortunes rarely come singly. . . . First we found a shortage of oil; with most rigid economy it can scarce carry us to the next depôt. . . . We are in a *very* queer street since there is no doubt we cannot do the extra marches and feel the cold horribly."

His men were suffering from frostbite; one, Titus Oates, was in agony, and it was plain that not only would he not last the march, but that while he stayed, he was a drag on all the rest. Scott wrote : "God help us, we can't keep up this pulling, that is certain. Amongst ourselves we are unendingly cheerful, but what each man feels in his heart I can only guess. . . ."

The next day, Sunday, there was a week's food left, but only enough oil for three or four days. They looked forward to the next depôt, still talking about what they meant to do when they got home, but they knew there was little hope in the face of a shortage of this sort.

On March 11, Scott ordered the means of suicide—tablets of opium—to be handed around, and each man received thirty tablets. From these hours on, the diary tells its story, of tragic weakening, with Titus Oates at the limit of suffering. While the blizzard howled past their tent, he said, "I am just going outside and may be some time," and disappeared. They dropped off one by one, these adventurers, until Scott writes in his heartbreaking message to the public—with his hand and eye failing, and the fatigue of cold sweeping over him: "We should have got through in spite of the weather but for the sickening of a second companion, Captain Oates, and a shortage of fuel in our depôts for which I cannot account . . ." and "For God's sake, take care of our people . . ." and at the end, in a last weak scrawl: "Send this diary to my wife." The word "wife" was crossed out when the book was finally found with their bodies; over it he had written the strange word "widow."

How deeply these adventurers were cut away from each other! And, so divided, how far away they were kept from their own selves! Even in one town, even in one university. . . . Charles Peirce had once got into trouble with the editors of the Century Dictionary by defining a university for them as an institution for purposes of study. They wrote back, demurring—their notion had been "that a university was an institution for instruction." He answered, saying that any such notion was grievously mistaken, that a university had not, never had had, anything to do with instruction. "Until we got over this idea we shouldn't have any university in this country," he had told them, and cited Johns Hopkins as the good example. This story is told by Henry Alsberg, who lived in a Cambridge rooming-house during his Harvard years. One day, the landlady asked him to come into one of the rooms to see an old gentleman, who had been ill and was very likely dying. When he went in, he saw a sick, worn body of a man obviously suffering from under-nourishment and lack of care; and when he asked his name, he was told, "Charles Peirce." In a wild confusion of emotions, Alsberg and a friend went to find William James, and caught him coming out of class. James listened to their story. "Why," he said, his face changing, "I owe him everything!" and swung them into a cab to call for Peirce and take him home, to the house he had left with the few cents he had in his pocket.

There seemed to be nothing for such men in America, these

mathematicians who "lived long and lived young." But the air
was here—air of expansion, air of democracy. It could hardly be
scented, sometimes. A New Haven story tells of the Wright
who was De Forest's teacher—Buffalo Wright, he was called,
from his appearance—who kept notebooks for years and years,
series of outlines and diagrams. When Röntgen announced the
X ray, friends who knew the contents of these notebooks understood that Buffalo Wright had been on the track of X rays for
a matter of twenty years. He had always said that nobody in
New Haven would believe him.

But to live in a New England city was one thing; too close,
perhaps, like living in a fishing town and never realizing the deep
metallic taint that overpowers strangers as they breathe. The
returning traveller, sensitive to an intensity which had been alive
all the time, could see the possibility. Henry James, whose sister
had written of the huge chance, said of America in 1907 :

The will to grow was everywhere written large, and to grow
at no matter what or whose expense. I had naturally seen it before,
I had seen it, on the other side of the world, in a thousand places
and forms, a thousand hits and misses : these things are the very
screeches of the pipe to which humanity is actually dancing. But
here, clearly, it was a question of scale and space and change, margin
and elbow-room, the quantity of floor and loudness of the dance-
music; a question of the ambient air, above all, the permitting
medium. . . . With so little, accordingly, within the great frame
of the picture, to prevent or to prescribe, it was as if anything
might be done there that any sufficient number of subscribers to
any sufficient number of sufficiently noisy newspapers might want.
That, moreover, was but another name for the largest and straightest
perception the restless analyst had yet risen to—the perception that
awaits the returning absentee from this great country, on the wharf
of disembarkation, with an embodied intensity that no superficial
confusion, no extremity of chaos any more than any brief mercy of
accident, avails to mitigate. The waiting observer need be little
enough of an analyst, in truth, to arrive at that consciousness, for
the phenomenon is vivid in direct proportion as the ship draws near.
The great presence that bristles for him on the sounding dock, and
that shakes the planks, the loose boards of its theatric stage to an
insubordinate unprecedented rumble, is the monstrous form of
Democracy, which is thereafter to project its shifting angular
shadow, at one time and another, across every inch of the field of

his vision. It is the huge democratic broom that has made the clearance and that one seems to see brandished in the empty sky.

. . . The clew is never out of your hands, whatever other objects, extremely disconnected from it, may appear at the moment to fill them. The democratic consistency, consummately and immitigably complete, shines through with its hard light, whatever equivocal gloss may happen momentarily to prevail. You may talk of other things, and you do, as much as possible; but you are really thinking of that one, which has everything else at its mercy. What indeed is this circumstance that the condition is thus magnified by the commanding value of the picture, its message and challenge to intelligent curiosity? Curiosity is fairly fascinated by the sense of the immensity of the chance, and by the sense that the whole of the chance has been taken. . . . As an explication or an implication the democratic intensity could always figure.

If the chance were taken, the whole of the chance! That would be the meaning of the imagination in America! In these years, with the great antagonisms still alive, to reconcile them by accepting the gifts of the imagination would be to take the whole chance. The acceptance of Gibbs is a good barometer of the democratic chance. To open the immortal eye, inward. To take, freely and imaginatively, the democratic intensity wherever it occurs—in war, in violent poverty, in the hard light of America, with its marvellous dream and its countless lives of failure. In Admiral Mahan's idea of the equilibrium of power between nations, in Justice Holmes's discussions of chance and practical life; in the World War, first breaking here with its crudities of blood and scepticism; the democratic intensity, seen in acceptance—even the acceptance of the great gift of the imagination made by a modest man, living and dying in the space of three New Haven blocks.

Even his modesty had been misunderstood. That Gibbs had the simplicity of response of the great man who is working in language, and is therefore ahead of his listeners in his speech, and learns a habit of directness and naïve address, is true; but it is not enough to say that. His students have carried away stories of extravagant modesty. They have also done him a disservice in taking this modesty for granted in all of his statements, as the thief takes for granted the honesty of any honest man. Peirce spoke of a trait of Gibbs's character that struck everybody who ever met him; he did not know what else to call it but diffidence. But Peirce, whose letter to William James from the Brevoort illustrates his own complex of self-consciousness which appeared as modesty, said diffidence was not a fit name. It was not, he said, that diffidence which consists of timidity; he disagreed with Bumstead that Gibbs was unconscious of his own superiority, and muttered about Périgord pigs and mathematical truffles.

One of the sayings of Willard Gibbs, that comes down through generations of Yale, has been interpreted as a maxim of the modest, as a shrinking from his own distinction. He illuminated his own attitude, the spirit with which he came to his work, when he said : "Anyone with the same desires could have made the same researches." It must have been some sadly passionless person who took that line to mean self-effacement, a cutting down of the value of the work, until it fell loosely into anybody's capacity. Gibbs is here speaking of the fiery impulse which brought him to his choices. He is laying the stress on desire itself, clearly pointing out the criterion for all effort. Rather than reducing himself, this is a way of indicating the chance of anyone to lift himself to the important levels of action. In the period of "dime-novel theories of the world," a time when great hunger and great power were the driving forces, he does not say, "Anyone with the same power could have made the same researches." It is the hunger that he recognizes, the strength of the wish itself. This quiet man has been spoken of so often as being self-sufficient, as working alone "without need of personal conversation upon the subject, or of criticism from others." The principle of understanding your own desires, so that you may know how best to feed them that they may be fertile, is a fortunate guide; it seems to have been Gibbs's. Its signs are in the concentrated applicability of his work, and in his prophetic images, so close to the wish of his age that they were found by other scientists independently during almost every year after he first enunciated them. During the period of his work's anonymity, Gibbs had begun to have his influence; that influence *without recognition* which has often been most socially appropriate.

John Quincy Adams, long before, had handed down the saying of an English Jesuit : "It is surprising how much good a man

may do in the world if he allows others to take the credit of it."
This takes on a new light; the successful chemists, the engineers
employed by big business, were able to present Gibbs's ideas effectively. But, for all their unfair start, the ideas carried themselves. Science has been defined as not only the discovery of
"new" facts for the experts, but also the finding of appropriate
combinations of existing knowledge in its human significance.
And here the relation of the finder to the fact reaches its chief
importance.

Masters of any art or science have by a convention come to be
known as the "father" of their gift, and the absurdity here is as
grotesque as if we called Columbus the father of the Indies.
These are all real, these discoveries; human beings have found
them, but they were always there. The endless chain of new
causalities following on the work of the discoverer is a complicated postlude to his responsibility; but he did not know the
future. Speaking of the scientist's lamp, George Sarton reminds
us of Melville as he says it sends only "a very small cone of light
into the infinite darkness," and he adds of the traveller with this
lamp, "He is the spiritual lord of the domain which his imagination could encompass, neither more nor less." These are dis-
coverers; we are very likely to share the lover's attitude with
them, and ask the lover's question of their discovery : Did you
live till we loved? But all of it existed; it did live. What the
love, what the desires did, that led to these researches, was to
bring a delicate and enormous human expansion to these discovered images, so that they might grow and grow in the imagination, filling thought, coming to religion, the dance of growth,
or industry and war, as Gibbs's work has come; enlarging, and
at the same time enlarging the capacity of those who see the
images, indeed enlarging their desire, until new gifts arrive.

CHAPTER EIGHTEEN
The Double Democracy

THE CHALLENGE of the American mind has been recognized for so long as a simple challenge of invention that the split between two kinds of imagination is likely to be overlooked. From the Constitution down to the complex pressures of the latest moment, that split exists; it is made ferociously clear in the antagonism between a Jackson and an Adams, wastefully clear in the cheerfulness of Edison. The director of the historical research department of Thomas A. Edison, Inc., N. R. Speiden, says :

I have no doubt that Mr. Edison, in his work, quite often profited by the results of Gibbs's work on phase rule, although it would be very hard for us to prove this unless we came across some reference in his notes to that effect, as the present biographies also fail to help out on this question.

Edison was working on the projects of his old age, making rubber from goldenrod, inventing a device to obtain nitrogen from the air, plunging into the Portland-cement industry and pouring low-cost homes, and at the end saying: "I am the zero of mathematics, but I don't have to moan over it any more, since I found out through my questionnaire that professors of Harvard and Yale are as ignorant as I am. . . ."

Science had been mobilized again. As quickly as the National Academy had been set up in the Civil War, the Naval Consulting Board of the United States was formed in October 1915. It set to work at once to take inventory of the entire manufactur-

[*383*]

ing resources of the country to back the army. "Science, invention, and industry became an impregnable line of defense behind the soldiers."

The work of the new committees was a response to the German discoveries. All the general staffs of the United States underestimated the power of explosives, according to later opinions; and the most pressing need was to learn about the "secret" method that was saving Germany from an explosives bankruptcy —the Haber ammonia synthesis. The United States had been dependent on Chile for its nitrates. The blockade had changed all the possibilities; but when it was made known that Germany was supplying its own explosives—and, incidentally, its own fertilizers—the Haber process was recognized in its full value.

One application of the phase rule had already gone to work in the war. When van't Hoff was conducting his later researches, he used, not his partial re-discovery, but the phase rule as Gibbs had written it to interpret the Stassfurt deposits—the immense German source of salts left by the deposit of a prehistoric inland sea. Crowther tells the story :

When solutions of samples of salts were evaporated, they did not reproduce a mixture of the same composition as the original sample. Van't Hoff and his colleagues analyzed the problem by treating it as an example of equilibria between sulphates and chlorides of sodium, potassium and calcium. They proved that the presence of the strange salts was due to the slow rate at which the evaporation had occurred.

They were able to deduce the order of the stages of drying of this sea which had vanished millions of years ago, and were able also to determine the temperature and pressure at which the evaporation had occurred, and how long it had taken.

These researches were of great help in dealing with the potash of these deposits, which are—

the world's chief source of potash. The growth of chemistry and chemical industry in Germany has been conditioned by their existence. Without them, Germany would probably not have become a great power capable of challenging the world. The composition of the deposits was of high economic importance, for it enabled estimates to be made of the quantities of the various components available for industrial use.

The Double Democracy

Van't Hoff had lectured on Gibbs and the salt deposits at an International Congress in Berlin in June 1903. But now, deep in war, Germany was resolved not to lose : no matter what defeat, no matter how far the losses went, Germany was to win. That is, Germany was to emerge in a stronger political and commercial position in the world.

Just after the International Congress, Karl Duisberg, then working on ersatz food and materials, urged the Kaiser to merge all the German chemical firms into one trust. He added that the world-wide rule of German industry—and he put special emphasis on the dye industry, which looked harmless enough for a front—would not only exist safely, but would be assured for the future.

At that time, Germany did control world markets for dyes, chemicals, and explosives. Ten years later, at the beginning of the war, all the chemical industries were merged by the Imperial government. Liebig was behind this created conquest. The three men living to carry on his work were Karl Duisberg, Karl Bosch, and Fritz Haber.

Nitrogen out of the air, poison gas, ersatz goods—they were the weapons.

In moments of deep crisis, any organism rallies all its resources, evoking and controlling energies it had allowed to lie dormant and forgotten. Society acts in the same way, calling up men and marshalling production. But the power behind these final instruments is the imagination in its most abstract form— not necessarily the inventing mind, but the discovery that may lead to a multiplicity of invention. We are double so long as there is a gap between the two creations as they work for society. We are not only double, but our effectiveness as a society is split. The waste of war is very immediate. We see shattered lives and the mutilations of the flesh, the wrecks of cities. But this is the waste of peace, the waste of history—and, above all, the waste of a pioneer country, eager to overcome its obstacles at any cost.

The only way to check that waste of energy, the only way to meet an enemy that was using its resources, was to go behind these processes, behind Haber, to the inclusive mind which reined in all the threads.

[385]

Willard Gibbs

In April 1939, the Department of the Interior released through the Office of Education a broadcast in a radio series called "Americans All—Immigrants All." The Narrator began, after the appropriate fanfare: "Willard Gibbs, of English descent, has been called the father of physical chemistry. . . ." He told, in a few words, how Gibbs had worked obscurely at Yale, how his work was too complicated to be explained casually. And went on: "But this can be said: wherever chemistry enters modern industry—which is almost everywhere—the work of Gibbs has been of supreme importance. And it can be proved."

The Announcer takes up the tale, saying: "The War Office . . . London . . . early in 1915 . . ."

MINISTER: Men, yes, we must have men . . . but this is a war of high explosives. We must have them.

2ND MINISTER: We must have them in tremendous quantities . . . and instantly. . . . Can your factories . . . ?

MANUFACTURER: We do what we can . . . but we are constantly delayed. I can't go into the process with you, gentlemen . . . but in brief, we are compelled to use quantities of ammonium nitrate . . . and as this is a complicated salt, we have to devise a method of manufacturing it rapidly. . . .

MINISTER: Then do it, if you want to save us. What stops you?

MANUFACTURER: There are only a few people who understand what we need. Again without scientific detail, let me say that it depends on the application of the phase rule—and that means we need someone who has studied the work of Willard Gibbs. . . .

NARRATOR: In time, followers of Gibbs were found, and the crucial problem of manufacturing explosives was solved in England.

The man who was found was Francis Freeth. He had studied in Holland with Schreinemakers, and had indeed learned the phase-rule applications with which the Dutch school was deeply concerned. When Freeth came to write about his master, Schreinemakers, he spoke of the handing down of methods, which made for influence, not for recognition. Freeth, carrying that influence back to England, was working for the famous munitions firm of Brunner, Mond & Co., when the appeal for cheap and ready explosives was made. He was able to respond to that appeal; as Captain Freeth, he supervised the organization of three methods by which the manufacture of ammonium nitrate was made possible. The method which was finally chosen was the direct production of ammonium nitrate from sodium nitrate and ammonium sulphate. It has been called "a splendid triumph of scientific industry"; and it is openly acknowledged that "without the exact data yielded by Captain Freeth's series of phase-isotherms, no successful process—indeed no process at all—could have resulted."

If Germany could not have entered the last war without the release of power granted by the knowledge of the Stassfurt deposits, England has said that "it is an open secret now that the work which this company [Brunner, Mond] did in this field alone saved the cause of the Allies at a critical stage." And, through this process, which balanced the military struggle, the science of heterogeneous equilibrium reached a new stage of its fantastic and world-shaking development.

The ignorance of the Haber process set American authorities to work on the same problem, of finding a direct process for the extraction of this explosive. Ammonium nitrate, TNT, and picric acid were the three most important explosives of the war, and the other two were two and a half times as expensive. We had been completely dependent on Chile for both explosives and fertilizers. In this year, 1915, the general staff woke up to the fact that it had made a fearful mistake in underestimating the role that high explosives were to play in the war; and the National Academy of Science, set up in the Civil War, at last appointed a committee to study nitrogen, to learn to duplicate the process which had saved Germany from certain "nitrate bankruptcy." Soon chemists here, under the leadership of Charles L. Parsons, the chief chemist of the Bureau of Mines, were working on the five crystalline phases of ammonium nitrate, from the needle crystals through the beta-rhombic, alpha-rhombic, to the fine powder which hardened, when moisture was added, to a white and stone-like mass. Great plants were under construction in the East by 1919—the Atlas Powder Company built one tremendous one at Perryville, Maryland; Sheffield, Alabama, is another center; and the most spectacular of all is the immense cyanamid project at Muscle Shoals.

Gibbs's great paper is behind this work, and Freeth's patents are derived directly from his researches. The industry is still in its infancy, and with the new advances in chemicals and aircraft, parallel advances in phase applications may be foreseen.

At the Atlas Powder Company plant in Maryland, for example, the process was used to produce three hundred tons of ammonium nitrate daily. Brunner, Mond, furnished the Atlas Powder Company with "the equilibrium diagrams for the four component systems involved in the process, together with what operating and design data it possessed," says M. T. Sanders, of the company's engineering division. "Technically the process was interesting because of the nice adjustment of conditions required for successful operation. A number of double salts can be formed. The equilibrium diagrams are necessary for devising a satisfactory cycle of operations."

The operations at Searles Lake, in California, and in New Mexico have also found the principles of Gibbs a Rosetta Stone. F. G. Cottrell, of the U.S. Department of Agriculture, speaks of the passage of agriculture from "its traditional empiricism toward scientific understanding," with its use of the Stassfurt deposits instead of wood ashes for potash, according to Gibbs's principles, which have since "done equal service as each new internationally important deposit of potash salts, such as our own Searles Lake and the New Mexican fields, has been discovered and put to public service in behalf of agriculture."

One other rebirth is traceable to the great paper, and during the war it was seen sharply in all its opening promise. The knowledge of the properties of metals goes back to Damascus —to the swords of Toledo—but, in another sense, say the physical chemists of the General Electric Company, "the possibility of one branch of scientific metals research dates from the enunciation . . . of the phase rule : a key which unlocked many of the secrets of the complex, and often confusing, alloy systems." Dr. John Johnston, the director of research of the United States Steel Corporation, has written with deep appreciation of Gibbs's equilibrium diagram, the map of alloy specialists, for "such a diagram is absolutely fundamental to a proper understanding of how to handle the particular alloy system so as to secure the best results."

With the rapid growth of the automobile industry, and the expansion of the aircraft industry past wartime needs into commercial aviation, and with the beginning of radio as an everyday commodity—to name only three uses for the new alloys—this map became the necessity of the chemist, until it was to him what the navigation chart is to the pilot, and Gibbs his Bowditch.

Tammann, who during these years was doing vitally important research in metals and crystals, wrote of alloys and crystals, of the processing of metals—roasting and smelting—of fluid slags and refractories in equilibrium with liquid metal. We have not only methods which let us understand the mutual behavior of two substances, he writes, but—

we also have, for many of the most important substances, binary and ternary equilibrium diagrams which have become the solid foundation of many technical processes by enabling us to interpret the structure as seen through the microscope, of many materials of construction, such as steels, brasses, and bronzes. These diagrams are of many different forms, yet they are all subject to one rule, the phase rule of Gibbs. Thus the abstract theoretical investigations of a studious recluse constitute the scientific basis for the main part of the knowledge of the modern metallurgist.

The Bureau of Mines has conducted wide researches on theoretical metallurgy, under the direction of Charles G. Maier at the Pacific Experiment Station at Berkeley. In four long papers of contributions to this data, K. K. Kelley has summed up much of the recent work. The files of libraries are full of the names of systems whose analysis depends on these maps: copper, nickel-zinc, iron-chromium alloys, ocean salts, iron-tungsten, iron-molybdenum—the Japanese work on tungsten and chromium, the Russian work in tin and copper, the success of the Aluminum Company of America in the alloying of high purity aluminum—these are only a few.

Many alloys are not used *in equilibrium*, but in some degree of approach to that condition. Sometimes the slowness of that approach may be a major virtue. Knowledge of this passage and awareness of the final state toward which they tend is a great and steady gain.

The editorial director of the *Magazine of Metallurgical Engineering*, H. W. Gillett, writes in a letter:

Application of Gibbs' principles has vastly shortened the labor of countless metallurgical researches. Only when this saving of labor was possible and when means of mapping the boundaries was available, did metallurgy shift from an art to a science.

Only when it became a science and the influence of temperature became realized did metallurgy apply the temperature control necessary for production in quantity and with quality. Modern industry and modern warfare depend on alloys whose properties would not be controllable without the sequence of scientific understanding of need for control, development of control instruments, and their commercial application, that resulted from the application of Gibbs' principles.

Gibbs's work had already been applied to metals; now the experts in other fields were beginning to mine this vein. The specialists in cement had learned the true constitution of Portland cement with the help of the phase rule; now the phase-rule diagrams were proving their use to the experts in ceramics. The strength and elasticity of clays, the composition of silicates, found their clues in the six books of Roozeboom and in the texts of Washburn, Taylor, and Findlay. Now the only task left to the expert was to go ahead, to make further diagrams for further applications, to open a scientific era in yet another field.

The agricultural chemists saw that this was a guide to soils. Their slogan was, "The soil is the stomach of the plant," and they realized that plant growth might be thought of as a three-phase system, with the liquid phase feeding the plant itself. Ecology—the study of the interrelations of living things and their environments—was passing from the hands of the botanists, to become a science of regions. The study of any region—the life-line of a place, with its soil, its plants and animals—follows physico-chemical groupings. If a field is plowed, made quite bare, and then left, the history of its "system" may be traced, with the invasion of weeds, the tough first plants and their insects, the plants replacing them to spread more quickly but survive a longer time, and finally the "climax," with the dominant plants and animals of that region, and their functions which compensate each other. The "climax" is the state of equilibrium of a place. It is an unstable equilibrium. Its components are traceable in physico-chemical terms—weather, with its temperatures and pressures; light and radiation; and the living factors, fungus, say, or beetles and mice, or suburban men and women. The territory with which the ecologist deals is the "biosphere," the space occupied by living things, that is, the whole ocean, the earth to some yards deep, and the air to some height—excluding salt lakes, boiling springs, and active volcanoes : places where survival is zero. This is a science of mutually dependent survival, and Gibbs's work is used here; the Department of Agriculture is working according to Gibbsian methods.

In petrology, too, the phase rule has found results that might seem on the surface distant from its original statement. Dr. Arthur L. Day, the director of the Geophysical Laboratory of the Carnegie Institute at Washington, once said, in speaking of Gibbs's profound influence on physical chemistry, "Professor Gibbs will therefore always stand in the same relation to the new science of petrology which we are endeavoring to establish." With E. T. Allen, Day has explained according to one application of the phase rule the volcanic action of Mount Lassen. Deep in the base of this active California volcano, the boiling point of its molten mixture changes suddenly from one temperature to another point at which explosive boiling takes place. Day and Allen proved this to be true for a system of silicates, as Roozeboom had proved it for certain solutions.

The first physiologist to apply Gibbs was Zwaardemaker, who in Holland, in 1906, proposed the application of the phase rule and the second law. He wrote defining "energetic histology" and "energetic physiology" : the task of the first would be to determine the number of phases and the phase relations, while the second would make experiments to determine equilibria and reversible processes. Zwaardemaker was the first to regard the human body at rest as a system of coexistent phases in equilibrium. All of the processes of the body are irreversible; its unit, the cell, is a system of heterogeneous phases. These can be determined by removal of the nucleus. He recorded the early speculations as to the nature of the equilibrium of the blood. He foreshadowed work in eye strain, for example, that regarded it as a change in equilibrium due to disturbance of the chemical potential.

In 1909, two profoundly influential papers were published, which fed new life into a tremendous range of work on equilibria. The first was Sørensen's classic work, which introduced the pH scale, and the concepts of buffer solutions and indicators—

concepts which again brought up Gibbs's surfaces of discontinuity and unimolecular layers.

In the same year, Lawrence Henderson began his work on blood. Even as an undergraduate at Harvard, he had been influenced by Gibbs, and in an unfinished manuscript called *Memories*, he records his early excitement as the possibilities opened up before him, so much larger than the stated ideas. He wrote :

Both in clear thinking and in revery I spend much time going over again and again the same problem, or the same set of facts, and my thinking seems to recur endlessly or to move in frequent, and therefore short, cycles. It would be easy to describe this in terms like persistence or tenacity of purpose, but I have the impression that the process is automatic and rarely subject to my conscious control. It applies alike to the study of undigested facts, though this, I think, has probably been the case only since I began serious experimental work, and to apparently finished conclusions or accepted propositions. In the latter case it seems to be accompanied by the feeling that there must be more implied by the conclusion than is explicitly stated, or, at least, than I clearly see. It is this latter phenomenon that I seem to remember, though often only vaguely, in my early undergraduate experience. But I think I remember it clearly in the case of Gibbs' *Phase Rule* and of the periodic classification of the elements.

The periodic table of Mendelieff delighted me and gave rise to much reflection which issued, at the time, in a strong conviction that there must be some explanation similar to that implied by Prout's hypothesis,—and in nothing else that I can remember. However, I think it more than likely that this experience of my sophomore year is an important source of my later interest in "the order of nature" and I can remember that I already had a vague feeling that there are not only many undiscovered simple uniformities behind the complexities of things but also undiscovered unifying principles and explanations. It is certain that the periodic system later came to be an important consideration in my thinking about the fitness of the environment.

The Phase Rule interested me in another way. I saw intuitively that it was not so much a generalized description of phenomena as a logical instrument useful in attaining a generalized description. I also remember that I at once saw without help why it is possible to choose the components of a physico-chemical system in more than one way if, and only if, each choice leads to the minimum number of components necessary for the constitution of the system.

The Double Democracy

I think I was still an undergraduate when I had a discussion of the Phase Rule with one of my teachers which left me with the impression that I understood this better than he did. I did not often form such impressions until I reached the Medical School.

In 1909, with the publication of his outline of acid-base equilibria in the blood, he had provided one of the most beautiful bases for analogous thought, opened up a new field, and dealt with the organic problems of the red blood of vertebrates in their living growth, and as a physico-chemical system. His conceptions, based on the most sensitive and profound use of analogy, deepened in quantitative and mathematical forms as he expanded them, as laboratory illustrations were offered, and as he repeated them in several versions—one a series of lectures delivered in London, and the final version of those discussions presented as the Silliman Lectures at Yale.

In the complete version, the biological sciences are described in relation to the other descriptive sciences, which can watch stiller processes; the first never attains "the abstractness, the elegance, and the simplicity which are the mark of the classical epoch of many of the physical sciences and the ideal of those who follow Newton and Willard Gibbs." Deriving many of the concepts of this marvellously suggestive treatment from Gibbs, Henderson describes the responsibility of the system—an organic responsibility which he had always emphasized, the bases for which had been laid by two masters whom he acknowledges in these lectures—Claude Bernard and Willard Gibbs. The French physiologist, with his investigations into the *milieu intérieure*—the secret native bath of the body, the internal flood in which we live—had insisted on the importance, always, of integration. He had been the great protagonist of physiology, showing in many ways how organization was the most striking characteristic of living bodies, and working in both physical and chemical terms within that framework. The system itself, the love and meaning expressed in the equilibrium of the system, came through his work, until the delicate structures of which he wrote could be related to other structures of life and art in moments of wish, or moments of illumination. He was working on his ideas during the same period of carelessness and general neglect as Gibbs, whose paper "On the Equilibrium of Heterogeneous Substances," "the greatest effort of sustained abstract thinking in the history of America," says Henderson, "was destined to awaken chemists from their empirical slumber and to make possible the study of the problems of general physiology at their deepest level, as Claude Bernard had conceived them, to provide a foundation, in short, on which a rational science of general physiology could be reared." Physiologists found themselves well into the twentieth century before they could use either of these men; for, early in the expansion of Gibbs's work, systems of only a few components were used. A living system, such as the blood, with its many components, came late; but the study of such a physico-chemical system was the beginning of another ideal construction, like the fictional systems of Gibbs, which were so fertile. This study led to an ideal equivalent of protoplasm, "and therefore an approach toward a description of the elementary condition of the phenomena of life."

It is for the specialist to go ahead with these studies, Henderson says, as the steel specialist has taken the phase-rule studies forward.

But Gibbs is again the guide in these regions. His favorite few assumptions hold here, also; here, in biology, the axiom is true that the whole is simpler than the parts. Henderson speaks now of the parts : scientists have avoided what Gibbs dared to consider, systems with many components, except when they could use the statistical treatment. In the problems, great complexity is reached immediately, for all these changing factors depend on each other as the members of a society, and secondary changes increase at breakneck speed as the number increases very slightly. "The nature of the case will be more readily appreciated by reference to another branch of biology in which our intuitions are better practiced. Consider a human society of n individuals and let n equal successively 2, 3, 10, and 20." With two or three persons, we have the short story, in which relationships are often successfully managed, Henderson continues; with ten individuals to keep alive, he doubts whether the greatest poets or novelists have done their work of description successfully; and with twenty characters, he says description is possible only if most of the figures are puppets. One thinks of Tolstoy, of Shakespeare or Balzac as masters of such equilibrium, but counting the few who have dared to consider systems of living complexity, one recognizes another possible use of Gibbs's powerful results.

The Double Democracy

It is in systems of many variables, with their high degrees of interdependence, Henderson points out, that "the application of mathematics, though difficult, is of peculiar interest." We are at once led into the region of economics. The growing school of economists who have applied mathematical principles—Walras, Pareto, Irving Fisher are three—have felt the implications of mathematical method here; indeed, they have felt that there was no other approach possible to these great numbers of dependent individuals.

Coming back to protoplasm, Henderson considers its equilibrium, which is not the equilibrium of a physico-chemical system, but of a candle-flame or whirlpool, a poise of form. The assumption that must here be made is that of the existence of the state of equilibrium which old Lucretius recognized does exist.

Referring to Whitehead, referring to the ideas of organic mechanism, Henderson speaks of the *milieu intérieure*, that bath in which the cells of all warm-blooded animals are bathed. Of startling stability, this has all the properties of a physico-chemical system. It in itself is the protection of the protoplasm. It is, in a paradox, the internal environment, and Henderson had already stated that the environment bore the stamp of purpose as the organism itself is purposive. The relations between the inner and outer systems, those subtle relationships which lock the universe in its own laws whose dramatizations are everywhere to be found, are seen at last in the blood itself.

Blood may be regarded as a physico-chemical system of two phases, to use the Gibbsian term. These two are the red cells and the plasma; and the components may be described, with the principal ones being water, certain acid bases, hydrochloric acid, carbonic and other acids, protein, and oxygen.

We are not dealing here with equilibrium states, but rather with states on the way to equilibrium, and in Gibbs's processes we have a means of measurement that had never before been possible.

Fritz Haber reached the United States after a painful defeat in the South Atlantic. He had sailed there on the vain expedition of his life, hoping to extract gold from sea-water, and finding that the gold of his experiments had been seduced from his laboratory instruments, from spectacles, from anything in the room rather than the sea-water he was testing. Haber arrived in Philadelphia for the centenary celebration of the Franklin Institute. The appearance of this patron saint of German warfare inspired the newspapermen; to them it meant the end of the war, it was the convincing re-entry of nations into solidarity.

Fritz Haber and F. G. Donnan spoke on successive days, that September week end of 1925. Donnan's address, "The Influence of J. Willard Gibbs on the Science of Physical Chemistry," made Gibbs headline news. From his first words :

It has often happened in the history of science that after or during a period of activity, there has come a man of genius, who, combining profound insight with the highest powers of logical reasoning, has presented the world with a precisely formulated and far-reaching synthesis of scientific principles. . . .

through his comparisons with Newton, Clausius, Kelvin, and Clerk Maxwell, his analysis of the great paper and the new applications that it was finding, Donnan moved to the graceful acknowledgment that Lawrence Henderson and his collaborators had conferred on the speaker "the incomparable honor of associating his name with that of Gibbs." The relation for membrane equilibrium which he derived has been found to·be a valuably suggestive interpretation of chemical potential in physiology. Henderson, as well as Jacques Loeb, Warburg, Van Slyke and McLean at Rockefeller Institute, and Wu in Peking had already contributed to the advance of physiology, and supplied a link in the chain of blood equilibria.

In speaking of Gibbs's work in adsorption and surface concentration, Donnan referred to Haber's recent researches, and concluded with a tribute to the power of rigorous deductive logic, "one of the greatest aids in man's effort to understand that mysterious universe in which he lives. . . ."

The world owes an immense debt of gratitude to the possessors of this power, and to none more than to Josiah Willard Gibbs. So faithfully and wisely did he use the splendid gifts which Nature had bestowed on him, that after half a century of time his work remains a potent and living force. Of such work it is, and always will be, true that the eager hand of Time may add something, but can take nothing away.

The Double Democracy

Donnan's words drew a line under the sum of much that Gibbs had already done. But Haber, in those same days, foreshadowed much of the unrecognizable future. As he said at the beginning of his speech, "Practical Results of the Theoretical Development of Chemistry" : "Commemoration days, festivals which revive the past and survey what has been done, are teachers of the future." It was easier, he said, for theoretical science to speak for itself on such days; applied science had to present a scene of deeds. And here the interrelations are tremendous; mutual influences are hard—impossible, very often—to sort out among the broad inclusive terms of human culture. But in the specific domain to which Haber was confining his words, he might outline three periods of science in the last forty years. The first—the period of structural chemistry—was followed at the turn of the century by the period of thermodynamics. Haber recalls his visit in 1902, when he saw how clearly the problems of nitrogen were forcing cooperation between theory and practice. He speaks of van't Hoff, and the statement of ammonia content in mixtures, which was made by help of this rule (which could be found in Gibbs). And, here, he mentions the part played by the Badische Anilin and Soda Works, using the ammonia industry as the key to all these relations.

The third period is that of electrochemistry—that time when theory is "beginning to interpret the structure of atoms by discrete electric constituents and the coherence of the atoms in the molecules by electric forces resultant from the action of the atomic constituents upon one another." He briefly mentions the unsatisfactory and necessarily limited relations here, for the present moment.

Haber goes on : "Among such common interests, however, there is one toward which development tends from all sides to such a degree that it is hard to tell whether it is of greater interest to the organic or the inorganic, to the experimental or the practical chemist. This bond is what we call capillary chemistry." This applies to vital processes, to the relation between the chemical nature of a substance and organic growth; to the industries including rubber, plastics, leather, silk, wool, oil, clay, milk products and other foodstuffs.

The theory behind this surging development is the adsorption theory. The bombshell of Haber's speech, in its shock to the American imagination, follows :

"The theory of adsorption owes its foundation to a conception of Gibbs."

Haber goes on with a detailed analysis of the phenomena of adsorption, with the work of Helmholtz, Debye and Hückel, Donnan, Powis, Otto Stern, and Gouy, with "the intimate relation of Gibbs' formula" to the entire history of this science. And he asks, in his summary, in the shadow of Benjamin Franklin, what these developments have meant to mankind—asks with a prophetic ring of armies and the reach of man to surpass himself in any way he chooses :

Within the thirty years previous to the World War, we enjoyed all the precious gifts that were given us by the power of advancing knowledge. The state of science enabled industry to produce a thousand new commodities of life, and the economic world welcomed any successful attempt to offer them to mankind. But, alas, life is not eternal, and the reverse of the medal is visible today. The new commodities of life have become necessities. Industry has educated man to needs that were formerly unknown and has aroused in everyone demands that must be granted for the sake of social peace. How can these demands be satisfied? There are two answers to this question. The one which is most adhered to in this country is that we should aim at a greater and cheaper production by increasing the utilization of natural resources. The other view, advanced as a new creed with the enthusiasm of a world conqueror, comes from Russia. It strives to attain success by disregarding personal competition and controlling production by the State. Neither of these ways will lead to the goal. The progressive education to new needs outweighs the progressive increase of production, while the elimination of free competition paralyzes the natural powers of man. To arrive at the goal we must have recourse to the primary origin of the difficulty. We produce goods as far as we know how to produce them, by virtue of our scientific and technical knowledge. But we are not able to produce those goods that we need most urgently. Nowhere else can we realize this malproportion more than in the sphere of chemistry, because, outside of chemistry, industrial efficiency is always restricted by the suitability of the material used, and because every transformation of the material belongs to the domain of chemistry. The most urgent chemical work, which we ought to but hitherto could not do effectively, is the providing for our sustenance and our health. Nutrition and cure are the tasks of natural science which open new fields to industry and new prospects of a happier state for man. We are scientifically far enough advanced in our knowledge of the minute difference between the structure of starch and that of cellulose. But we are not far enough advanced to be able to live on the stalk instead of the grain of wheat. To the first of the three periods of the above-mentioned cooperation between theoretical and applied science, we owe the discovery that nature can be surpassed. Our dyestuff industries offer a greater variety and far superior quality of products. To the same period, we owe certain remedies which combat devastating maladies and alleviate pain that formerly tormented man severely. To the second period of cooperation, we are indebted for a progressive development in the providing of agriculture with the indispensable vegetable nutriments. Of the third period, in which we are living, we expect the exploration of those paths on which nature brings forth her living products.

There was a past when scientific development was not limited by time. What one generation did not discover was left to the next generation. The social condition of the world was not dependent upon scientific progress. Today we are under some compulsion. Discontent with economic conditions arouses a strife amongst men, and only the progress of natural science offers the certain prospect of a greater contentment than prevails in the present world. This progress of natural science, however, can only follow from research work in the institutions of all civilized countries and from the cooperation of the politically distinct nations in this field of common interests.

The touches of prophecy summed up here—the key position of the dye industry, in India, in England, and then in Germany—the need for synthetic goods, the compulsion of today—have all been confirmed.

The press reported these statements half-heartedly, and without emphasis. But Haber really broke into the feature columns and editorials with what he told a newspaperman on the last day of the meeting. He was full of his new ideas about food in its new forms, about purification methods, among which he mentioned insulin as the purified form of an enzyme. He spoke to a reporter of the possibility of extending human life until a man might live for a thousand years.

It was this "Back to Methusaleh" conversation—as the New York *Times* called it—which was the news of the week. As for

the rest, with its images of the future, its threat and promise—
its real offer of the choice of life and death—America was not
particularly concerned.

Nobody could say that America, from the least educated on
up to the professors, was not deeply concerned in scientific issues
in 1925. The interest of the American public, in fact, was concentrated on a fierce and spectacular debate whose issue was the
lag between the facts of experimental science and the slow working of the American imagination. In a hot Southern county seat,
whose streets swung banners advertising, "Read Your Bible,"
and "Be a Sweet Angel," and on whose lawns crowded pennant-
venders, lemonade-men, and wandering preachers, the Monkey
Trial was going on. Darrow and Bryan were arguing the Anti-
Evolution Law of Tennessee in the first trial to achieve a nation-
wide broadcast. Sweltering in the direct sunlight of July, ripping
their limp shirts in the violence of this battle, they fought, and
fanned their faces, and fought again, while the crowd waited
for Bryan to maintain that evolution was not a theory, and
shouted "Amen" from the back of the courtroom. Virgin birth,
Northern outsiders, the satiric lament that Americans must
descend from European, not American, monkeys—were argued,
until Darrow turned and asked Arthur Garfield Hays, "Can it
be possible that this trial is taking place in the twentieth century?"

Bryan fought for the people against Wall Street, as Darrow
had so often done. But this trial, which included at least one
scene which could be described as the most amazing court scene
in Anglo-Saxon history, could have occurred only at a time
when the laws of a democracy were still outside of a science
already half a century old; that is, when democracy was so far
from being experimental in its own nature that it could still make
blunders so fatal as to allow Bryan to go on the stand as an expert
on the Bible, to name the exact date of the flood, to testify
happily that he had no idea that Chinese civilization antedated
the year he named—2348 B.C.—and to swear that he would make
this trial a political and even a presidential issue. Will Rogers,
unable to laugh in the face of this sickening display, wrote, "He
can't ever do that. He might make Tennessee the side show of

The Double Democracy

America, but he can't make a street carnival of the whole United States."

The judge on the bench at Dayton ordered that crucial testimony stricken from the record. That day might be nullified in court; but July 1925 has its monument in that trial, one of the eyesore memorials in the long history of cultural lag.

There was no lag in other quarters. In Germany, Fritz Haber, returned from his tour of Japan and China, was lecturing to a hand-picked group of general-staff officers. There were those unpublicized lectures; and there was also a milestone meeting in Berlin.

Haber, Duisberg, and Karl Bosch were at last triumphant. They had seen through to one end of Bismarck's dream, to an ending which Bismarck himself would have recognized at once, although he had not foreseen it. These men had not met for an ordinary board meeting, but for a victorious announcement. Heavy industry had at last been brought to the point at which it must make way for the chemical industries. And there were no more chemical industries! There was *a chemical industry*—I. G. Farben, one trust which included every important chemical firm in Germany. But Krupp and Stinnes were working fast. They were setting up dummy industries in Holland and Spain, and the chemical industry took its cue from this activity. The old bloody dream was on them. World conquest was in their hands; not the over-riding iron armies—not yet—but the slick, polite men who could filter into the countries of Europe, South America, and the East, prepared to undersell Du Pont and Imperial Chemical, prepared to fight the Guggenheims' American control of Chilean nitrate with weapons of division where that would work, and competition where only that would win.

Just home from Japan, Haber brought news. The United States, as he saw it a year before, was being developed. But Japan and China were ripe, as German markets. China, disorganized and in political chaos, was a simple problem. But Japan!—its nationalist military, its secret societies, its circulation of Haushofer's book on Geopolitics—Japan was not merely an outlet, it was a potential ally. And it was no longer a question of guns and explosives. Haber knew that better than anyone else. Synthetic nitrogen had played its role in the last war. This coming struggle was to be fought in more inclusive terms. The Japanese with

whom he had spoken were eager to learn—a German tie-up
would teach them more quickly than any other way the tricks
and short-cuts of the chemical industry. They would take
Farben men into the two controlling concerns : Mitsui and
Mitsubishi. They had already reached the basis for a deal on
synthetic nitrogen. And that one product could yet be the key
for international domination. Chile was willing to make terms.
An International Nitrogen Cartel would be a testing-ground in
the coming war—the first element of penetration.

Haber's report laid the groundwork for the huge Farben plan.
The firm would be prepared to dump materials on foreign markets—nitrogen first, then other chemicals, sold far beneath all
other prices. The army would be working along with these
plans. A new division—the War Economy Division—was just
being organized. I. G. Farben needed irritants to the Republic.
They even made contributions, when they were asked to,
toward the publication of a book that was printed in Munich.
Copies arrived, to show that their money had been used well.
They did not even bother to read them. The books lay on office
desks, testimony that a small part of the work that I. G. Farben
had set itself to do had been accomplished. They lay there, un-
opened, with the letters big on their stiff covers—MEIN KAMPF.

CHAPTER NINETEEN
Tendencies of History

THE LINES OF FAMILIES, like those of the culture of nations, mark the recurrence of energies, the lives of these daughters and sons curving response to their age in startling answers to their ancestors. These rises have been compared to the "faults" in geologic records; they are more like the many-based lines of those statues dictated by Gibbs's formulas, the statues of form itself, which may by analogy apply to any natural form. The analogy is as sensitive here as if itself were another form of life, delicate, vulnerable, and precious. It has stood service in many ways. For not only were the salts of the earth traceable by means of Willard Gibbs's succinct expression; he had a claim to more than empty priority. Boltzmann called him "the greatest synthetic philosopher since Newton," and his work was connected in so complete a consistent system that its general principles could be used in many ways.

The Gibbs family can be traced by its papers and legends. There are not many of these. We are given shreds; we see Samuel Willard stubbornly refused the title to which he had a right, President of Harvard, and taking the next best title rather than move into Cambridge, where he had to live according to the statutes of the University; and Gibbs living and dying on scarcely more than a length of three New Haven blocks. But of these great New England families, none is more closely documented than that line of kin—reticent, aspiring, involved with a belief in "God, education, and science"—the Adams family. The connection between the Adams family and the Gibbs family has

[*403*]

never been traced, but it swings through the history of the United States like a mystery saga, in which the clues are laid down by one generation which forgets and dies, until the traces are picked up unconsciously by their children and grandchildren.

If Josiah Gibbs met John Quincy Adams the day he came to New Haven to see the *Amistad* prisoners, Adams did not mention it in his diary, and the professor of philology left no record of the meeting that has not been destroyed. John Quincy Adams was lecturing on faith that autumn, and wondering privately how far faith might be violated. He saw with distrust the approach of new revelations, and he and Josiah Gibbs would have had much to talk about, if they could have been spared the haste and pressure of the trials, in which the work of Adams increased as Gibbs finished his part and withdrew. The stirrings in Massachusetts were disturbing the ex-President; he could defend freedom and fight new forms; he wrote :

A young man, named Ralph Waldo Emerson, a son of my once-loved friend William Emerson, and a class-mate of my lamented son George, after failing in the every-day avocations of a Unitarian preacher and schoolmaster, starts a new doctrine of transcendentalism, declares all the old revelations superannuated and worn out, and announces the approach of new revelations and prophecies. Garrison and the non-resistant abolitionists, Brownson and the Marat democrats, phrenology and animal magnetism, all come in, furnishing each some plausible rascality as an ingredient for the bubbling cauldron of religion and politics.

That cauldron, bubbling as Adams reached his old age, was prepared for his grandsons. As Josiah Gibbs had given John Quincy Adams his means of communication in the *Amistad* case by finding an interpreter, so Adams' grandson Henry was to be the first to bring Willard Gibbs into communication with the world beyond his science, to give to him the words which might let that world see that Gibbs's science could be brought to them.

Henry Adams looked all his life for a formula in history which might prove the richest ingredient in the "cauldron of religion and politics." He did not stop there; as consciously as Melville and Whitman, he fought for equilibrium; the balance of matter against mind, of men against women. After the tragic death of his wife, he was driven in that search. At one end of the quest, he found the great cathedrals of France, and the unified century for which they spoke, balancing their Gothic thrusts in arches he could understand slowly, and meet with a dance of worship in his heart. In the wish to be pure spirit, the Church had thought of life as a double-headed comet, with mind and matter travelling in ordained harmony. But he brought to these poems, these windows and legends, and this miraculous rose, the rest of his education. He brought with him the terrible world of the nineteenth century, where all the forces felt by Lord Kelvin as failure made our century. He brought this passionate experimental search for unity; he brought a heritage of power and the Presidency, and his own contemporaneity with the wishes of his grandfather, who also had failed. The only way one can see triumph among these imaginations is to link together, for our own moment, those men and women who in full consciousness knew they had failed. They make a sort of triumph, shining darkly down to us. Henry Adams brought along with him that light; he brought an acquaintance with Clerk Maxwell, Langley, Lord Kelvin; and he brought what he knew of Willard Gibbs. Roozeboom had called Gibbs "the sociologist of chemistry"; Adams wanted a chemistry of sociology, or, for a beginning, of history.

Henry Adams in protest against the driving evil of the nineteenth century went backwards into a vivid, pure, and exquisite past. When Mark Twain went backwards to his medieval dream, he returned with a vision of society fearful in its discrepancies, full of the avoidable—of poverty, epidemic, and brutal error—but that was because he fixed his look on society. Henry Adams looked at a religious flowering, and was able to set an island of unity, Mont-Saint-Michel, against the universal degradation of the heat-death. But this concentration on one dramatic product was to illuminate the background of our civilization more than Mark Twain could even suggest, since he brought back a mirror of his time. *Mont-Saint-Michel and Chartres*, which we can see as half of Adams' book—of which the other half is the *Education* —was privately printed in 1904. He had been working on it as Gibbs died in New Haven. The nervous great spring of the arch, whose roots lie deep in an earth of anguish and doubt, and whose head leaps into the black sky where comets lose themselves—that dangerous equilibrium is the theme of the first book. But behind that theme are sexuality and religious hope; and farther behind, the *Pteraspis* and *Terebratula* still, fossils of uniformity of whose existence Sir Charles Lyell first had told him. They had led him to a long study, paralleling his work in history, of physics and mathematics. He believed that history must be treated as a physical science, and this belief had come back from Europe with him, and had been fortified by every change in his life. He wanted, as the new century wanted, to arrange phenomena, to force unity under law upon the understanding.

Gibbs would have listened with patience to Adams' "disputatious questionings," for Henry Adams came to his subject with a passionate wish for knowledge as well as a passionate doubt. But Adams missed Gibbs when he was in Washington—he says in the *Education*, "The greatest of Americans, judged by his rank in science, Willard Gibbs, never came to Washington," and he never inquired closely enough about Gibbs to learn that he had been mistaken. Simon Newcomb did not take his wish to study seriously; Langley did, although like Gibbs he denied himself the "amusement of philosophy, which consists chiefly in suggesting unintelligible answers to insoluble problems"; he knew the problems, however, and did Adams the service of putting Stallo's book in his hands.

Henry was not the only member of his generation who was concerned with these questions. Brooks Adams, his brother, touched his deepest excitement with his book, *The Law of Civilization and Decay*, and Henry's answer is in a letter dated 10 November 1902 :

Your economical law of History is, or ought to be, an Energetic Law of History. Concentration is Energy, whether political or industrial. If I were ten years old, I would educate myself to write that book, and teach that lesson, but I care too little now for God or man to teach anything.

Some member of the Adams family was always trying to persuade himself that he cared too little for God or man to do the task that was beginning to consume his days and nights; and Henry Adams had by this time developed the passion toward which his whole life had led him. He would have to go farther in recoil against what he was doing before he could speak. A year later he wrote to Charles Milnes Gaskell, from Paris :

. . . The gentle mathematicians and physicists still cling to their laws of thermo-dynamics, and are almost epileptic in their convulsive assurances that they have reached there a generalization which will hold good. Perhaps it will. Who cares? Already it is like all the rest of our old structure. It explains nothing. Science has given up the whole fabric of cause and effect. Even time-sequence is beginning to be threatened. I should not at all wonder if some one should upset time. As for space, it is upset already. . . .

He was thinking in terms of his historic curves, and his science was still the science of Lyell and Lord Kelvin, bombed by the metaphysical bomb of Madame Curie, wrecked by the rays of Crookes, cut loose by Karl Pearson, "adrift on a sensual raft in the midst of a supersensual chaos." He transferred that collapse to history; and in his sudden synthesis of every change since the thirteenth century, he saw that "Matter was Motion—Motion was Matter—the thing moved." But he also saw what this disturbance meant, and he wrote, in this fear that it was *science* itself that was the evil, in the same terms that were used when people felt in their fear of machines that it was anything—learning, the machine, science—anything rather than human beings themselves who were to blame :

I apprehend for the next hundred years an ultimate colossal, cosmic collapse; but not on any of our old lines. My belief is that science is to wreck us, and that we are like monkeys monkeying with a loaded shell; we don't in the least know or care where our practically infinite energies come from or will bring us to. For myself, it is true; I know no care at all. But the faintest disturbance of equilibrium is felt throughout the solar system, and I feel sure that our power over energy has now reached a point where it must sensibly affect the old adjustment. It is mathematically certain to me that another thirty years of energy-development at the rate of the last century, must reach an *impasse*.

This letter to his brother Brooks was written in August 1902.

When Henry Adams said he knew no care, he was about to plunge into the work of Gibbs. He never lay claim to a technical understanding of Gibbs's work, of which only the great paper seems to have reached him—through Langley, or Newcomb or

Pumpelly, with whom he discussed Gibbs—but, as Townsend says, Adams "caught enough of the drift of the matter to speculate concerning its application to human history."

He grew to feel that science was lovely and metaphysical and idiotic, and delightfully human, more passionate than St. Thomas, who had supplied the formula for *Mont-Saint-Michel*. He grew to be glad of Lord Kelvin's confession of failure, since he felt that it was his own admission, which he had refused to face. And finally, at the end of September 1908, he wrote to Elizabeth Cameron,

. . . I have run my head hard up against a form of mathematics that grinds my brains out. I flounder about like a sculpin in the mud. It is called the Law of Phases, and was invented at Yale. No one shall persuade me that I am not a Phase.

The mystery of the Adams-Gibbs connection is given its last twist by the note added to this letter by its scholarly and careful editor, Worthington Chauncey Ford, who notes after the word "Yale" : "By Josiah Willard Gibbs (1790–1861)." In this confusion of the father's dates for the son's, he makes an error which underlines the ignorance of Gibbs's name, and ties the bonds of the two families that much closer.

During 1909, Adams used what James Truslow Adams has called "Willard Gibbs's book on phase" to follow the work begun by him fifteen years before in his letter on "The Tendency of History." He announced the new work to Charles Milnes Gaskell, as a book to be printed on his return from Paris : about a hundred pages of no consequence, he said it was, announcing the end of the universe. The book was called *The Rule of Phase Applied to History*, and although it was written in 1909, it was not published until ten years later, when his brother Brooks collected Henry Adams' papers on the dissipation of energy in history. The little book had been submitted to the *American Historical Review*, which held it for a long time, and finally rejected it because it did not believe that the paper would interest its readers.

Even in the first few lines of his book, Adams misreads the title of the chapter of Gibbs containing the phase rule, which he says became a means of great extension of static chemistry in the hands of the Dutch chemists. Adams continues :

Tendencies of History

Although the name of Willard Gibbs is probably to-day the highest in scientific fame of all Americans since Benjamin Franklin, his Rule of Phases defies translation into literary language. The mathematical formulas in which he hid it were with difficulty intelligible to the chemists themselves, and are quite unintelligible to an unmathematical public, while the sense in which the word Phase was used, confused its meaning to a degree that alters its values, and reduces it to a chemical relation. Willard Gibbs helped to change the face of science, but his Phase was not the Phase of History.

Henry Adams goes on to speak of equilibrium, as it may be used in literature and history, and of this new field, he remarks that it may be entered "only by timid groping for its limits, and with certainty of constant error; but in order to enter it at all, one must begin by following the lines given by physical science." And now he summarizes the steps in the exploration of energy, ending in the region of hyper-space—the hyper-space of Thought, the region of pure mathematics and metaphysics—the last and universal solvent, where even mathematics must stop.

He quickly outlines the reasons why the phase rule is favored by physicists as well as mathematicians, and going ahead with his description of dividing lines, he comes to the matter of Direction, ignored by the mechanists. "The matter of Direction," he says, "was more vital to science than all kinematics together. The question how order could have got into the universe at all was the chief object of human thought since thought existed; and order,—to use the expressive figure of Rudolph Goldschied, —was but Direction regarded as stationary, like a frozen waterfall."

So far as it considers progress, history deals only with Direction. Adams makes the analogy of the attractive forces, such as Thought, which in history play the same part as pressure does in a physical system. Acceleration, according to this way of reasoning, would be the same as temperature; and the third main variable, Volume, would remain unchanged. The history of the thought of man would follow the analogy of water, passing from phase to phase determined by Attraction, Acceleration, and Volume, and might be watched for ten thousand years, and— still following Gibbs—be divined for a hundred thousand; and geologically followed back perhaps a hundred million, until its origins are lost in the rocks.

In this long and—for our purposes—infinite stretch of time, the substance called Thought has,—like the substance called water or gas,—passed through a variety of phases, or changes, or states of equilibrium, with which we are all, more or less, familiar. We live in a world of phases, so much more astonishing than the explosion of rockets, that we cannot, unless we are Gibbs or Watts, stop every moment to ask what becomes of the salt we put in our soup, or the water we boil in our teapot, and we are apt to remain stupidly stolid when a bulb bursts into a tulip, or a worm turns into a butterfly. No phase compares in wonder with the mere fact of our own existence, and this wonder has so completely exhausted the powers of Thought that mankind, except in a few laboratories, has ceased to wonder, or even to think. The Egyptians had infinite reason to bow down before a beetle; we have as much reason as they, for we know no more about it; but we have learned to accept our beetle Phase, and to recognize that everything, animate or in-animate, spiritual or material, exists in Phase; that all is equilibrium more or less unstable, and that our whole vision is limited to the bare possibility of calculating in mathematical form the degree of a given instability.

Thus results the plain assurance that the future of Thought, and therefore of History, lies in the hands of the physicists, and that the future historian must seek his education in the world of mathematical physics. Nothing can be expected from further study on the old lines. A new generation must be brought up to think by new methods. . . .

This was the most daring use of Willard Gibbs that had yet been attempted. It laid Henry Adams open to all the charges, and he was at once called a crazy old man and a charlatan, by the specialists. It also made him the pioneer in scientific history. He recalled to his readers the laws which Auguste Comte and Tur-got had formulated, years before Willard Gibbs defined the phase rule; but he set up a new character in the world : the physicist-historian, who would recognize a change of form— that is, a change of phase. He pointed at one marker of such a change, a generally admitted renaissance which we have been forced to call The Renaissance, and which includes Galileo, Descartes, Bacon, as well as Newton, Huygens, and the discoveries of printing, the telescope, and America. That the moment was the most vital that history ever recorded, "and left the deepest impression on men's memory . . . hardly expresses its scientific value. As a change of phase it offered singular interest, because, in this case alone, the process could be followed as though it were electrolytic, and the path of each separate molecule were visible under the microscope."

After Newton, the acceleration became "even measurable" in terms of the utilization of heat as force : "Society followed the same lines of attraction with little change, down to 1840, when the new chemical energy of electricity began to deflect the thought of society again."

In these three hundred years, ending at the time of the birth of Gibbs, and especially, Adams notes, in the nineteenth century, the acceleration suggests the law of squares, and the curve, whose resemblance is fantastically close, is the curve of the vaporization of water. He accepts the law of inverse squares experimentally as a general law of history.

Nature is rarely so simple as to act rigorously on the square, but History, like Mathematics, is obliged to assume that eccentricities more or less balance each other, so that something remains constant at last, and it is compelled to approach its problem by means of some fiction,—some infinitesimal calculus,—which may be left as general and undetermined as the formulas of our greatest master, Willard Gibbs, but which gives a hypothetical movement for an ideal substance that can be used for relation.

So, then, he has one phase, the period between 1600 and 1900, which he calls the Mechanical Phase. And he has a rule for its acceleration.

Using these rules, he goes about to fix his points, with the daring of a fortune-teller or an inspired analogist. He casts about in nature for a figure of thought that can speak to us of phases, casts out the nebula for being beyond measurement, and takes the comet. Not so much for phases, he says, but because it resembles thought. No one knows what it is, says Adams, and it seems to be immaterial, and its body may show no nucleus at all. "If not a Thought, the comet is a sort of brother of Thought, an early condensation of the ether itself, as the human mind may be another, traversing the infinite without origin or end, and attracted by a sudden object of curiosity that lies by chance near its path."

He takes the swing of the comet of 1843 as his example, and with one inclusive gesture, accepts that flying onrush as his image for history. "Nothing in the behavior of Thought is more paradoxical than that of these planets, or shows direction or purpose more flagrantly"; they furnish the only parallel for the tremendous acceleration of the last Phase of Thought. But the acceleration of society is even faster than this; 1900 was fully a thousand times greater in tension, vibration, so-called progress, than 1800, according to any measurement; the speed approached infinity. This proved only that the comet *was* material; thought was not. Nature is not "so simple as to obey only one law." The figure only introduces the problem.

Assuming the lag after the change of phase to its announcement by Galileo, Bacon, and Descartes, the date is set at 1296, with a preceding religious phase of thirty-six years, and the twentieth century following these two with a tremendous speed —"a straight line to infinity."

But if you reverse this curve, a curious result appears, and you have the time sequence. Fetish force ruled for thousands and thousands of years, and then mechanical force for the years from 1600 to 1900, and then the quick phase of electrical force, to 1917, at which time, this calculation predicts, it passes into an "Ethereal Phase"! That is, we reach pure mathematics—or, possibly, "The only consequence might be an indefinitely long stationary period, such as John Stuart Mill foresaw. In that case, the current would merely cease to flow." But it might also mean the control of cosmic forces on a cosmic scale, as startling as the changes of the worm, or of radium. Adams concludes:

Such seem to be, more or less probably, the lines on which any physical theory of the universe would affect the study of history, according to the latest direction of physics. . . . The figure used for illustration is immaterial except so far as it limits the nature of the attractive force. In any case the theory will have to assume that the mind has always figured its motives as reflections of itself, and that this is as true in its conception of electricity as in its instinctive imitation of a God. Always and everywhere the mind creates its own universe, and pursues its own phantoms; but the force behind the image is always a reality. . . .

Tendencies of History

When Brooks Adams added a long introduction to his edition of this book, he called the introduction "The Heritage of Henry Adams," and compared his mind to that of his grandfather in a brilliant double biography. He took his work, with its references to Gibbs, to be checked by H. A. Bumstead, a pupil of Gibbs who was best qualified to make such a check, in the opinion of Worthington Ford; and, says Brooks Adams, "the professor entirely relieved my mind." Henry's work was of an intense—a painful—interest to Brooks Adams, and he surrendered entirely to his brother's views. Henry had named 1917 as the date at which a revolutionary acceleration of thought would occur. In that year occurred the Russian Revolution and the participation of the United States in the World War, and a balance was struck for the future years. As for the scientific developments : Rutherford's work in 1911 was called by Eddington "the greatest change in our idea of matter since the days of Democritus"; in 1913 Bohr elaborated the quantum theory, and in 1915 Einstein extended the earlier theory of relativity. J. T. Adams says, triumphantly : "A change of 'phase' in Adams's sense, comparable only to those at preceding 'critical points,' had occurred." In 1925, Heisenberg's new quantum theory and, two years later, his principle of indeterminacy announced the new phase. And in this new arrangement, Gibbs's work still held. Mathematicians announced that there was no future refinement; "beyond this point," said Bridgman, "meaning ceases." But this, too, had been said before. If Adams had found another success, he had also found another failure, for the methods of science were changing. The advances sometimes confirmed him, but sometimes they seemed to undermine the whole of the intrepid analogy. His whole structure could be toppled, but the *method* was what he wanted, and that held. It was not for nothing that Henry Adams spoke of the "certainty of constant error." He was not afraid of it, as the specialists are. Speak to an expert today, and he will tell you that if you mention such a theory—not that he knows Adams' work—you must not say a word for it yourself. Put everything between quotation marks, he will tell you; protect yourself. J. T. Adams asks : "Was he wholly on a wrong tack? I do not think so." Remember what John Quincy Adams said about Emerson.

William James burst out, in fear and rage; he could not bear the notion of the heat-death. While Brooks Adams was measuring pressures in terms of the Versailles Treaty, speaking of economic warfare as the fiercest and most pitiless of all wars, since to make a lasting peace in competition implies either the extermination or enslavement of the vanquished. James did not have the edge on history. He answered right after Adams' paper arrived. A month before James's death, he was soaking in the baths at Nauheim; he wrote a long sceptical letter back to Adams, reminding him that they were both old men, asking him "whether an old man soon about to meet his Maker can hope to save himself from the consequences of his life by pointing to the wit and learning he has shown in treating a tragic subject. No, sir, you can't do it, can't impress God in that way." His letter went on to say that the statistical drift downwards of energy was a false idea; that the *amount* of energy did not matter, that a dinosaur's brain had as much energy-exchange as a man, but could only unlock the dinosaur's muscles, while a man could use his feebler muscles and the same energy to make proclamations or write books or describe Chartres Cathedral—"in short, *make* history." The second law, James held, had nothing to do with history. The law sets a terminus, and history is what happens before that terminus is reached. Canalizing, that is the thing, as far as energy is concerned. Why, the moment before the most possible moment might be the millennium, when—

a maximum of happy and virtuous consciousness would be the only result. In short, the last expiring pulsation of the universe's life might be, "I am so happy and perfect that I can stand it no longer." You don't believe this and I don't say I do. But I can find nothing in "Energetik" to conflict with its possibility. You seem to me not to discriminate, but to treat quantity and distribution of energy as if they formed one question.

This book had got under James's skin; he sent along a postcard after his long letter. The card read :

P.S. Another illustration of my meaning : The clock of the universe is running down, and by so doing makes the hands move. The energy absorbed by the hands and the *mechanical* work they do is the same day after day, no matter how far the weights have descended from the position they were originally wound up to. The *history* which the hands perpetrate has nothing to do with the *quantity* of this work, but follows the *significance* of the figures which they cover on the dial. If they move from O to XII, there is "progress," if from XII to O, there is "decay," etc. etc.

W. J.

Adams answered at once, arguing his own case, but grateful for having got a rise out of one person, and telling James that nobody else had commented at all. And James wrote this last tart and laughing postcard on the subject—one month, to the day, before his death at home :

Constance, June 26

Yours of the 20th, just arriving, pleases me by its docility of spirit and passive subjection to philosophic opinion. Never, never pretend to an opinion of your own! that way lies every annoyance and madness! You tempt me to offer you another illustration—that of the *hydraulic ram* (thrown back to me in an exam. as a "hydraulic goat" by an insufficiently intelligent student). Let this arrangement of metal, placed in the course of a brook, symbolize the machine of human life. It works, clap, clap, clap, day and night, so long as the brook runs *at all*, and no matter how full the brook (which symbolizes the descending cosmic energy) may be, it works always to the same effect, of raising so many kilogram-meters of water. What the *value* of this work as history may be, depends on the uses to which the water is put in the house which the ram serves.

W. J.

This one attempt of Henry Adams, rejected and put away until after his death and not printed at all until after the first World War—it was not published until 1920—was, for all its curious stretching of an analogy, the sum of the work of the Adams family, the fusion of science and history. The observatories that the old ex-President had almost forced on us, the JUS SUUM, the risk of a religious and scientific vision of a free country—would lead to a country that would be free to see the laws by which it moved, free to choose a tradition from its past, as well as free to fight for its own future. Henry Adams groaned and shrieked with the rest of his world under the assaults of violent Nature :

No one could say that the social mind now failed to respond to new force. . . . The railways alone approached the carnage of war; automobiles and fire-arms ravaged society, until an earthquake became almost a nervous relaxation. An immense volume of force had detached itself from the unknown universe of energy, while still vaster reservoirs, supposed to be infinite, steadily revealed themselves. . . .

All about him, the analogy was being carried too far. Gibbs had made his models, and thrown them away, seeing that the overlapping and combining which he needed could be found in an idea rather than a physical model. He moved away from the familiar image in this way; but his austere and rigorous progress kept him within the bounds of his own analogies.

Others had gone out of bounds. Woodrow Wilson, the following year, was saying :

No living thing can have its organs offset against each other as checks, and live. On the contrary, its life is dependent upon their quick cooperation, their ready response to the commands of instinct or intelligence, their amicable community of purpose. Government is not a body of blind forces; it is a body of men, with highly differentiated functions, no doubt, in our modern day of specialization, but with a common task and purpose. . . . Living political constitutions must be Darwinian in structure and in practice.

Woodrow Wilson stormed against the Newtonian theory of government, pointing out lapses and failures, from the Constitution on down, as this theory had prevailed over the

very different theory of Hamilton, that government was not a thing which you could afford to tie up in a nice poise, as if it were to be held at an inactive equilibrium, but a thing which must every day act with straight-forward and unquestionable power, with definite purpose and consistent force, choosing its policies and making good its authority, like a single organism—the theory which would have seemed to Darwin the theory of nature itself, the nature of man as well as the nature of animal organisms.

But this use of "equilibrium" was not the physicist's use; it was a rigid balance he was describing, not a dance of process in which the steps would be predictable within limits. Wilson was illustrating how far the lag had separated government and science, when he must hold up Darwin as the only scientist of process. But he fell into the same error, not stopping at *method*, but hanging onto models. Here Gibbs's neglect of consciousness carried another penalty to him. If he had been the great and poised citizen that Benjamin Franklin was, there would not have been these gaps. But this was not Philadelphia and Paris, this was New Haven, and Gibbs bears his own penalties. He had given abstract truth; it could be taken up by the specialists, and applied according to their characters. There is no priesthood of learning, for the priests failed long ago, and that idea was always false. We can see in the applications only this : the greatness of the system with which Gibbs dealt, and the characters of those who came after him to use his work.

Far on the other side of the meanings, his work was paralleled by Vilfredo Pareto. The product in revolt against the violent Mazzini partisanship of his father, an exile from Italy, Pareto was brought up in France, and when he returned after the amnesty of 1858, the ten-year-old boy brought all the results of his conflict with his father to a general rebellion against revolutionary influences. His assertions about his own serenity threw into lightning-flash chiaroscuro his abuse of every humanitarian gesture. Over seventy years old when he wrote his four-volume *Trattato di Sociologia Generale,* not only this boiling hatred finds its expression here, but a lifetime of mathematical training, with his standing as an engineer, a physical scientist, and a director of the Ferrovie Italiane. His attention was called to Walras, "the creator of mathematical economics," and Pareto took over Walras' chair at Lausanne in 1893. His suggestively worked-out system is based on the paradox of an attempt to keep a liberal economic policy, and at the same time to wreck every move toward political freedom. In the most extreme revulsion, he turned on his own early liberalism, and his life was gnawed by the question of what had been wrong with his young beliefs, what disease had eaten his youth. Like all those who turn for the sake of a machine-perfect system or for the sake of power against their own best beliefs, his hatred corrodes all his writing, leaving these acid-eaten places in a brilliant edifice.

His central structure is the scheme of the social system itself, seen with the same largeness of view and in analogy with Gibbs's physico-chemical system. Pareto's work is not an application of science; it is, however, a metaphor of a scientific scheme. He was aware of the newest work done in physical chemistry; he reached the concept of society as a system in heterogeneous equilibrium, led by the statement of a general theory in Sensini's *Teoria dell' Equilibrio di Composizione delle Classi Sociale*. He built up the idea of a society composed of individuals who could be dealt with according to the laws of statistical equilibrium, whose components were the governing elite, the non-governing elite, and the non-elite.

His social system was one of molecules set in motion by tastes, and subject to checks. These checks took the form of obstacles to the acquisition of social values. He tried to determine measurable components, like economic and moral and intellectual prosperity, military and political power, and various kinds of utility. There was no vocabulary for these measurable quantities. Pareto suggested, for example, the unwieldy word "ophelimity" for the useful and the desirable in economic life. He moved guardedly on these border lines of discovery, remarking, "I say that, but I am sure I am wrong, there may be no way of reconciling the literary approach to sociology with the scientific approach." And all the time his books are full of suggestive sociological material, as wonderful as the touches in Sumner or *The Golden Bough*—clues to the behavior of competitive individuals in war and business. The involuntary cry of the sea gull as he first sights his prey, which calls the other gulls, but also protects him when he is not the first to see food—the movements of an individual as he passes from the non-governing elite to the governing elite and renounces, among the rigors of the class transition, his early views—these keys to behavior are analyzed with the care that Gibbs spent on critical points and unimolecular surfaces.

Lawrence Henderson, looking for further relations of Gibbs's work than he had already worked out for blood physiology and metallurgy, has written a study of Pareto in the light of Gibbs. The social system of Pareto bears the same relation to examples in society that Gibbs's physico-chemical system bears to the branches of science. The social system is a fiction, not the result of the application of facts. Gibbs reduced his variables to a minimum, as did Pareto. The long, intuitive work as each of these men began his work in science became a flower of development in their hands. Often their criteria were the same. Equilibrium, in Pareto, is the same as Gibbs's equilibrium, and is often of such a character that some function like entropy or energy assumes a maximum or a minimum value or . . . vanishes. In the case of Pareto's social system the definition of equilibrium takes a form that closely resembles the theorem of Le Chatelier in physical chemistry, who expresses a property of physico-chemical equilibrium, and which may be deduced from the work of Gibbs.

From these likenesses, both fruits of the same wish that moved Henry Adams, the great dream of order which moved any man or woman living in protest against the forces of the nineteenth century, Mussolini derived fascism, literally acting according to Pareto in the early years at Rome. And Pareto, an old man, found himself unable either to repudiate or accept this rigid-minded use of the fiction which he had laid down, making no allowance for the human being and railing against human political liberty at every step. He called from his estate, his villa Angora, named after his flood of cats, that he wanted freedom of opinion, freedom of speech, and no alliance with the Papal See. But it was too late. The analogy had been handled mechanically; the hatreds were set in motion, and their momentum was "a straight line to infinity"—unless it could be stopped by greater force.

In America, the analogy was also in motion. From the meeting in Saratoga that had set a group of economists—including R. T. Ely and John Bates Clark—against Sumner, and for the "historical and statistical study of actual conditions of economic life" to bring the young science of political economy to its maturity, to the work of the students of Gibbs, the attempt to bring the methods of science and the methods of economics together grew. J. B. Clark went to water for his symbols, and the equilibrium he chose was the equilibrium of water which is never achieved in the living lake, to which flow streams which keep a state of change. He thought of society with an ideal counterpart, the classic reflecting pool, still as the pools described by Hawthorne, too still for reality.

"Gibbs himself never contributed to the social sciences," notes Irving Fisher. "Apparently I am the only one of his pupils who, after first doing some teaching in mathematics and physics, became professedly an economist," although he mentions that a pupil of Gibbs became president of the American Statistical Association. "It is one of the handicaps of mathematics in the social sciences that there are so few who are trained in both lines for such study, and this particularly applies to any applications of Professor Gibbs's vector analysis." The concept of time's arrow is needed in our thought; now we learn other methods all year and this new method at the end of the term; one teacher has said that it is as if we lived in Columbus' time, and learned all year that the world was flat, only to be told in the last week of school that indeed it was round.

"There are several fairly distinct branches of social science to which mathematics has been, or may be, applied. The chief of these may be distinguished as (1) pure economics, (2) the 'smoothing' of statistical series, (3) correlation and (4) probabilities, all of which overlap to some extent." Fisher's graduate work with Sumner and Gibbs ended with the writing of his thesis on "Mathematical Investigations in the Theory of Value and Prices." "Professor Gibbs showed a lively interest in this youthful work," he said, "and was especially interested in the fact that I had used geometric constructions and methods including his own vector notation." In his *The Nature of Capital and Income*, dedicated to Sumner, Irving Fisher has taken as a key Gibbs's maxim, "The whole is simpler than its parts," and leaned on the definition of Walras and Pareto of wealth as including men. He cites Pareto's "distribution curve" of incomes, which is really the tail of the probability curve. In this and in other books, Fisher's debt to J. B. Clark, who discovered the concept of "marginal utility," as well as to Jevons, Walras, and Pareto, is acknowledged. What he drives towards—however one may feel about his economic beliefs—is a methodology of economics that will approach the completeness and style of the physical sciences. Both Ragnar Frisch and Irving Fisher have ventured far into statistical measurements. The available statistics are not yet sufficient, but a way is indicated here, a flexible method that may be used according to belief. Through these new attacks, the influence of Gibbs shines clear, changing the remote fields of life insurance and the calculation of incomes. Gibbs had said, "Mathematics *is* a language." Irving Fisher adds that it is necessary in the social sciences, when the relations are so involved that language becomes less precise and complete than mathematical expression.

This is a challenge to poets and makers of language, as well. The unwieldy word of Pareto exists only because nobody has made a better one. These new methods have been chosen almost accidentally, often by experts who remained unaware of the links in other fields, as the scientists have remained ignorant of Henry Adams' book and its implications for twentieth-century culture. If we end in the dead and level waste of Adams' prediction, or if we approach that end and escape it by some huge and fighting chance, as South America, say, has escaped being the dissipated end of Spanish culture, it is experimental fact for the scientists. Henry Adams had to choose 1300 and 1900 by their symptoms; we have the two Compiègnes, as critical points from which to measure.

In 1751, Horace Walpole proposed another unwieldy word, which never came into use. In a letter to Horace Mann, he suggested the word "serendipity," taken from a fairy tale about the three princes of Serendip, that is, Ceylon. "As Their Highnesses travelled," the old tale went, "they were always making discoveries, by *accident* or *sagacity*, of things they were not in search of." The word is a possibility word, a word for luck. It means the luck of finding new proofs or relations which were not looked for; it is a word for induced sensitization, as one writer has shown, a luck that is a luck of use, a deftness in using good fortune; and the good fortune is nothing more than one's own prepared awareness. This quality, serendipity, is the luck of the discoverer, and those who find new applications have it. The knotted myth of the voyages of Gibbs's ideas is a myth of this quality.

The giant companies of the United States have acknowledged their debt to Gibbs, which is so difficult to trace because it is so broad a foundation.

Dr. John Johnston, director of research of the United States Steel Corporation, says of Gibbs's methods : "They have entered, directly or indirectly, into almost all lines of manufacture and have thus enriched the world immeasurably."

R. H. Ewart, of the United States Rubber Company, in

pointing out the importance of Gibbs's work to the rubber industry, speaks of the knowledge of the properties of rubber solutions derived from statistical mechanics, and of the applications of Gibbs's work on the chemistry of surfaces, which is "of extreme importance in the study of natural rubber latex and the preparation of synthetic rubber."

F. B. Jewett, of the American Telephone & Telegraph Company, says with Karl K. Darrow :

The difficulty in describing the work of Gibbs lies precisely in the fact that it is fundamental. It is like a ponderous foundation on which so great a superstructure has been built that no one notices the foundation any more unless it is specially pointed out. We do not describe Newton's work in mechanics by citing a few phenomena of motion and saying that Newton explained them; rather, we speak of "Newtonian mechanics" and imply that it extends to all such phenomena. It would be equally justifiable to speak of "Gibbsian thermodynamical chemistry." Many a famous chemist has gladly made public announcement that his own fame rests on his verifications of the predictions of Gibbs. If I were asked to indicate how the work of Gibbs has influenced the arts of communication, I might indicate our chemical laboratories, which are staffed by chemists every one of whom was partially formed by Gibbs, even though it is probable that no one of them ever saw the master.

In New Haven, while Gibbs's ideas were being used in industry, history, economics, and sociology, recognition was slow. When Irving Fisher went to Germany in 1922, Nernst asked what had become of the five hundred dollars, his fee for the Silliman lectures, which he had given to Yale as his contribution to a Gibbs memorial. Since the beginning of the war, no news from New Haven had reached him.

The news was simple. The fund had finally been used, in the absence of further money, to pay for a Gibbs plaque by Lee Laurie, which was mounted on the wall of the staircase at Sloane. During the next years, the decade around the centenary of his birth, the first general notice of Gibbs's achievement was given him, in the form of a Gibbs fund at Yale for a lectureship, the first American edition of his collected works, the establishment of a lectureship by the American Mathematical Society, and the awarding of a Gibbs Medal by the Chicago branch of the American Chemical Society.

In 1926, fifty years after the publication of the phase rule, at a meeting of the Chemical Union in New York, scientists, arrived from abroad to attend the convention, reminded the people of his own country of Gibbs. And this reminder reached the press. Gibbs himself had refused to talk to reporters, recognizing that while actions may often be successfully interpreted and diluted into headline journalism, the wish and method of a person engaged in complicated expression can only be translated into a terribly debased form, if it is not generally familiar. The best a scientist—or a poet or artist—may hope for is the *haute vulgarisation* that cannot carry his true attitude or the whole of his meaning, however simpler than its parts that meaning may be.

This, too, carried its penalty to his name. Pupin once described a dinner at the University Club with twelve Yale graduates. After dinner, he and William Welch, dean of the Johns Hopkins medical school, wagered that nobody present could name the man who in their opinion was the greatest scientist to come out of Yale; and not one Yale man guessed the name of Gibbs.

Pupin went on as he had done, spreading the fame of the man who he said should be set up as the patron saint of idealism in science. The following year, at the Graduates Club in New Haven, a dinner was held for the presentation of a portrait of Gibbs, done after death from the heliograph Gibbs had made at the request of Ostwald. At the dinner, Ernest Brown remembered what John Johnston had said: that before Gibbs, it looked as though chemistry had nothing left but to work out the details. Gibbs had changed all that. Now Pupin had arranged for the gift of this portrait to the Club; and it proved at least that the administration of the Club was more effective than that of the University.

When Pupin began to speak, the story of the portrait was told for the first time. It is all of a piece with the rest of the Gibbs story. Pupin himself had gone to the donor, who had paid for the painting and given it anonymously to the Graduates Club. But he said, curiously, to Pupin, before he made the gesture : "Who is Josiah Willard Gibbs? I never heard of him." And Pupin answered, "Yes, Jim, you never heard of him, but neither did he ever hear of you, and so don't worry about it." "But," said the man, piqued, "tell me who he was." Pupin began the story, with its sparse details and vast implications. After a few minutes the business man interrupted : "I have heard enough," he said, "you can have the money for the portrait. I shall gladly give it on one condition, that you cut the story short. It makes me feel unhappy to realize that I am ignorant of so great a fact connected with the history of Yale."

Another story that Pupin remembered about Gibbs was the story of his own disappointment, when he had not been allowed to teach physical chemistry. Gibbs could answer that. The last time Pupin had seen Gibbs was when Gibbs had brought a Japanese gentleman connected with the postal and telegraph system in Japan to see Pupin at his laboratory at Columbia, to examine the apparatus connected with telephony.

Since that time, Yale tells the story, which it is impossible to withhold, and which many Yale people wish remedied, of the drive to raise a small sum for a Gibbs laboratory and $180,000 for a Walter Camp memorial. The larger sum was raised; schoolboys and businessmen paid for the Camp Gate; there still is no Gibbs laboratory at Yale.

In a real and terrible sense, the world has become a Gibbs laboratory, although many steps of this development are blurred by re-discovery. There is no question here of priority; rather the point is the foreboding, the prophetic imagery which exists in Gibbs's work, and which has been made a dominant pattern in the world as it lives today. If there has been dissipation of energy—energy of all kinds—there has also been the reaction to explosive and creative force. There has been the varied acceptance and rejection of sources such as Gibbs, which in their way mark the change of historical phase, which in their way offer direction and momentum to the flow of human history.

From the conception of the elite without personal freedom to the compulsive force of fascism was an easy step. In Germany, the problem was more complicated, but because of the poverty of the country and because of the restrictive settlement at Versailles, it was necessary to accept every gift of the imagination that could be seen as directly marketable, of direct "ophelimity." The New York *Times* cited the synthetic-nitrogen plant at Muscle Shoals as a by-product of Gibbs's work. The synthetic-nitrogen industry was not only a key to German industrial power and to Germany's relations with Japan, it was a model for the growing chemical trust. During the war, Karl Bosch, working with the Badische Anilin and Soda Works, had been experimenting with his process of hydrogenation—a process to extract oil from coal. Now Bosch and Haber, with Duisberg, were the chemists behind I. G. Farben.

In 1927, a "Leunabenzine" plant was built; and in 1933, Hitler was informed that Farben could create a Germany independent of gas and oil imports.

In 1934, "Neue Werkstoffe" was the order. New production materials for Germany! And in addition to the synthetic fabrics, synthetic foods, and plastics, as well as Buna synthetic rubber, were added to the list.

This period locked the chemical industries of Germany and Japan. Haber's trip had been fruitful : an agreement signed in 1928 formally acknowledged that I. G. Farben was to "take over the Japanese chemical industry and train the Japanese in the manufacture of explosive, synthetics, light metals, and other war and civil material."

And in the meantime, Farben agents had been perfecting an economic strategy that would involve not only Europe but the countries of North and South America in powerful German-dominated cartels, whose grip could only be broken—as they were in the early months of 1942—by exposure in wartime and the ruthless nullification of enemy-held patents. The patent office had reached its full power, had entered into its share of democracy, and was fighting with its nation. But it had been dangerously slow. It had not recognized, any more than the State Department, that the Japanese invasion of Manchuria and the Franco-Nazi-Fascist alliance against the people of Spain and the.Spanish government were linked by ties of business and will, and the incredible ties of accepted imaginative acts.

While war drove the age down the slope of entropy, many arrived to speak about the preparations of science and the imagination.

Henry Adams had spoken of the brilliant possibilities of inert Czarist Russia; if Russia were swung "into the Western movement," he said, it would very likely "become the most brilliant constellation of human progress through all the ordered stages of good." In April 1942 the most conservative newspapers were pointing out to a lately allied people the results in Russia of mobilization of science by the state. If the theorist thrives more slowly because he must concern himself with discoveries that can be applied at once—in field and factory and hospital—the fruit of the policy is found in the efficiency of airplanes, surgical improvements, and the *better utilization of raw materials*. Peter Kapitza is the example chosen—a brilliant master of technique whose career, between England and Russia, has already proved dramatic and productive. Kapitza cites the Haber process as war-inspired science. Synthetic ammonia, which gave Germany explosives and fertilizers, was found through the utilization of that raw material which is the most important—the creative imagination. Haber openly acknowledged his debt to Gibbs before he died in exile from the nation whose war had inspired him; but that is the least important of all the points that might be made. The sight of the truth is the crucial vision; the sight of the chance of America, or the chance of people anywhere in the world, to use the gifts that are offered. War is made by imagination, and the peace that follows is made in the same way.

The tendencies of history are directed by the acceptance or rejection of the imagination. Economic pressures and the will of the people, aroused to resistance or producing in the full vividness of conscious life—they make these tendencies, which may go burning to war, or flow toward creative belief and the wish for a living order.

The analogies reach their full flowering here. Many have looked, not for the rigid "order" that is being held over us as if it were a novelty, while it is really the dead hand holding a whip —many have looked for the living order, in their own ways. Sir William Bragg, who brought X-ray analysis and the phase rule together and found new knowledge of the nature of the phase, has worked with metals and the atom, according to the Rutherford-Bohr model. He said, "The transition from disorder to order does not involve latent heat and is therefore not an ordinary phase-change," and he and Hume-Rothery have worked in definitions of order in structures known as super-lattice structures, or *ordered* solid solutions, such as the alloys which have been combined according to the map of the phase diagrams. Sir William Bragg has recently shown that each phase had its own characteristic atomic pattern; and this *phase pattern* holds, no matter what bonds exist between atoms. It is this work, following in the field of Westgren, Tammann, and Hume-Rothery, that leads to the following statement, which carries the analogy even farther than Henry Adams dared. It is the tremendous and hair-raising likeness, that, in its flash, strikes at those narrow souls who will not dare the metaphor, and sets a limitless possibility for the application of Gibbs—and beyond Gibbs, for the use of truth. In a passage on "The Thermodynamics of the Order-Disorder Transformation," the following sentences arrive :

. . . We may say that "demoralization sets in," there is a complete collapse of the ordered state. . . . This is no isolated phenomenon. Similar reasoning has been employed to explain the Curie point in ferromagnetics. . . . It is a general thermodynamic feature of an organized structure, where the energy keeping any given member in its right place is dependent on the degree to which its neighbors are in their right places, on "public opinion" if I may venture the analogy. Any such structure is subject to a rapid demoralization culminating at a critical temperature in the way I have indicated.

As one small example of a freak of possibility, it may be noted that this statement of a contemporary English scientist brings the idea of history of Henry Adams into focus, with the hope for a method which he first outlined. Henry Adams' interest in a scientific method of history was first excited by Sir Charles Lyell; he said that his active life began with the writing of a confession of geological faith at this friend's bidding. And Sir Charles Lyell, a hundred years ago, spoke with Noah Webster in New Haven. He asked Webster about the Dictionary, inquiring particularly about the words appearing now for the first time. How many of these new words had Webster himself invented? he asked. "Only one," answered Noah Webster, smiling; "only one—the word 'demoralize.'"

From the New England concern with demoralization to the twentieth-century world, with its war and its vision of the crystal as a set of flakes whose molecules lean over like blown wheat in a windy field—this is the life-span of Gibbs, as surely as his other markers are the fantastic voyage of the *Amistad* and the fantastic flight at Kitty Hawk. And the issues of the latest moment, however much they depend on him, depend on these two. The war, we know, will ultimately be decided by air power —since this is a struggle for control of the air over the earth, the new continent which has been discovered, invaded, and disputed in this century—supplies, and their transportation—since the Nazi armies are based on the reality of a growing chemical empire which is in economic conflict with another chemical empire—and the issue of personal liberty, wherever there is a human being in the world; as well as by the actual fighting. And all of these are interdependent. They are factors in the drive, through war and peace, to a dynamic equilibrium. Gibbs's truth, even in application to the atom and the ordered state, in relation to aircraft, electrophoresis, and ideas of history, shines on these factors. They are victorious while they use their gifts of the imagination. Gibbs's steady look can be seen among these processes of history : in the light alloy of the plane, faster and more powerful across the sky; in the industry which is daily becoming vaster, more important to American economy and more clearly a battle-front of the world—the chemical industry; and the parable of his acceptance and rejection, of his background and his emergence, becomes a parable of human freedom and a free attitude toward the gifts which the imagination makes. Truth, belonging to no group, no leader, no army, may be chosen by a free people; that is a test both for freedom and for truth. This power, which may emerge from the stillest of centers, which has emerged from the imagination of Gibbs, is to be used. It belongs to the stream of that great tradition from which free people are at liberty to choose their own ancestors. Gibbs is an ancestor and a contemporary of our moment in history. We bear many of the penalties he bore; many of the narrownesses are what we suffer from today, in our time and in our war; but in the generosity of his spirit he made his gifts. They, in their turn, enter into history; they are an image of its tendency.

CHAPTER TWENTY

The Long Discovery of Willard Gibbs

To COME TO THIS DEAD MAN, hoping to know him, seeing in him the gifts of the imagination raised to their most creative level and hoping to find him there, is to come away with something other—the growth of the idea in America; and, beyond.that, the fine and unlimited flowering of thought in the world. The unpredictable child is forgotten among the memories of the dead; and afterward, in the curbed adolescence of that town, the years of nourishment, the colorless youth arises, sad and rebellious, fading on a daguerreotype; the passionate full man follows, beard grown, his mind controlled and flowing, the source of a flashing river, his eyes impelled, driven by flame; and at the end, an old and kingly prophet's head blanks out the rest in its spell of restrained generous features and white hair. During these years, somehow his work was planted in the world. Coming to these years to understand a life, one may come away with a failure richer than that narrow success might ever have been.

The life he lived is in the rooms he slept in, torn down with new brick built over the wooden ghost; the offices he brought his days to, torn down to make room for new-equipped strong halls; the gardens where he walked, whose swords of iris fell in petals down, and which bred swords standing in Connecticut now. And the dark wood on which he wrote, the tables where he ate—the chairs scattered, the sofas covered with new pattern, the items of a dead man's inventory scattered like the iris. And the names he knew, now the names of changed streets : the college names, ringing their bell-notes over the hurried boys : High

Street, Chapel Street, Wall Street, Elm Street, Grove Street. And the lost faces.

That was the pale life, whose faces were read distantly, and slipped away, whose letters were torn up, burned, anyway destroyed. The life behind that burned. Hill-slopes, scattered yellow and blue with the familiar flowers and the flowering trees, and the darker wooded hills of Germany and the light-pointed Riviera; the return forever home, to know these streets, only these few streets except for the handful of trips made to Washington, Baltimore, Philadelphia, Buffalo, at which the sparks of contact with the men who could possibly find his thought were struck. But of his life there is left only a husk of legend, the cast-off and repudiated anecdotes, and the little stories that suddenly illuminate one side of greatness. The other side has its own youth and strengthening; to that side his death was only a minor episode. That life began with the shaping of the first images; he thought in images, and as these designs and balances, the strict intricate dances of equilibrium, came through, the new sciences took root. And they grew with a jungle growth, not in the restricted avenues of commerce, but in their applications which are the applications of any kind of truth purified; used for all the uses of good and evil by the specialists of action.

He is remembered as the professor's voice, as the kindness which helped a boy through an examination, or a wise man through his difficult problem. That is for the biographical man; for the life of his gifts, one need not speak in terms of memory. They are still being re-discovered, known as a full continent may be known, in which a bay is seen from whose banks the early sailor guesses what weather and what enemies lie within that darkness; and then to the next wave of exploration the first slopes of the mountains are made known; and another generation crosses these into different weather and the color of different grasses; until a further range known only to the snows and more intrepid birds stands big on all horizons; and finally the great-grandchildren may smell another sea. That wires should be cast, and the brave metals roll in a white passion from the furnaces; that men may be killed in explosions which the artists of hell have never written down; that a thousand unimagined industries may feel the vision and voyage by the charts of this one man—that is what grows upon the sight when one looks for the life of

The Long Discovery of Willard Gibbs

Gibbs. Newton had his London years, with the dinners and entertainments of the capital, and the stir of his employment at the Mint; he was "carried to kiss the King's hand." The legends of Gibbs's daily life are the small traces of genius recognized afterward, for the most part. If there was not in his listeners the greatness of time, that they could recognize the possible circles flung by his mind out over many kinds of thought and habit, they gave us what they could : the little chronicles of the student and affectionate disciple.

He comes down more clearly to us in the nature of his assumption. *Unassuming* in every meaning of that word, yes; there still are a few axioms which stand at the head of his days, as the couplet of Clausius stands at the head of the great paper. This was the man who permitted himself little, whose lack of trust in the external world is obvious in every habit which has been rumored, and in every trick of phrase, every rejection of offers made. He had been asked to come back to Europe and deliver his lectures; to come and be recognized, as Wolcott Gibbs had been fêted in his place. He refused. And, for the most part, he refused the world of recognition. His faith lay in the few often-repeated words which come down through the memory of his friends, his friends' children, his students :

"*Mathematics is a language.*"

"*The whole is simpler than its parts.*"

"*Anyone having these desires will make these researches.*"

These three statements come down to us in a great and terse communication of his spirit.

A psychiatrist has said of him : "But how can you deal with his life? Do you know anything of what happened to him before the age of three?" The products of his life answer for him; and one comes away, caring for his life in the way he cared for it, taking its real depth from its impact on the lives of strangers and the unborn, giving such greatness of meaning and such purpose to the future as few have been able to give.

Influence, not recognition. Recognition becomes a very strange follower when the influence is as wide as Gibbs's already is, and can be seen still growing at this moment of history, when all influences are snapped by the curving force of time and the whirlpool, war. But, in such a time, one looks for the sources of

Willard Gibbs

power. War, and the general darkness of struggle, attack the imaginative lives of men and women, cut off from much of the future by the need to fight for precisely that future they have imagined. A woman, seeing the men about her going off to war, caught in the need for all the hope that the present may afford, looks at the sources, believing that a country is richest when it comes most near to using all its energies. Behind the energy that can be evoked at this moment—behind the energy of the people —are the sources in belief and creation. Willard Gibbs is one source.

At a London dinner some years ago, the modern counterpart of those dinners of Newton's which drew the society of men of science, members of a British scientific society met; and afterward, twenty or thirty continued the evening at a near-by café. The talk veered and returned to scientific discoveries, and their relative importance; and being men of mathematics, they soon proposed a ballot. The vote was to be on the classification of the greatest scientists since the Renaissance. Each member turned in a numbered list; and when the names were ordered, Newton stood first, Darwin second, and Faraday and Einstein tied for third place. These names stood at the top because of the number of votes ranking each first. The next name was placed in order for a different reason; Willard Gibbs had been voted very high by nearly *all* of the assemblage. He had touched their lives and their work. Looking about that table, one saw biologists, who believe that "the next fundamental advance in their science will be due to discoveries of a Gibbsian type"; chemists, who have made lifeworks out of the equilibrium studies, fragment by fragment; physicists and mathematicians, who know the great beauty of his vector analysis and statistical mechanics.

Since that dinner, the technicians have added praise; the scientists of rubber, of steel, of the telephone industry, the plastics industry; and the economists, the historians, the sociologists, persons who are searching for a language for complexities that have added consciousness to their variables. Models had been supplied for those moments which needed illustration; and then removed, with always the double-edged battle-cry, "Go ahead; faith will follow!" Names had been found, and new techniques; the new masters of technique had found, as a bridge and a symbol of relationships, Gibbs's work.

The Long Discovery of Willard Gibbs

Of the meaner kinds of recognition—for anything is less living than this touch on the lives of millions—the story is slightly different. There are the Gibbs Medal, the Gibbs lectureship, a plaque at Yale, the proposal of Gibbs's face for a United States postage stamp; the toys of fame begin to appear. The mark of that kind of recognition is clear in the "career" of Gibbs at the door of the Hall of Fame, a corridor of elected immortals set up by New York University. Gibbs became eligible for this kind of immortality seventeen years after his death; his name was proposed then, and if he had won, a bust of him would have been set up on University Heights. Among the ballots several were sent out to members of the committee who had been dead for a good number of years. Many of those who voted had expressed their debt to pure science, in various ways. In 1920, Gibbs's name was voted on for the first time : he received 9 votes out of a possible 100. A three-fifths vote is required. In the next election, he was not considered; but in following elections, with the last vote being taken in 1940, he received 40, 55, and 56 votes. At this rate of increase, he should officially become a Great American at the next election. But, in the meantime, merely the proposal of his name as a candidate capable of being ranked with Agassiz, Gray, Joseph Henry, Simon Newcomb, Maria Mitchell, Maury, and Audubon has served to announce him to a public which was completely unconscious of his existence. Dr. Fisher, of Yale, and Dr. Theodore Shedlovsky, of Rockefeller Institute, have been to a large degree responsible for this wider acknowledgment.

In the meantime, critics have approached his life to wonder sadly at the penalties he carried. All the burden of withdrawal has been his; and since he himself spoke of popularization, since he wished his gifts to go to the world, there are even harsher penalties involved in the infrequent references to his name as "Joseph" Gibbs, as "William" Gibbs, as "Dr. Sibbs." Historians with a mature sense of the social responsibility of the discoverer have pointed at his omission of preparatory classes, at the kind of publication he received, at his refusal to submit himself to the long regime of dilution of his meaning which a re-translation of his work would mean. His students were solicitous that his real greatness should reach its audience : E. B. Wilson edited the *Vector Analysis,* Irving Fisher—in his wish to see a memorial to

Willard Gibbs

Willard Gibbs—conceived and initiated the 1300-page *Commentary*, contributing generously toward its publication.

In a society whose culture is an adjunct to the court, men of genius may be blamed according to two standards for having failed to communicate their discoveries. The first attitude condemns them if they fail to adjust to their age, and never reach the graces of the only patron; the second dismisses both the men and their language if, having reached the court, they do not continue to find a historic audience. More is to be expected of a democracy, whose greatest promise is that it is the "huge chance"; that is, we may expect everything. In a democracy, there is a mutual obligation. Gibbs made his contribution from the place from which it might have been expected that it would be quickly sown : a rich and powerful university. It was up to the circle around him to carry on. His gifts are those of the poet and discoverer; and if that language is not the language of the current maps, it will be accused of obscurity, *particularly if it deals with relationships*. But the burden rests on the group; the statement has been made. The language it assumes must be as delicate as the control-panel of a power-house, as inevitable as the plunge which releases the high explosive. One does not criticize these controls for being sensitive or complex. The reason for that is partly in the speed with which their results are shown; the water races enormous around the turbines, the entire mountainside lifts itself up into the air, and no spectator is innocent. It is partly in the respect which a certain group of experts have earned for themselves. But most of all, it is in the eager gesture of acceptance which greets their work.

When whole peoples suffer from the stress of bursting cultures, these expanding gifts seem very great. If Willard Gibbs, with all his penalties, with the narrownesses he endured and lived among persevering even after his death, can have penetrated through peace and war until he becomes, possibly beyond anyone who has yet lived, the type and emblem of the imagination in America—he stands as a great sign to the people of the world. While still he is unknown to the wide unspecialized audience in America, praise of a new order arrives from abroad. Gibbs is called one of this country's most *representative* intellectual figures. Here is the man, comes the voice of another country, here is the man who freed the dogmas of industrial civilization. He belonged to an ascetic and mystical minority, which, in order itself to grow, changed the face of the world. *"O grande pais norte-americano,"* ends a paper from Portugal in praise of Gibbs, America which has become the country of powerful enterprise, and at the same time the country where human thought has found its highest level.

The highest level, that level of our thought at which Gibbs stands, looks to the past with re-affirmation and to the future with foreboding. Such foreboding is not the dark gaze, but the creation of images which speak for the future *as it arrives*, with the speed of the poet, and not the attendance on the fact of the reporter. The re-affirmations are on the side of human chance. And it is this combination that permits Gibbs to play his immense part in a world in rearrangement, whose developments he, as a mortal man, did not foresee.

The nature of the war was predictable from its early days in China and Spain. When it was made clear on those proving-grounds—in those bloody laboratories—that the big guns of this coming war would include the factories, and supplies would need to be fired almost as fast as shells, one point was made. The other was made when the whole population of a country became its army, and it appeared that the conduct of civilians, in the factories and on the roads, was a part of military strategy. It was then that the war became the concern of all the people of the world. Everyone had a stake in this. And for the most completely dispossessed, the poor and suffering, the only riches lay in use. On another level, the only riches lay in release of whatever energy could be found, present or past—and this was only another kind of use. In this war of supplies, in this struggle of the chemical empire on which Hitler has founded his army against the maturing chemical empire of the Allied Nations, Gibbs leaped into a fiercer, more dramatic role than any he had yet played. From the experts the cries of waste came—"If we had known!" and part of that cry was loss, for ignorance of Gibbs's applications. But in many fields, steadily through these years between the wars, his work was known, and moving forward.

"Gibbs lives," says Millikan, "because, profound scholar,

matchless analyst that he was, he did for statistical mechanics and for thermodynamics what Laplace did for celestial mechanics and Maxwell did for electrodynamics, namely, made his field a well-nigh finished theoretical structure. . . ." That can be echoed along twenty roads of culture, and in the innumerable boundary lands between·"fields," where the future of our culture lives.

Einstein has said, in a recorded conversation : "Now I believe that events in nature are controlled by a much stricter and more closely binding law than we recognize today, when we speak of one event being the *cause* of another. We are like a child who judges a poem by the rhyme and knows nothing of the rhythmic pattern. Or we are like a juvenile learner at the piano, *just* relating one note to that which immediately precedes or follows. To an extent this may be very well when one is dealing with very simple and primitive compositions; but it will not do for the interpretation of a Bach fugue."

We have been given many clues by Gibbs's work, clues to the pattern. The rich history of how his work came to live its life gives us still further clues. For his life is that of a shadow; shadowy in all its details, in its destruction as well as in its love, it braces itself against the framework of the pressures on him and that work which was its marvellous result. He becomes a shadow radiating light; by that light we see the map of possibilities.

It is said that to tell of a person's life is to *thin* it out—to simplify while seeking to enrich. Whoever speaks of Gibbs must come to him willing to fail at thinning. His mythological touch did enrich. A little business man remarked, with some sly narrowness of his own, and a sigh, "If he had stayed in one line, think what he could have made of himself!" The head of a social agency asked, "Was he prolific?"

He has answered his critics, from the most responsible to the most loudly selfish. He carried the tragedy of his own restraint, and it grew into an immense and jungle growth. He refused to set down what was not essential, as he refused to assume; and he was prolific as nature, in the limits he allowed himself. So much of his story breaks its bonds, washes away his dead constraining days, and floods through these years with its prodigal vitality, so much of it touches on the terrible American wish for integrity of life and spirit in an immense country—that integrity which few have approached, which perhaps no American has ever completely known. But, as Lincoln reminds us of our wish with every word, every portrait, so Gibbs reminds us, even by his caution and denial, of that tradition—that *chance* which lies before us, and has left clues in our own past.

The abundance he made was a gift of imagery. Again like the great poet, he was able to speak, not in the prophetic mouthing which is nothing but acting, or in the important concrete prophecy of invention, but in the real language—that imagery which might be called the imagery of history. There is a language which can find itself in a future immediately ahead. Readers come to it later, and see the events foreshadowed, for they were felt *as they arrived*, when they still seemed symptoms. Truth arrives always a little before the fact, and the great men and women have all spoken in terms of truth as it appeared. That is another reason why it is so much to the point to look at a time half a century ago for today's clues, for there we all may see our own moment, its outline and its tendency toward equilibrium. And, too, if it is in one set of symbols, as Gibbs's work was in mathematics, we have that further sensitization which time has given us; we may go on with the analogies, going very delicately, and looking continually toward the young, for their foreboding of the next event.

The young come up, asking their questions. Perhaps the questions, in this world, are worth the most, as far as talking goes. They are, after all, the critical part of speech; and the rest can be better answered in action, for it wishes response. But, in these days, in this only life we know, the women and men ask the questions of freedom that may be asked in such a war as our time is reckoning with : questions of freedom, asking how can we find our energies? how can we make release? what lies behind that wish, these energies? And living in a changing disorder, wishing for the light of the chance of order to touch the forms we see, we come to this still man, with his touch of richness and death on the world. Richness and death, for it was pure life, and it could be used in any way, according to any follower's wish and energy. This life had been sown in the near past; it could go on in its own formal beauty, bringing relationships nearer to order, nearer to unity; and still could be unsatisfied. For in that treatment of possibility—as the angel of possibility— we find an angel of necessity. The thing is possible; therefore, in human terms, it is necessary. These are laws, disembodied as angels, bearing the same relation to the other creative laws that the angels of myth bear to men and women; without humanity, they show us what we might be, and in that *might be,* what indeed we are. Which they insist that we become.

Gibbs knew that imperative in his loneliness, the creative loneliness of the impelled spirit. Let him seem satisfied, the future must come to meet him! Let death be but a minor event, his life would grow in a courageous flowering. It signifies to us here, and to the people with whom we stand. It becomes a search for process and freedom, with the dance of relationship, and the blur and loss of wars which must be fought. He was unfree, and made his own freedom; hedged in, and disproved barriers. And what he gave may be used in countless complex usages, as is the great hope of the poet, of the planner, of all who fight for the full acceptance of the gifts of the imagination. They change into strength from their pure law; they can be used. And the search for them need not, like many searches, fail. This search, with its appalling midnight adventures, its little light, its madnesses and blessing and defeat, which yet can say to the lost, You shall be found, and to the lonely, There are others to speak to you, and to all who live for it, Freedom will come.

For the sake of persons of different types, scientific truth should be presented in different forms and should be regarded as equally scientific, whether it appears in the robust form and vivid coloring of a physical illustration, or in the tenuity and paleness of a symbolic expression.

CLERK MAXWELL

The paradox is now fully established that the utmost abstractions are the true weapons with which to control our thought of concrete fact.

A. N. WHITEHEAD

Appendix

ACKNOWLEDGMENT

ONE OF THE REASONS that I wrote this book was that I needed to read it. I was aware from the beginning of my limitations; and, as I went deeper into the material, of course I became more deeply aware of them. I knew, too, that there were people alive who seemed to be eminently qualified to set down what they knew of the life and work of Willard Gibbs, and I knew the names of some of them. They were academic persons, they had personal knowledge of Gibbs, and backgrounds of training rigid enough to be equal to what I could never have : a critical knowledge of the details of his most complicated achievements and influence. However, eager as they were to acknowledge their qualifications, it was clear that they did not mean to write this book; indeed, in the mandarin tradition, they set themselves against even the thought of such a book. I hope that they will now go ahead and outreach this book with their specialized knowledge. The best I can hope for this or any other work is that it will be taken up and outdone as soon as possible; in the same way, the best I can hope for our age is that it will do well enough so that by the twenty-fifth century, say, all we shall have done will be outworn. Let the twenty-fifth century believe that all we said was trash; that belief will prove that it has used us well.

This book has relied on information and attitudes from many sources. It will be understood that everything I have said directly about the past comes from books and periodicals. A reading list follows this Acknowledgment; but it is partial only. Because of the nature of this book, information has been derived from many seemingly distant origins. Even after my poem "Gibbs" had been written and published, it was difficult to indicate—even to close friends—the nature of the work in which I was engaged; until trust in my object became a greater gift than the offering of facts. And then the facts I needed seemed so unrelated—from the material of the early chapters, dealing with the *Amistad* story, the strange wrecked career of the poet Percival, and the Adams family, there was little assistance I could ask from specialists.

Three people, in particular, from the very beginning, almost before they could be well aware of the design of my work, gave me their help and confidence, and maintained that attitude throughout. They are Dr. Theodore Shedlovsky of the Rockefeller Institute, from whom I first learned about Willard Gibbs, and who offers the imaginative approach of a scientist who is alive to many purposes; Mr. Norman Holmes Pearson of Yale University, whose sympathy I may always trust in the delicate interrelations of cultural and social history as well as of personal complexity; and Mr. Donald Elder of Doubleday, Doran & Co., whose aware-

Appendix

ness and friendship have seen me through many of the silences of this work.

Dr. Lee De Forest sent me a portion of his journal, with his comments, as well as the page of notes reproduced in the illustrations; and Professor Crane Brinton sent me the section of Lawrence Henderson's manuscript of *Memories* which I quote. Neither of them had seen any of my manuscript or had any token of my capability; and I thank them for their generosity as well as their material.

Among the others whose confidence reminds me of them now are especially : the tellers of the anecdotes named in this book, Rebecca Pitts, Joseph Jablonower, Leonard Bacon, Mr. and Mrs. Walter E. Bezanson, John Schoolcraft, Edna Guck, T. B. Costain, Ethel Hulse, Irving Fisher, and W. J. V. Osterhout.

I thank Henry James for his suggestions about the James family, Charles Francis Adams for his advice about the Adams papers, Ralph Barton Perry and Mrs. Bailey Aldrich for their interest and search through the papers of William James, and George Eaton for his material dealing with the Connecticut Academy of Arts and Sciences.

I thank the Yale Library for the kindness with which its staff helped me, and for permission to publish documents from the Gibbs manuscripts and the Baldwin manuscripts.

The Widener Library staff and the staff of the Engineering Library have been very kind, and I am grateful.

Susan S. Pearson and Norman Holmes Pearson have been very generous in giving time and special effort to the historical check of the last uncorrected draft of this manuscript; and Theodore Shedlovsky has done as much in reading the manuscript for scientific accuracy. I have wished the truth, imaginative and factual, to be in these pages; and I thank those who have in any way helped me to reach it.

I here thank all those who have helped me. I wish at the same time to say that I assume full responsibility for the attitudes and statements of this book. The imagination of Gibbs, emerging and expanding against his own background and the background of the present, can and should be treated in many ways; what I offer here is my own treatment.

M. R.

FIVE DEFINITIONS

SYSTEM—Any portion of the material universe which we choose to
separate in thought from the rest of the universe for the purpose of
considering and discussing the various changes which may occur
within it under various conditions is called a system.

PHASE—The physically homogeneous but mechanically separable portions of a system are called its phases.

EQUILIBRIUM—An equilibrium exists in any system under a fixed set of
conditions when the parts of the system do not undergo any change
of properties with the passage of time and provided the parts of the
system have the same properties when the same conditions are again
arrived at by a different procedure.

COMPONENTS—The number of components of a system at equilibrium
is defined as the smallest number of independently variable constituents by means of which the composition of each phase may be
quantitatively expressed.

DEGREE OF FREEDOM—In the application of the Phase Rule to the
type of system under consideration, the system may be defined by
the number of variable conditions. This number is called the variance,
or degree of freedom, of the system.

READING LIST

(This list, a partial bibliography, does not pretend to be complete; it is rather a grouping of materials that might attract the interested reader. I have tried also to list references that are easily accessible.—M. R.)

ABRO, A. D'. *Decline of Mechanism in Modern Physics*. Van Nostrand, 1939.

ADAMS, BROOKS. Intr. to *Degradation of the Democratic Dogma* (H. Adams). Macmillan, 1919. *The Law of Civilization and Decay*. Macmillan, 1895.

ADAMS, CHARLES FRANCIS. *John Quincy Adams, His Connection with Emancipation under Martial Law*. Mass. Historical Society, 1902.

ADAMS, HENRY. *Degradation of the Democratic Dogma*. Macmillan, 1919. *The Education of Henry Adams*. Houghton Mifflin, 1918. *A Cycle of Adams Letters, 1861–1865*—ed. W. C. Ford. Houghton Mifflin, 1920. *Letters of Henry Adams, 1892–1918*—ed. W. C. Ford. Houghton Mifflin, 1938.

ADAMS, JAMES TRUSLOW. *The Adams Family*. Little, Brown & Co., 1930. *Henry Adams*. Boni, 1933. *The Tempo of Modern Life*. Boni, 1931.

ADAMS, JOHN QUINCY. *Memoirs*—ed. Ch. Fr. Adams. Lippincott, 1876. *Oration at Cincinnati Astronomical Society*. Shepard & Co., 1843. *Speech for the Amistad Defense*. Washington, 1842. *Report of the Secretary of State upon Weights and Measures*. Wash., 1821.

AMERICAN GUIDE SERIES: *Connecticut*. Federal Writers Project. Houghton Mifflin, 1938.

ARRHENIUS, SVANTE. *Theory of Solutions*. Yale Univ. Press, 1912.

ATWATER, EDW. E. (ed.). *History of the City of New Haven*. W. W. Munsell & Co., 1887.

BALDWIN, ROGER. *Amistad Defense* (published with Barber, q.v.). Connecticut, 1839–42.

BARBER, JOHN W. *A History of the Amistad Captives*. New Haven, 1840.

BARUS, CARL. "Suggestions by Josiah Willard Gibbs in Geophysical Research." *Amer. Jour. Sci.*, 1906.

BEARD, CHARLES, and BEARD, MARY. *The Rise of American Civilization*. Macmillan, 1937.

BELL, ERIC TEMPLE. *The Development of Mathematics*. McGraw-Hill, 1940. *Men of Mathematics*. Simon & Schuster, 1937. Etc.

BENSON, ADOLPH B. "James Gates Percival, Student of German Culture." *New Eng. Quart.*, 1929.

BEZANSON, WALTER E. Ms. *Henry Adams, Historian*. 1938.

Appendix

BIRKHOFF, GEORGE D. "Fifty Years of American Mathematics." *Science,* 1932.

BIRTWHISTLE, GEORGE. *The Principles of Thermodynamics*—2nd ed. Macmillan, 1929.

BLAKE, HENRY T. *Chronicles of New Haven Green.* New Haven, 1898.

BORDEAUX, ALBERT. *Histoire des Sciences.* Paris et Liège, 1920.

BOYLAN, JOHN. "Sequel to the Apocalypse." *Booktabs,* 1942.

BRAGG, W. C. "Atomic Arrangements in Metals and Alloys." *Jour. Inst. Metals,* 1935.

BRIDGMAN, P. W. *Logic of Modern Physics.* Macmillan, 1927. "Statistical Mechanics and the Second Law of Thermodynamics." *Science,* 1932.

BROOKS, VAN WYCK. *Flowering of New England.* Dutton, 1936. *New England: Indian Summer.* Dutton, 1940. Etc.

BROWN, ROLLO WALTER. *Lonely Americans.* Coward-McCann, 1929.

BRUNHES, BERNARD. *La degradation de l'energie.* Flammarion, 1922.

BRYAN, GEORGE S. *Edison. The Man and His Work.* Knopf, 1936.

BUCHANAN, SCOTT. *Poetry and Mathematics.* Day, 1929.

BUCHLER, JUSTUS. *Charles Peirce's Empiricism.* Harcourt, Brace, 1939.

BUMSTEAD, H. A. *Josiah Willard Gibbs*—in *Collected Works J. W. Gibbs* —q.v. Etc.

BURROUGHS, JOHN. *Whitman: A Study.* Houghton Mifflin, 1896.

CAJORI, FLORIAN. *A History of Mathematics.* Macmillan, 1929.

CANTELO, R. C. "J. W. Gibbs. A Summary of His Contribution to Chemistry." *Canad. Chem. & Met.,* 1924.

CARROLL, LEWIS. *The Complete Works of Lewis Carroll.* Modern Library, 1936.

CATTERALL, H. T., and J. J. HAYDEN (eds.). *Judicial Cases Concerning American Slavery.* Carnegie Institute, 1936.

CHEMISCH WEEKBLAD. Gibbs Number, 18 September 1926. "A Half-Century of Phase"—including Work by Jorissen, Le Chatelier, Ostwald, Van der Waals, W. Lash Miller, Schreinemakers, Tammann, Vogt, Van Laar, Terwen, Donnan, Freeth, De Baat, and a bibliography.

CHITTENDEN, RUSSELL. *History of the Sheffield Scientific School of Yale University.* Yale University Press, 1928.

CLARK, BENNETT CHAMP. *John Quincy Adams, "Old Man Eloquent."* Little, Brown, 1935.

CLARK, W. MANSFIELD. "Equilibrium." *Jour. Ind. & Eng. Chem.,* April 1936.

CLIBBENS, DOUGLAS A. *Principles of the Phase Theory.* Macmillan, 1920.

COGSWELL, F. H. *J. G. Percival and His Friends.* Conn. Soc. of the Founder and Patriots of America, New Haven, 1902.

COHEN, E. "The Semi-Centenary of Willard Gibbs' Phase Rule, 1876–1926." *Science,* 1926.

CROWTHER, J. G. *Famous American Men of Science.* Norton, 1937. *Men of Science.* Norton, 1936. *The Social Relations of Science.* Macmillan, 1941. Etc.

Appendix

CRUM, RALPH B. *Scientific Thought in Poetry*. Columbia Univ. Press, 1931.

DAMPIER, WHETHAM, SIR CECIL. *A History of Science*. Cambridge Univ. Press, 1929. Etc.
   and CATHERINE WHETHAM. *Science and the Human Mind*. Longmans, Green, 1912.

DANTZIG, TOBIAS. *Number, the Language of Science*—3rd ed. Macmillan, 1939.

DAVIS, THOMAS B. *Chronicles of Hopkins Grammar School*. New Haven, 1938.

DE MILLE, GEORGE E. *Literary Criticism in America*. Dial, 1931.

DEXTER, F. B. *Biographical Sketches of the Graduates of Yale College*. Yale, 1912.

DONNAN, F. G. "Influence of J. Willard Gibbs." *Jour. Franklin Institute*, 1925.

DUHEM, PIERRE. *J. W. Gibbs—à propos de la publication de ses mémoires scientifiques*. Paris, 1908.

DUNBAR, SEYMOUR. *History of Travel in America*. Bobbs-Merrill, 1915.

DWIGHT, TIMOTHY. *Memories of Yale Life and Men*. Dodd, Mead, 1903.

EDDINGTON, SIR ARTHUR. *Nature of the Physical World*. Macmillan, 1933. Etc.

EINSTEIN, ALBERT. Papers in the *Annalen der Physik*, 1907. Gibbs Lecture. Etc.
   and LEOPOLD INFELD. *The Evolution of Physics*. Simon & Schuster, 1938.

ELIOT, ELLSWORTH. *Yale in the Civil War*. Yale Univ. Press, 1932.

ELLIOTT, S. H. *Attractions of New Haven*. New Haven, 1869.

ENCYCLOPAEDIA BRITANNICA—11th edition.

FAURE, ELIE. *History of Art*. Harper and Bros., 1930.

FINDLAY, ALEXANDER. *A Hundred Years of Chemistry*. Macmillan, 1937.
Phase Rule and Its Applications. Longmans, Green, 1904.

FISHER, GEORGE P. *Discourse Commemorative of J. W. Gibbs (Sr.)*. New Haven, 1861. *Life of Benjamin Silliman*. Porter & Coates, Phila., 1866.

FISHER, IRVING. Gibbs Lecture, "Mathematics in the Social Sciences." "Mechanics of Bimetallism." *Economics Journal*, Sept. 1894. Ms.— "Memorandum Regarding J. Willard Gibbs, LL.D., as a Candidate for Election to the Hall of Fame." *Nature of Capital and Income*. Macmillan, 1906.

FORJAZ, A. PEREIRA. *Gibbs e o genio norte-americano*. Academia das Ciências de Lisboa. Lisbon, 1939.

FOWLER, R. H., and E. H. GUGGENHEIM. *Statistical Thermodynamics*. Macmillan, 1937.

FURNAS, CLIFFORD C. Ms.—*Significance of the Work of Willard Gibbs in Applied Science*.

GABRIEL, RALPH. *The Course of American Democratic Thought*. Ronald Press, 1940.

GARRISON, FIELDING H. "Josiah Willard Gibbs." *Pop. Sci. Monthly*, May–Aug. 1909.

Appendix

GIBBS, JOSIAH WILLARD (SR.). There is a bibliography in Dexter, *Biog. Sketches*, q.v. Periodicals, esp. *Amer. Jour. Science & Arts*, 1833–48; *Quarterly Christian Spectator*, 1834, 1837; *Theol. & Lit. Jour.*, 1851, 1856; *New Englander*, 1843–63; *Jour. Amer. Orient. Soc.*, 1849–54; *Mass. Teacher*, 1859. . . . *Annals of the American Pulpit*, I, 164–67. *Hebrew & English Lexicon of the Old Testament inc. the Biblical Chaldee—from Gesenius*. Codman Press, Andover, 1824. *A Latin Analyst on Modern Philological Principles*. New Haven, 1858. *Philological Studies—with English Illustrations*. New Haven, 1857. *Storrs' Essay on the Historical Sense of the New Testament—tr.* J. W. Gibbs. Wells & Lilly, 1817. *Teutonic Etymology—The Formation of Teutonic Words in the English Language*. New Haven, 1860.

GIBBS, JOSIAH WILLARD. *Collected Works*. Longmans, Green, 1928. *A Commentary on the Scientific Writings of J. Willard Gibbs*—ed. F. G. Donnan and Arthur Haas. Yale Univ. Press, 1936. *Diagrammes et surfaces*—tr. M. G. Roy, introd. M. B. Brunhes. Scientia, Nov. 1903. *L'equilibre des substances heterogenes*—notes by Georges Matiss. Paris, 1919. *Scientific Papers of J. Willard Gibbs*. Longmans, Green (London), 1906. *Thermodynamische Studien*—tr. W. Ostwald. Leipzig, 1892. *Vector Analysis—founded upon the lectures of J. Willard Gibbs*—E. B. Wilson. Yale Univ. Press, 1901. Mss. at Yale in the Gibbs Collection: "On the Form of the Teeth of Wheels in Spur Gearing," 1863. "The Proper Magnitude of the Units of Length and of Other Quantities Used in Mechanics," 1866. Three notebooks, 1866–1869. Letters, papers, etc. . . . Gibbs Lectures, 1923– : American Mathematical Society, including papers read by Pupin, Henderson, Pierpont, Williams, Brown, Hardy, Fisher, Wilson, Bridgman, Tolman, Einstein, Bush, Russell, Kraus. Bibliographies in *Collected Works*, *Chemisch Weekblad*, Garrison, Commentary, Crowther (*Famous American Men of Science*), Ency. Brit., 11th ed., in articles on "Energetics" and "Thermodynamics."

GIBBS, J. W. *Memoirs of the Gibbs Family of Warwickshire*. Phila., 1879.

GOOD, H. G. "To the Future Biographers of John Quincy Adams." *Sci. Monthly*, Sept. 1934.

GRADUATE OF '69, A. *Four Years at Yale*, 1871.

GUGGENHEIM, E. A. *Modern Thermodynamics by the Methods of Willard Gibbs*. Methuen, 1933. Etc.

GUMPERT, MARTIN. *Trail-Blazers of Science*. Funk & Wagnalls, 1936.

HABER, FRITZ. "Practical Results of the Theoretical Development of Chemistry." *Jour. Franklin Institute*, 1925. *Thermodynamic Gas Reactions*. Longmans, Green, 1908. Etc.

HARROW, BENJAMIN. *Eminent Chemists of Our Time*. Van Nostrand, 1920.

HASTINGS, CHAS. S. *Biographical Memoir of Josiah Willard Gibbs*. Natl. Acad. Sci., 1909.

HENDERSON, LAWRENCE J. *Blood*. Univ. London, 1925. *Blood—A Study in General Physiology*. Yale Univ. Press, 1928. Ms.—*Memories*. Pareto's

Appendix

General Sociology—A Physiologist's Interpretation. Harvard Univ. Press, 1935.

HILL, EVERETT G. *Modern History of New Haven.* S. J. Clarke, 1918.

HOGBEN, LANCELOT. *Mathematics for the Million.* Norton, 1937. *Science for the Citizen.* Knopf, 1938.

HUME-ROTHERY, W. "Rationale of Phase Form in Alloys." *The Metal Industry,* London, 1936.

JAFFE, BERNARD. *Crucibles.* Simon & Schuster, 1930. *Outposts of Science.* Simon & Schuster, 1935.

JAMES, ALICE. *Alice James: Her Brothers, Her Journal*—ed. Anna Robeson Burr. Dodd, Mead, 1934.

JAMES, HENRY. *The American Scene.* Harper & Bros., 1907. Etc.

JAMES, WILLIAM. *Collected Essays and Reviews.* Longmans, Green, 1911. *Letters of Wm. James*—ed. by H. James. Atl. Monthly Press, 1920. *Memories and Studies.* Longmans, Green, 1911. *Pragmatism.* Longmans, Green, 1907. *Principles of Psychology.* Henry Holt, 1890. *Varieties of Religious Experience.* Longmans, Green, 1902. Etc.

JEANES, SIR JAMES. *An Introduction to the Kinetic Theory of Gases.* Macmillan, 1940.

JOHNSTON, JOHN. "Applications of Science to the Metallurgical Industry." *Sci. Monthly,* June 1939. "Willard Gibbs: An Appreciation." *Sci. Monthly,* Feb. 1928.

JORDAN, DAVID STARR (ed.). *Leading American Men of Science.* Henry Holt, 1910.

JULIN, CHARLES E. "New Haven, Connecticut. A Dual Civic Personality." *New England Mag.,* 1911.

KILLEFER, D. H. *Eminent American Chemists.* Amer. Chem. Soc.—no date.

KINGSLEY, WM. H. (ed.). *Yale College.* Henry Holt, 1879.

LANGER, R. S. "Josiah Willard Gibbs." *Amer. Math. Monthly,* 1939.

LEONARD, JONATHAN NORTON. *Crusaders of Chemistry.* Doubleday, 1930. Etc.

LEVY, S. I. *Introduction to Industrial Chemistry.* G. Bell, 1926.

LEWIS, G. N., and MERLE RANDALL. *Thermodynamics and the Free Energy of Chemical Substances.* McGraw-Hill, 1923.

LINDSAY, R. B., and HENRY, MARGENAU. *Foundations of Physics.* John Wiley & Sons, 1936.

LUCRETIUS. *De Rerum Natura.*

MACINNES, DUNCAN A. "The Contribution of Josiah Willard Gibbs to Electrochemistry." *Trans. Electrochem. Society,* 1937.

MAGIE, WM. F. *Principles of Physics.* Century, 1911.

MALONEY, JOHN A. *Great Inventors and their Inventions.* Univ. of Knowledge, 1938.

MARGENAU, HENRY. *Ms.—Gibbs' Statistical Mechanics.*

MARSH, J. I. *Principle of Phase Diagrams*—foreword by John Johnston. McGraw-Hill, 1935.

MATTHIESSEN, F. O. *American Renaissance.* Oxford Univ. Press, 1941.

Appendix

MAXWELL, JAMES CLERK. *Scientific Papers of J. C. Maxwell*—ed. W. D. Niven. Camb. Univ. Press, 1890. *Theory of Heat*—4th ed. Longmans, Green, 1875. *James Clerk Maxwell. A Commemoration Volume.* Camb. Univ. Press, 1931.

MELLENCAMP, FRANK J. *Application of Gibbs-Helmholtz Equation to Concentration Cells.* Univ. of Michigan, 1909.

MELVILLE, HERMAN. All works. The novels and stories have been published in the United States, the poems in England only. A good selection is in: *Representative Selections*—ed. Willard Thorp. Amer. Book Co., 1938.

MERZ, JOHN T. *A History of European Scientific Thought in the Nineteenth Century.* Wm. Blackwood & Sons, 1903.

MILLER, FRANCIS TREVELYAN. *Thomas A. Edison.* John C. Winston, 1931.

MILLER, W. LASH. *Method of Willard Gibbs in Chemical Thermodynamics.* Toronto, 1925.

MITCHELL, MARY HEWITT. *History of New Haven County, Conn.* Pioneer Hist. Pub. Co., 1930.

MUMFORD, LEWIS. *Brown Decades.* Harcourt, Brace, 1931. *Golden Day.* Norton, 1934. *Herman Melville.* Harcourt, Brace, 1929. *Technics and Civilization.* Harcourt, Brace, 1934. Etc.

MURRAY, ROBERT H. *Science and Scientists in the Nineteenth Century.* Sheldon Press, 1935. "Needs of the University." Yale College, 1871.

NERNST, WALTER. *The New Heat Theorem.* Methuen, 1926. *Theoretical Chemistry.* Macmillan, 1911. Etc.

NETTLETON, GEO. H. (ed.). *The Book of the Yale Pageant.* Yale Univ. Press, 1916.

NEWTON, HUBERT ANSON. *Scientific Papers.* Yale Library (author's collection).

OSTWALD, WILHELM. *The Historical Development of General Chemistry.* Columbia Univ., 1906. *Individuality and Immortality.* Houghton Mifflin, 1906. *Lebenslinien—Eine Selbstbiographie.* Berlin, 1926. Etc.

PAGE, LEIGH. Ms.—*Gibbs' Vector Analysis.* Yale.

PARETO, VILFREDO. *The Mind and Society.* Harcourt, Brace, 1935.

PARRINGTON, VERNON LEWIS. *Main Currents in American Thought.* Harcourt, Brace, 1927, 1930.

PEARSON, KARL. *The Grammar of Science.* London, 1895. *The Chances of Death, and Other Studies in Evolution.* Edward Arnold, 1897.

PEIRCE, CHARLES S. *Collected Papers*—ed. Chas. Hartshorne and Paul Weiss. Harvard, 1935. Review, *Gibbs' Collected Works*—in the *Nation*, Jan. 1907.

PERCIVAL, JAMES GATES. *Poems.* John Miller, 1824. *Poetical Works.* Tichnor & Fields, 1859.

Periodicals, including: *African Repository, Bull. Amer. Math. Soc., Bull. U.S. Bureau of Mines, Science, Scientific Monthly, Nation, Atlantic Monthly, New Haven Palladium, Columbian Register, N.Y. Times, N.Y. Herald Tribune, Time, Journal of Physical Chemistry, Proc. Amer. Acad. Arts and Sciences, Trans. Conn. Acad. Arts and Sci-*

ences, *Jour. Amer. Ceramic Society, Nature, Philosophical Magazine and Physical Review, Chemical and Met. Engineering, Chemical Review, Annalen der Physik, Jour. Ind. Eng. Chem., Metals, The Metal Industry, Jour. Inst. Metals, Journal of the Franklin Institute, Amer. Journal of Science and the Arts, Chemisch Weekblad.*

PERRY, RALPH BARTON. *The Thought and Character of William James.* Little, Brown, 1935.

PHELPS, WILLIAM LYON. *Autobiography with Letters.* Oxford Univ. Press, 1939.

Physics in Industry. American Institute of Physics, 1937.

PITTS, REBECCA. Ms.—*The Valley of Decision.*

PLANCK, MAX. *Theory of Heat,* Macmillan, 1932. *Treatise on Thermo-dynamics*—3rd ed. Longmans, Green, 1927. *Universe in the Light of Modern Physics.* Norton, 1931. *Where is Science Going?* Norton, 1932. Etc.

POINCARÉ, HENRI. *Foundations of Science.* Science Press, 1913.

Professor's Theory, A. Yale University, 1939.

PUMPELLY, RAPHAEL. *My Reminiscences.* Henry Holt, 1918.

PUPIN, MICHAEL. *The New Reformation.* Scribner's, 1927.

Report of the Electrical Conference at Philadelphia in Sept. 1884. Washington, 1886.

REYNOLDS, FISHER, WRIGHT (eds.). *Two Centuries of Christian Activity at Yale.* Putnam's, 1901.

RHODES, J. E. W. *Phase Rule Studies.* Oxford Univ. Press, 1935.

RIVETT, A. C. D. *Phase Rule and Study of Heterogeneous Equilibrium.* Oxford, 1923.

ROOZEBOOM, H. W. B. *Heterogene Gleichgewichte vom Standpunkte der Phasenlehre.* 1901.

ROSENHEIM, FREDERICK. "Flight from Home." *American Imago,* Dec. 1940.

RUHEMANN and RUHEMANN. *Low Temperature Physics.* Cambridge, 1937.

RUKEYSER, MURIEL. "Gibbs" in *A Turning Wind.* Viking, 1939.

SHAW, JAMES BYRNE. *Vector Calculus.* Van Nostrand, 1922.

SILLIMAN, BENJ. *American Contributions to Chemistry.* Phila., Collins, 1874.

SLOSSON, EDWIN E. In Jordan, D. S., q.v.

SMITH, PERCY F. "Josiah Willard Gibbs in Pure Mathematics." *Bull. Amer. Math. Soc.,* 1903.

SNYDER, CARL. *New Conceptions in Science.* Harper & Bros., 1903.

STALLO, J. B. *General Principles of the Philosophy of Nature.* Crosby & Nichols, 1848.

STEVENS, F. W. "Josiah Willard Gibbs and the Extension of the Principles of Thermodynamics." *Science,* Aug. 1927.

STOKES, ANSON PHELPS. *Historical Prints of New Haven.* New Haven, 1910. *Memorials of Eminent Yale Men.* Yale Univ. Press, 1914.

SULLIVAN, J. W. N. *The Bases of Modern Science.* Bevan, 1928. *Contemporary Mind.* Tonlinn, 1934. *Isaac Newton.* Macmillan, 1938.

Appendix

The Limitations of Science. Viking, 1933. *Science : A New Outline.* Nelson, 1935. Etc.

SUMNER, W. G. *Andrew Jackson* (American Statesmen Series). Houghton Mifflin, 1890. *Folkways*—with a preface by Wm. Lyon Phelps. Ginn & Co., 1940.

TAYLOR, HUGH S., and H. AUSTIN TAYLOR. *Elementary Physical Chemistry.* Van Nostrand, 1937.

THOMSON, JAMES. *Collected Papers in Physics and Engineering.* Camb. Univ. Press, 1912.

THOMSON, SIR J. J. *Recollections and Reflections.* Macmillan, 1937.

TOWNSEND, H. G. *Philosophical Ideas in the United States.* Am. Book Co., 1934.

VERRILL, H. E. "How the Works of Prof. Willard Gibbs Were Published." *Science,* Jan. 1925.

WARD, JULIUS H. *J. G. Percival—Life and Letters.* Tichnor & Fields, 1866.

WARFEL, HARRY. *Noah Webster.* Macmillan, 1936.

WARREN, AUSTIN. *The Elder Henry James.* Macmillan, 1934.

WATSON, DAVID LINDSAY. *Scientists Are Human.* Watts & Co., 1938.

WHITMAN, WALT. All works. *Leaves of Grass*—Inclusive Ed. Doubleday, 1924. *Democratic Vistas.* London, Walter Scott, 1888. Etc.

WHITNEY, MARGARET. Ms.—*One of the Prophets.*

WILLIAMS, HORATIO B. "Mathematics and the Biological Sciences"— Gibbs Lecture, 1926.

WILSON, E. B. "Reminiscences of Gibbs by a Student and Colleague"— Gibbs Lecture, 1931.

WILSON, WOODROW. *Constitutional Government in the U.S.* Col. Univ. Press, 1921.

YALE. Mss., memorabilia, etc., including : Baldwin Collection; Gibbs Collection; *A Sacred Wreath;* Risteen mss.; Classbooks; Memorabilia Room files; Graduates Club dinner, presentation Gibbs portrait; L. C. Lichty—"Application of Professor Gibbs work to Internal Combustion Analysis," and other mss. by various writers; Faculty Club dinner, 100th anniversary of Gibbs's birth.

SOURCES OF QUOTATIONS

Thanks are due to the following authors, publishers, publications, and agents for permission to use the selections indicated :

J. McKeen Cattell—for extracts from the *Scientific Monthly, Science*, publications of the Science Press, and for extracts from his letters to Miss Rukeyser.

Columbia University Press—for selections from *Constitutional Government in the United States*, by Woodrow Wilson.

Dr. Thomas B. Davis—for selections from *Chronicles of Hopkins Grammar School*.

Dodd, Mead & Company, Inc.—for selections from *Alice James : Her Brothers, Her Journal*, edited by Anna Robeson Burr; selections from *Scott's Last Expedition*, by Robert Falcon Scott.

Dr. Martin Gumpert—for selections from his book, *Trail-Blazers of Science*.

Harper & Brothers—for selections from *The American Scene*, by Henry James, with special permission from Henry James, for the Estate.

Houghton Mifflin Company—for selections from *The Education of Henry Adams : An Autobiography*, by Henry Adams; selections from *Letters of the Adams Family*, edited by Worthington Chauncey Ford; selections from *Letters of Henry Adams*, edited by Worthington Chauncey Ford; and selections from *Whitman, a Study*, by John Burroughs.

Bernard Jaffe—for selections from the Introduction to his book, *Outposts of Science*.

Alfred A. Knopf, Inc.—for selections from *Edison*, by George S. Bryan.

Little, Brown & Company and the Atlantic Monthly Press—for selections from *The Adams Family*, by James Truslow Adams; and from *The Thought and Character of William James*, by Ralph Barton Perry.

Longmans, Green & Co., Inc.—for selections from *The Collected Works of J. Willard Gibbs*, edited by W. R. Longley and R. G. Van Name.

Dr. Duncan A. MacInnes—for selections from his article, "The Contribution of Josiah Willard Gibbs to Electrochemistry."

The Macmillan Company—for selections from *Degradation of the Democratic Dogma*, by Henry Adams; from *The Elder Henry James*, by Austin Warren; and from *Recollections and Reflections*, by J. J. Thomson.

Oxford University Press—for selections from *American Renaissance*, by F. O. Matthiessen.

Appendix

Walter A. R. Pertuch, and the Franklin Institute of the State of Pennsylvania—for selections from the "Report of the Electrical Exposition, 1884," and from articles from the *Journal of the Franklin Institute*, April 1925.

George Bernard Shaw—for a quotation from his book, *The Irrational Knot.*

Professor Willard Thorp—for selections from his book, *Herman Melville, Representative Selections, with Introduction, Bibliography and Notes*, published by American Book Company.

D. Van Nostrand Company, Inc.—for selections from *Decline of Mechanism in Modern Physics*, by A. d'Abro.

Ann Watkins, Inc.—for selections from *Famous American Men of Science*, by J. G. Crowther.

Yale University Press—for selections from *Commentary on the Scientific Workings of J. Willard Gibbs;* from "A Professor's Theory," a pamphlet; from a speech by Charles Kraus; and from the Classbook of the Class of 1858.

Prof. Crane Brinton, for excerpts from the manuscript, *Memories*, by Lawrence J. Henderson.

Elizabeth Mayer, for the translation from Ostwald's preface to *Thermodynamische Studien.*

To all those who have entered into correspondence with Miss Rukeyser and the press, and particularly to those from whose letters of critical estimate or personal recollection of Willard Gibbs passages are quoted in this book: Harold Urey, Wilder Bancroft, M. T. Sanders, Frank Jewett, R. H. Ewart, H. W. Gillett, and Lee De Forest.

The Department of the Interior, for a passage from *Americans All— Immigrants All.*

Margaret Whitney, for her kindness and her permission to read and quote from her manuscript, *One of the Prophets*, a sympathetic account of Willard Gibbs in his personal relations.

Walter E. Bezanson, for his manuscript, *Henry Adams, Historian.*

Rebecca E. Pitts, for the manuscript of a part of her book, *The Valley of Decision.*

The *Nation*, for permission to quote from articles and reviews.

Yale University, for manuscripts, privately printed material, and other information.

Yale Library, for manuscripts in the Gibbs Collection, the Baldwin Collection, the Memorabilia Room.

(Note: The translation from Lucretius was done by Muriel Rukeyser.)

INDEX

Index

Index

De Forest, Lee, 275, 307–9, 328
Degradation of energy, 242, 341
Democracy, double stream, 5, 76; loss of belief in, 123; split in direction, 171, 383; betrayal and reaffirmation, 352; vitality, 379
Devonshire, William Cavendish, Duke of, 181, 210
Dexter, Lord Timothy, 100
Dickens, Charles, 54
Dickinson, Edward, 100
Dickinson, Emily, 174, 175–76, 261, 305
Donnan, F. G., 200, 396–98
Du Bois-Raymond, Emil, 151, 297
Duisberg, Karl, 385, 401, 425
Dyadics, 270, 343

East Rock, steamboat on, 101
Edison, Thomas A., 173, 179; work on telegraph, 196; laboratory at Menlo Park, 228, 230, 274, 275; experiments with incandescent lamp, 264
Edwards, Jonathan, *Freedom of the Will*, 50
Einstein, Albert, 243, 270, 373; law of sedimentation equilibrium, 375; concept of universal unity, 436
Electric waves, 294
Electrochemistry, 243, 246
Electrolytes, theory of, 236, 247, 312
Eliot, Charles William, 180, 206, 212
Emerson, Ralph Waldo, 48, 111, 146, 192; "Poetry and Imagination," 101; *Representative Men*, 101; transcendentalism, 404
Energetics, 148, 374
Energy, factor in thermodynamics, 187, 231; significance of concept, 230
Entropy, factor in thermodynamics, 187–90, 231; definition, 206
Entropy-temperature diagram, 189
Equilibrium, in systems, 234–36; effect of gravity on, 244; for solids in contact with fluids, 245; modification by electromotive force, 246
"Equilibrium of Heterogeneous Substances," publication by Connecticut Academy, 225; appraisal of, 232; recognition by Maxwell, 237, 243; publication in German translation, 285–87; a Rosetta Stone for science, 314; industrial possibilities of theory, 331; notes for supplement

to, 349; development of chemical industry from, 371; basis of metal industry, 388–90; application of theory in history, 404–15, 427; in government, 416; in society, 417–19; in economics, 419–21
———, analysis, 231–42, 243–47; energy and entropy, factors in, 231, 233; behavior of systems, 234–36; effect of solidity on mass, 236; equations of condition, 236; equilibrium of osmotic forces, 236; phase rule, 237–39; thermodynamic surfaces, 240; critical phases, 241; gas mixtures, 241; effect of gravity on equilibrium, 244; equations of ideal gases, 244; surfaces of discontinuity between fluid masses, 245; modification of equilibrium by electromotive force, 246; galvanic cell, 246, 271, 287, 311
Ether theories, 289
Expert, emergence of, 316
Explosives, 243; manufacture in Germany, 384; in England, 386; in America, 387

Fabian Society, 184
Faraday, Michael, 110
Father-and-son relationship, 108
Fellowship of the New Life, 184
Films, liquid, 246; semi-permeable, 321
Fisher, Irving, 270, 310, 433; *The Nature of Capital and Income*, 420
Fisk, James, 171, 173, 229
Fitch, John, 183
Förster, Wilhelm, 151, 157
Fort Sumter, attack on, 123
Fourier infinite series, 322
Franklin, Benjamin, 117; opposes balanced system of government, 78
Franklin Institute, 275
Freeman, Mary, 173
Freeth, Francis, 386
Fuller, Margaret, 173, 174, 178

Galiani, Abbé, 204, 273, 331
Galvanic cell, 243, 246, 271, 287, 311
Garfield, James A., President, 268
Gases, ideal, 241, 244
Gauss, Karl Friedrich, 157
Gauss's law of least constraint, 264
Gedney, Lieut., 25, 37

Index

Gene, theory of, 370

George, Henry, 265

German scholarship, permeation in United States, 50, 93, 105; debt of Adams family to, 114; induces wave of American students, 146.

Germany, emergence as chemical power, 371, 384, 426; development of industrial control, 385, 401, 424

Gibbs, Anna Louisa, 51, 93, 151; home life, 176; death, 330

Gibbs, Eliza, 85, 93

Gibbs, Emily, 85, 142

Gibbs, Henry, 33

Gibbs, Josiah Willard, Sr., 6; visits *Amistad* mutineers, 32, 82, 404; finds interpreter, 34–36, 52; antecedents, 33; interest in languages, 50–52, 105–8; work on Gesenius' *Hebrew Lexicon*, 50, 51; glossary of Mendi language, 52; admission to Yale, 94; *Philological Studies*, 105; last years, 114–16; death, 118–20; character, 119; epitaph, 120

Gibbs, Josiah Willard, source of power, 2–7, 315; obscurity, 6, 12; national background of early life, 7; creation of system based on unity, 11; childhood, 47–66; education, 83–103; school life, 86–92; described in school poem, 88; picnic, 89; student at Yale, 92–103; college honors, 97–98; relations with father, 104–20; elected to Connecticut Academy, 104; letters about camping party, 114, 134; graduate work, 136; "On the Form of the Teeth of Wheels in Spur Gearing," 136; invents railroad brake, 136; work on meteors, 139, 221; advocates metric system, 140; devises formula for lenses, 143; invention of governor, 144; friendship with H. A. Newton, 144, 292; loneliness of work, 145, 231, 438; European trip, 145–63; study in Paris, 150, 162; in Berlin, 151–58; notebooks, 154–56; study in Heidelberg, 159–62; return to America, 163–82; re-establishment in New Haven, 167–69; professor of mathematical physics at Yale, 182, 184, 204, 206, 208; at Keene Valley, 183, 191–94, 299; "Graphical Methods in the Thermodynamics of Fluids," 185–91; second paper, "A Method of Geometrical Representation of the Thermodynamic Properties of Substances by Means of Surfaces," 197–201; recognition of work, 201; skating, 219–21; modesty, 219, 250, 289, 381; friendship with Maxwell, 221; stories of, 223; "The Principles of Thermodynamics as Determining Chemical Equilibrium," 224; "great paper," 227–47 (*see also* "Equilibrium of Heterogeneous Substances"); awarded Rumford Medal, 231, 265–68, 284; theories applied in industry, 243, 331, 371–73, 383–88, 421; work on crystals, 243, 288; lectures at Johns Hopkins, 252–55; invited to join Johns Hopkins, 255; founds Yale Mathematical Club, 259; work on vapor densities, 263; "Fundamental Formulas of Dynamics," 264; interest in Hopkins Grammar School, 265, 324; elected member of National Academy of Sciences, 265; work in vector analysis, 268–70, 301–5, 433; on statistical mechanics, 269; on electromagnetic theory of light, 270, 302; "On the Fundamental Formula of Statistical Mechanics . . ," 272; at National Conference of Electricians, 276; statements expressing his spirit, 280, 303, 431; address on multiple algebra, 280–83; recognition in Holland, 284; in Germany, 285, 310, 314; re-discoveries of work, 287; work on electrostatic force, 289; on elliptic orbits, 290; political views, 291; enjoyment of Lewis Carroll, 292–94; writes a paper on Clausius, 149, 299–301; honored by scientific societies, 307; entertains Yale classmates, 310; work on galvanic cell, 311; as classroom teacher, 319–21, 328, 343, 346; work on osmotic pressure, 321; on thermodynamic theory of capillarity, 322; recognition in journals, 322; advises students on theses, 327; writes note on H. A. Newton's death, 329; *Elementary Principles of Statistical Mechanics*, 335–43; concept of truth, 339; receives Copley

Index

Index

James, Henry, Sr., 109–12; *The Secret of Swedenborg*, 174; description of William James, 216

James, Henry, 109, 134, 168; childhood, 111; early stories of, 153; description of Peirce, 217; *Daisy Miller*, 242, 261

James, Henry, III, 326

James, William, 109, 111, 134; with Agassiz expedition, 152; winter in Berlin, 153, 160; growing interest in psychology, 158, 159, 215; marriage, 184, 217; instructor in psychology at Harvard, 215–17; *Principles of Psychology*, 305; *Varieties of Religious Experience*, 334; denies phase rule in history, 413–15

James family, 109–13

Japan, industrial collaboration with Germany, 425

Johns Hopkins University, 252–57

Johnston, John, 367, 388

Joule, James Prescott, 148, 149

Journal of Physical Chemistry, 322, 372

Kelvin, William Thomson, Lord, 181, 265, 276, 289; work on Atlantic cable, 102, 147; on motive power of heat, 149

Key, Francis Scott, 43

King, Clarence, 114, 178, 214

Knott, C. G., 303

Konawalow, D., 287

Kowalewski, Sonia, 161, 258

Kronecker, Leopold, 151, 157, 184

Kummer, Ernst Edward, 151, 157

Kundt, August, 151, 157

Labor movement, 170, 259

Lafayette, Marquis de, 31

Lagrange, Joseph Louis, Count, 148

Langley, Samuel P., 334, 370

Laski, Harold J., 80

Lavoisier, Antoine Laurent, 148

Light, electromagnetic theory of, 270, 288, 294, 302

Lincoln, Abraham, President, 2, 130; authorizes photographs of war, 132

Locke, John, 76

Lodge, Sir Oliver, 276, 311

London *Times*, 126

Loneliness, of great minds, 52, 378; of children inheriting great traditions, 113; of Gibbs's work, 145, 231, 438

Lucretius, 10, 14, 131

Lyell, Sir Charles, 54, 147, 406, 427

Magazine of Metallurgical Engineering, 389

Marryat, Frederick, 48

Martin, Newell, description of Gibbs, 193, 194

Marx, Karl, 205, 261

Mathematical physics, significance in scientific progress, 206

Mathematics, backward condition in America, 117; as a language, 280, 420

Maupertuis, P. L. M., 148

Maxwell, James Clerk, Cambridge professor of physics, 181, 204; *Theory of Heat*, 199, 201; recognition of value of Gibbs's second paper, "A Method of Geometrical Representation of the Thermodynamic Properties of Substances by Means of Surfaces," 199, 201; character and achievement, 209, 222; head of Cavendish Laboratory, 209–12; interest in meteors, 221; recognition of Gibbs's "Equilibrium . . . ," 237, 243, 247, 248–51, 311; "demons," 241; "On the Equilibrium of Heterogeneous Bodies," 243, 261; poetry, 249; death, 251; place in science, 251; *Electricity and Magnetism*, 270

Mayer, Robert, discovery of law of conservation of energy, 14, 147

Melville, Herman, 2, 146; *Moby Dick*, 101, 354, 356; relations with Hawthorne, 223, 354–56; reaffirmation of freedom, 353–57; *Billy Budd*, 357; poems, 361

Metals, structural, electrical study of, 277

Meteors, 138, 147, 221

Metric system, advocated by Gibbs and H. A. Newton, 139; by J. Q. Adams, 140

Models, 186, 199, 202

Montesquieu, Baron de, 73, 77, 79; *L'Esprit des lois*, 76

Montez, Don Pedro, owner of *Amistad* slaves, 18, 28, 45

Index

Morse, S. F. B., 131
Munitions industry, Gibbs's influence on, 383–88

Nation, 153, 170, 179, 273; criticizes Yale scholastic level, 182, 208
National Academy of Sciences, 139, 265; in World War, 387
National Conference of Electricians, 276
National Labor Congress, 170
Nature, 201, 288, 289, 321
New England, attitude toward art, 54; decline of religious feeling, 84; loss of population to West, 122, 169; scholar type, 170; immigration from Europe, 170
New Haven, setting for Gibbs's life, 9; in Josiah Gibbs's time, 47–49; important figures in, 53–65; divided between college and town, 92; in 1854, 93; Fourth of July celebration, 95; in Civil War, 133; in 1867, 164–67; moral conditions in, 174; activity in invention, 180, 242; industrial development, 259; first telephone switchboard in country, 242, 261; in 1902, 346
New London Gazette, 27, 28
New York Times, 399, 424
New York Tribune, 124
Newcomb, Simon, 273, 276
Newton, Hubert Anson, 104, 167; study in Europe, 137; interest in meteors, 138, 147, 221; advocates metric system, 139; friendship with Gibbs, 144, 292; installs cameras in Yale observatory, 290; described by Gibbs, 291; house decorated in comets, 292; death, 329
Newton, Sir Isaac, influence on American political structure, 76–78, 209
Nightingale, Florence, 258
North American Review, 214

Osmotic forces, equilibrium of, 236, 321
Ostwald, Wilhelm, 285–87, 306, 374; publishes translation of "Equilibrium . . .," 314
Owen, Robert Dale, 52

Paalzow, Adolph, 151, 157
Palladium, 52
Panic, of '69, 178, 194; of '73, 194–96
Pareto, Vilfredo, 417–19, 420, 421
Pearson, Karl, The Grammar of Science, 295, 297
Pedro (Dom Pedro de Alcántara), Emperor of Brazil, 228
Peirce, Benjamin, 139, 269, 280, 284
Peirce, Charles S., 217, 250, 280, 378
Percival, James Gates, 107; campaign song, 48; life, 57; poetry, 59–65, 108, 199; scientific work, 63
Perry, Ralph Barton, 216, 218
Petrology, 391
Phase rule, deduced by Gibbs, 11, 235, 237–39; recognition, 331, 333, 337; application in industry, 384–95; in history, 408–13; combined with X-ray analysis, 426
Phase space, 339
Phases, critical, 241; of dissipated energy, 241
Phelps, Elizabeth Stuart, 173
Phelps, William Lyon, 319, 347
Phillips, Wendell, 124
Philosophical Magazine, 253
Phrenological Journal, 180
Pinkerton, Allen, 132
Planck, Max, 335, 373
Poe, Edgar Allan, 146
Poggendorff, Johann C., 147
Poincaré, Henri, 322, 334, 336
Porter, Noah, 194; president of Yale, 181, 208
Portugal, recognition of Gibbs in, 435
Potash industry, 384
Power, obsession of the time, 100; of industry, 145
Pragmatism, 217, 373
Princeton University Sesquicentennial, 321
Proceedings of the American Association for the Advancement of Science, 272
Proceedings of the Cambridge Philosophical Society, 243
Pumpelly, Raphael, 114, 262, 296
Pupin, Michael, 279, 423

Quantum theory, 335, 342
Quaternions, system of, 269, 301
Quincke, Georg, 151, 157

Index

Index